MW00805979

"One of the most important books on natural resource management ever done. It elegantly combines the intricacies of science with the vast knowledge of managers on the ground and gives equal weight to both; an epic undertaking, one that we could all strive to emulate, whether in science or the field."

Bob Budd, executive director of the Wyoming Wildlife and Natural Resource Trust; former president of the Society for Range Management

"This book is a call to arms to embrace, value, and combine all forms of knowledge. It shows that practical experiences and scientific insights must sit side-by-side to better connect and respect people, animals, and the places they inhabit to truly achieve multiple benefits."

Dr. Dean Revell, principal scientist, CSIRO Sustainable Agriculture Flagship, School of Animal Biology, University of Western Australia

"Fenced-in mind-sets about land management and livestock are set to change with the release of this book. It is a step toward moving us all closer to environmental and social repair by validating the work of herders and tapping into the benefits of grazing animals strategically in landscapes. This comprehensive exploration into the important art of shepherding is a must-read for animal handlers, scientists, agricultural educators, and government workers who manage both urban and rural landscapes."

Rachael Treasure, author of Jillaroo *and* The Stockmen

"The introductory paragraph of a range management textbook I had in college referred to the 'art and science of range management.' For the most part the science it reported was irrelevant and after that introductory statement there was no mention of the art. The science reported in this book is relevant and exciting. The art practiced every day by the herders described in this book is nothing short of a masterpiece."

Dave Pratt, Ranch Management Consultants, Inc.

Art & Science of Shepherding

"A book that will change the way you think about landscapes, livestock and the not so simple act of herding sheep."

Mark Schatzker, author of Steak: One Man's Search for the World's Tastiest Piece of Beef

"An outstanding, clearly written, and comprehensive book that gives a voice to shepherds and does not present us as folk relics."

Antoine Le Gal, shepherd, president of the Provence and Southern Alps Shepherds and Cowherders Association

"The value of this book is spelled out in the subtitle: "Tapping the Wisdom of French Herders." By changing the focus from animal husbandry to animal science, great gains of knowledge have been made. Sadly, there has been a great deal of knowledge lost because 'peasant wisdom' is seldom verifiable by the scientific method. The authors deserve our thanks for putting husbandry back into the discipline."

Walt Davis, rancher and author of How to Not Go Broke Ranching: Things I Learned the Hard Way in Fifty Years of Ranching

"A delightful book that describes the value of managing sheep and other livestock for manipulating rangeland vegetation. This book provides an insightful view of the life and outlook of French shepherds and likely reflects experiences of herders around the world."

Derek Bailey, professor, Department of Animal and Range Sciences, New Mexico State University

THE ART & SCIENCE OF

Shepherding

TAPPING THE WISDOM OF FRENCH HERDERS

THE ART
& SCIENCE OF

Shepherding

TAPPING THE WISDOM OF FRENCH HERDERS

Michel Meuret & Fred Provenza
EDITORS

Bruce Inksetter & Melanie Guedenet
TRANSLATORS

ACRES U.S.A. *Austin, Texas*

The Art & Science of Shepherding

Acres U.S.A.
P.O. Box 301209
Austin, Texas 78703 U.S.A.
512-892-4400 • fax 512-892-4448
info@acresusa.com • *www.acresusa.com*

Printed in the United States of America

Publisher's Cataloging-in-Publication

Michel Meuret, 1960-
    [Un savoir-faire de bergers. English]
    The art and science of shepherding / edited by Michel Meuret and
Fred Provenza ; translated from the French by Bruce Inksetter and
Melanie Guedenet. – Rev.
Austin, TX, ACRES U.S.A., 2014
            xii, 434 pp., 23 cm.
    Includes bibliographical references, index, illustrations, tables.
    ISBN 978-1-60173-069-5 (trade)
    1. Agriculture—environmental aspects.   2. Herders—France.
3. Grazing—France.   4. Rangeland management
I. Provenza, Fred, 1951-   II. Title.

SF85.M48   2014   636.3

Contents

The Authors

Isabelle BAUMONT: *Shepherd.* Route des Blancs, Le Pré Claux, 04700 Entrevennes, France - baumontisabelle@gmail.com

Olivier BEL: *Sheep farmer-herder and instructor at Le Merle Herding School.* Ferme des Roux, 05400 La Roche des Arnauds, France – olivier.bel4@wanadoo.fr

Olivier BONNEFON: *Agricultural adviser.* Chambre d'agriculture des Bouches-du-Rhône, Maison des agriculteurs, 22 avenue Henri Pontier, 13626 Aix-en-Provence Cedex 1, France

Émilien BONNET: *Sheep farmer-herder.* Les Cabanes, 84229 Lioux, France – emilienetemilie@orange.fr

Jean-Pierre DEFFONTAINES[†]: *Researcher in agronomy and geography.* INRA, Unité Versailles-Dijon-Mirecourt, Route de Saint-Cyr, 78026 Versailles Cedex, France

Christian DEVERRE: *Researcher in sociology,* INRA, UMR1048 SADAPT, AgroParisTech, 16 rue Claude Bernard, 75231 Paris, France – christian.deverre@agroparistech.fr

Rémi DUREAU: *Pastoralist engineer.* CERPAM (Centre d'Études et de Réalisations Pastorales Alpes Méditerranée). *Contact address:* Campagne les Craux, 04110 Villemus, France – campagne-les-craux@orange.fr

Mathieu ERNY: *Shepherd.* Conservatoire d'Espaces Naturels Rhône-Alpes, Antenne de l'Ain, 1 rue de la Poste, 01360 Béligneux, France – ernymathieu@aol.com

Patrick FABRE: *Pastoralist engineer.* Maison de la transhumance, Domaine du Merle, route d'Arles, 13300 Salon-de-Provence, France – patrick.fabre2@aliceadsl.fr

Jean-Michel GASCOIN: *Goat farmer-herder.* La Combe, 26400 Cobonne, France – michelle.gascoin@orange.fr

Pierre GASCOUAT: *School instructor.* Lycée des Métiers de la Montagne, BP 144, 1051 route du Gave d'Aspe, 64404 Oloron-Sainte-Marie, France - pierre.gascouat@educagri.fr

Jean-Do GUYONNEAU: *Shepherd,* INRA, Domaine du Merle, route d'Arles, 13300 Salon-de-Provence, France – Jean-Dominique.Guyonneau@supagro.inra.fr

Bernard HUBERT: *Researcher in ecology and social sciences.* INRA (Institut National de la Recherche Agronomique) & EHESS (École des Hautes Études en Sciences Sociales), President of Agropolis International, 1000 avenue Agropolis, 34394 Montpellier cedex 5, France – bernard.hubert@avignon.inra.fr

Michelle JALLET: *School director.* École de bergers du Merle, route d'Arles, 13300 Salon-de-Provence, France – Michelle.Jallet@supagro.inra.fr

Pascaline KROPP: *Shepherd.* 6 avenue du col de l'Izoard, 05100 Briançon, France.

Marie LABREVEUX: *School instructor.* Cfppa de Die, avenue de la clairette, 26150 Die, France. *Contact address*: Ribière, 26150 Saint-Andéol, France – yosanoso@free.fr

Étienne LANDAIS: *Researcher in animal science and livestock farming systems.* Director of Montpellier SupAgro, 2 place Pierre Viala, 34060 Montpellier Cedex 1, France - emplandais@gmail.com

Danielle LASSALLE: *School instructor.* Association pour la formation en milieu rural, 64120 Etcharry, France

Elisabeth LÉCRIVAIN: *Researcher in animal eco-ethology.* INRA, UR767 Écodéveloppement, Agroparc, 84914 Avignon, Cedex 9, France – lecriv@avignon.inra.fr

Jean-Pierre LEGEARD: *President of the Association Française de Pastoralisme (AFP),* Director of Centre d'Études et de Réalisations Pastorales Alpes Méditerranée (CERPAM), route de la Durance, 04100 Manosque, France – jplegeard@orange.fr

André LEROY: *Shepherd.* Le Chatelard, 05260 Champoléon, France

Pierre MARTINAND: *Researcher in livestock farming economy.* CTGREF, Division Techniques et Économie des Exploitations d'Élevage et de Polyculture, Montpellier, France. *Current address:* Irstea, UMR-TETIS, Maison de la Télédétection, 500 rue J-F. Breton, 34093 Montpellier Cedex 5, France - pierre.martinand@teledetection.fr

Michel MEURET: *Researcher in animal science and ecology, Visiting Professor at Montpellier SupAgro.* INRA, UMR868 Selmet (Mediterranean and Tropical Livestock Farming Systems), 2 place Pierre Viala, Bat 22, 34398 Montpellier Cedex 1, France – meuret@supagro.inra.fr

Jean-Lou MEUROT: *Sheep farmer-herder.* Le Village, 26150 Vachères-en-Quint, France

François MILLO: *Agricultural adviser,* Société coopérative de l'agneau de Haute-Provence, boulevard Gassendi, 04000 Digne, France

Roger MINARD : *Shepherd and vice president of the Provence and Southern Alps Shepherds and Cowherders Association.* Le Plan, 04110 Aubenas-les-Alpes, France– minard.roger@gmail.com

Francis MULLER: *Natural area conservancies.* FCEN, Pôle relais-tourbières, Maison de l'environnement de Franche-Comté, 7 rue Voirin, 25000 Besançon, France – francis.muller@enf-conservatoires.org

Fred PROVENZA: *Researcher in plant and animal ecology and nutrition, professor emeritus.* Utah State University, College of Natural Resources, Department of Wildland Resources, Logan, Utah 84322-5230, USA – fred.provenza@usu.edu

François SALMON: *Natural area conservancies, project director.* Conservatoire d'Espaces Naturels Rhône-Alpes, Antenne de l'Ain, Château Messimy, 01800 Charnoz, France – salmon@gceip.fr

Isabelle SAVINI: *Pastoralist.* INRA, Collège de direction, 147 rue de l'Université, 75338 Paris Cedex 07, France – isabelle.savini@paris.inra.fr

Pascal THINON: *Researcher in geography.* INRA, UMR0951 Innovation, 2 place Pierre Viala, 34060 Montpellier Cedex 1, France

Hervé TRIPARD: *Sheep farmer-herder.* Longo Maï, Le Pigeonnier, 04300 Limans, France

Sandrine VERDIER: *School instructor.* Cfppa de Lannemezan, 131 rue du Bidalet, 65300 Lannemezan, France

Marc VINCENT: *Pastoralist and animal scientist.* INRA, UR767 Écodéveloppement, Agroparc, 84914 Avignon, Cedex 9, France – vincent@avignon.inra.fr

Acknowledgments

T HE editors wish to extend their heartfelt thanks to the authors and to everyone who placed his or her unwavering support and talent at their disposal during the seven years that it took to complete this book not only in French but also in English.

Gérard BALENT – INRA, Toulouse, France
Ben BALDWIN – National Park Service, Rocky Mountain National Park,
    Estes Park, Colorado, USA
Jessica BARDEY – Shepherd, France
Claude BÉRANGER – INRA, Paris, France
Didier BÉTORED – INRA, Avignon, France
Marc BOUILLON – Shepherd, France
Mark BRUNSON – Utah State University, Logan, Utah, USA
Beth BURRITT – BEHAVE Network, Utah State University, Logan, Utah, USA
Olivier CLÉMENT – INRA, St Pée sur Nivelle, France
Vinciane DESPRET – University of Liège, Belgium
Hermann DODIER – Association Française de Pastoralisme, Digne, France
Michel ETIENNE – INRA, Avignon, France
Jean-Claude FLAMANT† – INRA & Mission Agrobiosciences, Toulouse, France
Laurent GARDE – CERPAM, Manosque, France
Michèle GASCOIN – Shepherd & Major, Cobonne, France
Sylvain GOLÉ – CERPAM, Digne, France
Rae Ann F. HART– Utah State University, Logan, Utah, USA
Jocelyn K. HASKELL – Cowherder, Wyoming, USA
John HASKELL – Ranch Manager and Cow herder, Wyoming, USA
Jana HUHN – Shepherd, France
Yolande JANKENS – Shepherd, France
John JANKENS – Shepherd, France
Roy KADY – Shepherd, Master Weaver & President of the Teec Nos Pos Chapter,
    Diné bé' Iina', Arizona, USA
Antoine LE GAL –Shepherd, President of the Provence and Southern Alps
    Shepherds and Cow Herders Association, Saumanc dc Vaucluse, France
Christophe MAITRE – INRA, Paris, France
René MEZUREUX – INRA, Mirecourt, France
Pierre-Louis OSTY – INRA, Toulouse, France
Jean PLUVINAGE – INRA & University of Lyons 2, France

Sue PROVENZA, Colorado, USA

Michèle QUIBLIER – CERPAM, Briançon, France

Camille RAICHON[†] – Publisher, Versailles, France

Sophie RASPAUT – INRA, Grignon, France

Jacques RÉMY – INRA, Ivry-sur-Seine, France

Laura SAYRE – INRA, Dijon, France

Courtney WHITE – Quivira Coalition, Santa Fe, New Mexico, USA

James WRIGHT – National Forests Authority, Nancy, France

Sylvie ZASSER-BEDOYA – INRA, Toulouse, France

A very special and warm thanks to Pierre-Louis Osty (INRA Toulouse) and Pierre Martinand (Irstea Montpellier).

The translation of this book into English would not have been possible without the financial support made available by INRA's Science for Action and Development department (www.sad.inra.fr/en). We are deeply grateful to Jean-Marc Meynard, head of the department (2004–2012), and Benoit Dedieu, head of the department (2012–present), for their confidence and endless patience.

Speaking of patience, commitment, and tenacity, we are also so grateful to our translators Bruce Inksetter and Melanie Guedenet. They faced a diversity of French dialects and mind-sets, from those of the shepherds to the scientists, as they labored on one chapter after another. We think they respected everyone as they translated written and spoken expressions from French into North American English.

We want to sincerely thank Fred Walters for agreeing to work with us to get this book published. He knows well the benefits from mutual respect and shared knowledge between science and art/craft in small-scale agriculture. We helped him discover that France has not only artisan cheesemakers but also some skilled and nature-friendly herders.

We also want to thank Amanda Irle for her meticulous work in helping with the editing of the book.

Last but not least, we are deeply grateful to all the shepherds who recommend that we "be as patient with the book manuscript as they must be with their flocks of sheep."

Why Would Anyone Read a Book about the Art and Science of Shepherding in France?

Fred Provenza & Michel Meuret

DISCOVERING THE ART OF SHEPHERDING IN FRANCE

WHEN a hiker in Provence, France, out for a day in the mountains, sees at some distance a shepherd and his herd, he may think at first glance the shepherd does little — he could probably be replaced with fences. The shepherd walks, scans every so often with binoculars, sits sometimes for a long while, searches his bag, relaces his shoes, then suddenly gets up, cries loudly, and sends his herding dog off like a rocket. He maintains what appears to be a rather unstable relationship with the herd. Sometimes the sheep or the goats graze calmly and quietly across the mountain slopes, some practically between his feet, and all seem to be unaware of his presence. At other times the shepherd and the dog prod and drive the herd much as a sailor does a boat during a storm. The impression is that the shepherd acts only to coerce the herd, preventing it from going up or down the hills too much, scattering itself into small groups, or exceeding some borders. Judging by the number and diversity of swearwords, his efforts are not always fruitful, reinforcing the notion that a good fence would suit just as well.

But if the hiker will chance to stay awhile, to observe more diligently, he will observe a different scene, one that will cause him to change his conclusions. A call of the shepherd is followed by silence. Then the sheep or goats that in the former instant had their noses buried in grasses and bushes raise their heads and begin to move calmly in a multitude of small single files. The shepherd, with his dog mute at his feet, indicates to the animals the direction to move to another part of the pasture or to the night resting place. He turns, and the herd follows, as if a mutual trust once established is never called into question. The hiker will see in this perhaps a scene of biblical appearance, but he will wonder especially about the relationship between the man, the dog, and the herd, made by an alternation of short authoritarian actions and long instants of laisser-faire, the collective being obviously guided by reciprocal knowledge and mutual trust. On the way back down to the nearest village, the hiker will follow all kinds of fences, but, his mind now residing with the shepherd and the dog, he will no longer tend to these boundaries.

Thirty years ago, Michel Meuret was this hiker. Native to Brussels in Belgium, with no parents or grandparents from the rural world, he was as naïve of livestock as any city dweller nowadays. Luckily, he was able to meet goatherders, then shepherds, in the south of France. He appreciated their farm-made cheeses and lamb, but he especially noticed how much most of them wanted to share their experiences. Michel became a researcher in animal science and ecology, but he was pleasantly surprised to see to what extent shepherds described to him in detail their trials and errors, their groping to understand, their ways of managing the grazing of the herd, whenever he took time to participate in their activities. They did not aim to apply technical recipes, even after fifty years, the age when you are considered in the profession an old shepherd, the one who knows, the one from whom the trade is learnt. Learning for them means trying, adjusting, making mistakes without becoming demoralized, and considering the absence of scientific and technical norms about herding as both a challenge and an opportunity. At times, on the way back to the farm in the valley or to the mountain shepherd's cabin, a herder will remark with a smile that he feels he has become a bit of a researcher himself. Michel could only admit, upon seeing their endless curiosity about animals and plants, that their enthusiasm and tenacity came from being inventive and testing new ways of interacting with them.

The herders Michel befriended came in the great majority, like him, from the city. They were educated in classical schools, and some even had previous occupations in cities, where they learned only certified knowledge about pre-established norms of various occupations they once had in the city. They hoped to move away from that, to find in pastoralism and the use of natural resources life in the open air and, chiefly, a space of autonomy of imagination and creation. That's why this book is called *The Art and Science of Shepherding* and not *The Textbook of the Talented Shepherd*. It is also why herders, as well as some researchers and other experienced people in France, readily agreed to contribute to the book.

A PROPOSAL FROM THE NORTH AMERICAN WEST

The idea for this book originated with a proposal from the BEHAVE network (Behavioral Education for Human, Animal, Vegetation, and Ecosystem Management, behave.net). Founded in 2001 in Utah, this network is an association of researchers, livestock farmers, and private- and public-land managers from across five continents. It aims to stimulate sharing of scientific and experiential knowledge about how to nurture the health of soil, plants, animals, and people by interacting more skillfully with animals and people and more respectfully with soil, plants, and the environment.

Breaking from the classical approach of animals as machines guided merely by genes and instincts, BEHAVE favors understanding adaptive behaviors and capacities for learning, those of both animals and the human beings who care for them. From life in the soil to plants and animals including people, creatures are constantly challenged to transform as all facets of earth continually change. The BEHAVE network integrates understanding of behavioral principles and processes with local knowledge to facilitate transitions as people adapt to change—socially, economically, and ecologically. Appreciating the importance of change and adaptation transforms peoples' philosophies and practices from rigid and unyielding to fluid and malleable. People no longer view creatures, including ourselves, as machines helpless against genetic destiny. Rather, they grasp how to use behavioral interrelationships to create an array of opportunities to match the challenges people face as they embrace constant change.

As early as 1995, Fred read Michel's first writings in English on the design of grazing circuits by herders in France aiming to optimize intake of less palatable forages. Working himself on the effects of different combinations and sequences of eating foods on the appetites of herbivores, Fred was interested in how herders sequenced within a meal, offering the herd different sectors of pasture to stimulate appetite. With his colleagues and graduate students, Fred showed that what animals learn from very early stages of life—beginning in utero—has a lifelong influence on food and habitat selection and encourages animals to mix plants of complementary nutritional characteristics by eating different forages and foraging in different locations. He recommends therefore that animals be allowed to graze areas composed of a diversity of eatable plants, where each animal will have the opportunity to express its competence as a wise consumer.

Such knowledge moves radically away from conventional ways of thinking and of acting, both in science and in management. In the United States, Europe, Africa, Australia, and other countries, people have often recommended homogenizing pasture by eliminating all plants of unknown or uncertain nutritional value in favor of mostly "improved varieties" of plants classified as "good fodder." For decades, the mostly unsuccessful attempts to remove brush and replace it with introduced grasses such as crested wheatgrass (*Agropyron cristatum* L.) were methodically implemented on millions of hectares of sagebrush steppe (*Artemisia tridentata* Nutt.), a shrubby wormwood from the North American West. In so doing, people rejected the fact that herbivores can learn to mix grasses, forbs, and shrubs in their diet, and that mixing different forages has value at different times of the year. The protein and tannin in shrubs complement the energy in grass during winter. This knowledge assimilated by herbivores results in a kind of "food culture" that can be acquired by the herd and transmitted across animals' generations with appropriate management. Of course, to acknowledge the ability of domestic animals to develop food cultures raises questions about human knowledge and of technical cultures, those of the managers of herds and land.

When in 2006 Fred asked Michel to come talk at a BEHAVE conference in Utah about French shepherds' know-how, Fred specifically wanted Michel to address two questions: "Who are they, and especially, how did they learn their trade?" Fred suggested, with respect to the mind-set and practices of the network, that Michel invite also an experienced shepherd. Michel first thought it would be a challenge to find a French shepherd willing to come to Utah and describe in English his occupation. He was wrong. Over thirty shepherds declared themselves candidates via the internet. Yolande, a shepherd of many years' experience, was selected. Yolande and Michel had never crossed paths before, and she didn't have any knowledge of his research. She said to Michel, "I will read your scientific writings after my stay, to avoid blending them with my personal experience." After Yolande and Michel's respective talks, and following discussions with the audience, people suggested Michel write a book so participants in BEHAVE and elsewhere could learn more. Michel opted for a joint publication with the herders, because neither he nor the herders alone could describe the diversity of their various experiences working in France.

REASONS FOR RENEWING INTEREST IN HERDING KNOW-HOW

Compared with hi-tech tools and techniques prevalent today in livestock husbandry and land management, the practices of shepherds seem to belong to a separate, archaic, folk world. This idea is reinforced by the fact that their practices remain mysterious for whoever is not a shepherd or does not share time with them.

Nonetheless, with growing concerns over the high costs and consequences of technology, the practices of shepherds represent another way to manage livestock, wildlife, and landscapes. Their approach is apropos given rising interest in managing grazing intensively and using stockmanship to move and place animals. Even with a herder's salary, skilled herding is a low-cost way to address ecological, economic, and social challenges and opportunities for improving the vigor of soil, the biodiversity of plants for the health of domestic and wild herbivores, and the health of people who rely on plants and herbivores for their well-being.

Many French books illustrate with superb photos the persistence of shepherds in the countrysides of southern France. Most are dedicated to the long-range transhumance (seasonal movements of herds under the care of herders or livestock owners) to high mountain summer ranges, a living culture now hidden by the transport of herds in trucks — no more shepherds and herding dogs in public view. Some books highlight the "last shepherds," with empathy but mostly with fatalism. French shepherds, more or less young and experienced, tell us they are quite offended by this form of muséification — feeling that they are put on display in a museum – of their profession.

In the United States, the "cowboys" of the West have been romanticized into an image of gun-toting, bronco-riding symbols of a rugged western tradition now manifest mainly at rodeos. The less sensational livestock-husbandry skills of the cattlemen who moved cattle long distances, nurturing them along the way, are unknown to most urban and many rural folks as well nowadays.

Offering an alternative to the folklorization or premature muséification of shepherds and their practices demanded we consider what bias to give this book, what part of "know-how" to favor? The shepherds in France assert a savoir-faire that can be roughly divided into four activities: 1) production of the herd, including lambing/kidding and cheese-making in the case of dairy animals; 2) health of the herd, including giving urgent care to individuals in need, notably in the high mountains or when the shepherd finds himself alone with the herd; 3) proper feeding by herding at pasture in mountains, hills, or plains; and 4) protecting the herd against predators. In France, herding to properly nourish the animals, to facilitate the health of plants, and to rejuvenate land occupies shepherds' time most of the year. Paradoxically, it is the most mysterious activity for anyone not dedicated to it, which is why we decided to favor herding in this book.

A few works by French researchers, closely cooperating with shepherds, try to understand and model herding practices conceived from experiential knowledge. They do so not to standardize and reduce their complexity, but to make them more comprehensible, thus more attractive and teachable, and to give urban and rural people a sense of the herders' profession. Even twenty years ago in France, these research works provoked deep interest, not only by pastoralists and technical advisers in animal husbandry but also by managers of national and regional nature parks, many who lacked arguments to enable them to promote herding for practical and ecological reasons, not just cultural ones.

We suggest three reasons to renew interest in herding knowledge and practices at the dawn of the twenty-first century: economic and social benefits from less oil and chemicals and more skilled herders; ecological benefits to soil, plants, herbivores, and people from herding livestock as opposed to using fences as livestock-sitters; and using herders as "ecological doctors" to provide ecosystem services.

Less Oil and Chemicals and More Skilled Herders

The economic crisis, especially in the sheep meat husbandry sector, has led to changes in supply and demand due to the globalization of trade. In France, the sheep population, which traditionally contributed 80 percent of the animals for meat production, lost more than half of its producers in the last thirty years: from 197,000 in 1979 to 58,000 in 2010. In spite of the increase of sheep numbers within herds, the income of sheep breeders is less than half of the agricultural national mean income. European agricultural subsidies included, the income is often barely the minimum wage, and it is impossible to maintain the farming activity if there is not a second income either on the farm, such as a bed and breakfast, or from outside the farm. Imported sheep meat, notably from the United Kingdom and New Zealand, accounts for more than half the sheep meat consumed in France. The French consumer doesn't hesitate, during economic crises, to favor a leg of lamb from New Zealand sold for only 5 to 7 €/kilogram ($2.99 to $4.19/pound). The price of lambs slaughtered in France is barely 2 to 2.5 times as high as the wholesale price of a European standard chicken grown in a battery cage.

As in France, the number of sheep operations in the United States has declined since the end of World War II, especially since the mid-1970s—from 110,000 in 1974 to 81,000 in December 2010. Nor has it been possible in the United States to maintain a sheep operation without a second income from outside the ranch. However, the price for feeder lambs ($1.75/pound or more) and for lamb meat ($7.00 to $15.00/pound depending on cut) is currently very high, due to low numbers of sheep being produced in the United States.

This raises a question: Is it reasonable to produce lambs in France or the United States? We think yes, but perhaps not at any cost. The cost of fossil fuels is high and likely to increase. While technologies such as lateral drilling and fracking are increasing access to harder-to-get oil, concerns about ecological, social, and economic costs are soaring and the price of oil is continuing to escalate. It is thus critical to consider the advantages of thriftier and more autonomous modes of livestock production, those less dependent on fluctuating grain prices, industrial food, forage seeds, herbicides, oil, gas, and chemical fertilizers.

One solution that has endured the test of time is using local fodder resources, as herders can do on natural pastures, or using a combination of natural and cultivated pastures in daily grazing circuits. As discussed in this book, livestock make good use of fallow lands, shrubby areas, weeds, moorlands, and bushy undergrowth, with nutrition and production benefits that can be comparable to those obtained from cultivated pastures. A key role of the herder in generating such benefits is to intervene during the course of the daily meals to stimulate appetite, especially when forages vary in their chemical characteristics.

As the manager of a large cattle ranch in Utah told Michel, "One of our herders was originally a sheep guy who worked with cattle. I don't know how he did it, but he grazed cattle in the same part of the range two or three times longer than I expected and I saw no overgrazing or erosion. At dawn, cattle were satiated and calm. He gave them no supplemental feed, but most of the cattle were in good condition at the end of the season. That's why I decided to pay the guy twice the regular salary. I also offered him a bed at the ranch, not in one of our herder wagons."

Michel decided to look at the range. From the window of a pick-up truck, sagebrush steppe looks an endless, monotonous, dusty plateau, a kind of shepherd's despair. But, just a few steps out of the pick-up, Michel found shallow dry washes, or ravines, that contained fresh grasses including sainfoin (*Onobrychis viciifolia* Scop.), a highly palatable legume. In such a landscape, what would non-herded cattle doubtless do? First, they would graze daily in the ravines searching for their preferred forage: sainfoin. Then, they would continue to roam around in the ravines, losing time and body condition searching for more sainfoin and fresh grass. Finally, they would be resigned to climb the plateau to graze the fibrous and less palatable vegetation of the sagebrush steppe, while frequently interrupting their meals to check for any regrowth of sainfoin and fresh grass in the nearest ravine.

On the other hand, a knowledgeable shepherd and his dog will limit access of cattle to the shallow washes. Within each grazing circuit, the herder will sequence the forages on offer, allowing access to sainfoin as an appetizer at appropriate times during the day to stimulate the appetite of cattle for the more fibrous plants. As will be discussed in this book, such a herding technique can double the amount of total forages eaten from a given area compared with grazing in fenced pastures without a herder to intervene in the forage selection process. Less oil, less chemicals, and more herder know-how — that's an alternative that in spite of the cost of the herder's salary can yield great economic benefits.

From Fences as Livestock-Sitters to Intensive Herding

European landscapes evolved with centuries of intense use, which created a need to divide grazing lands into sectors a skilled herder could efficiently combine in daily grazing circuits. They are not "let the livestock roam" landscapes. In contrast, the western United States evolved during the past twelve thousand years with extensive grazing by wild herbivores. Livestock were introduced into the United States in the sixteenth and seventeenth centuries. More recently, in the late 1800s and early 1900s, most rangeland in western United States was devoted to extensive grazing by cattle and sheep. Before the killing of their livestock in the 1930s, Navajo shepherds grazed large herds of sheep and goats on their land, Dinétah, in the Southwest. Nowadays the West is changing dramatically: land is becoming fragmented by real-estate development and subdivisions; suburbanization and the sprawl of large cities with people eager to recreate year-around on wildlands, nature reserves and parks; and energy developments. These changes have created a need for a more controlled and sequenced use of the land, including more intensively managed livestock, even in large cattle ranches.

In the United States we've come to rely on fences and various grazing systems to influence the foraging behavior of livestock and in turn the health of soil and plants, herbivores, and people. But that wasn't always the case. In 1918, Moroni A. Smith, a shepherd who wrote *Herding and Handling Sheep: On the Open Range in U.S.A.*, described the collective knowledge he and many other herders gained during their careers of moving and placing sheep on open ranges in the West.[1] He wrote about the importance of unlimited patience, kindness, and gentleness when moving sheep; getting the right start in the morning so that sheep foraged along the path the shepherd desired; the correct way to turn and place sheep during the day; and how to encourage sheep to make the moves the herder wanted them to make. In essence, Moroni A. Smith could have written a chapter in our book describing how to use low-stress techniques to move and place sheep (or cattle) on rangelands, blending herding and grazing as people did long before we turned fences into babysitters. We should rekindle our relationships with livestock and landscapes rather than relying on fences as livestock-sitters.

Fences can't do what a knowledgeable herder can to optimize grazing from a diversity of forage resources over days and weeks. Shepherds move livestock from meal to meal during the day and across a landscape in ways that stimulate appetites, thus improving the nutrition, health, welfare, and production of animals. By designing daily grazing circuits, a skilled shepherd can stimulate appetite of individuals by encouraging the flock to use different forages from a mix of plants, some highly palatable and others less palatable. By far the highest level of sophistication in targeted grazing with goats, sheep, and cattle can be achieved through the relationship between a herder, a flock, and a landscape of "weedy" species, some categorized as "desirable" and others "undesirable." The United States has over 50,000 species of invasive animals and plants, and the number is rising. We spend over $120 billion annually in attempts to control these species and their damages. Sadly, we've had little impact. Indeed, the United States has the greatest number of herbicide-resistant plant species on the planet, nearly 125 species. We need to learn how to "love them to death" with shepherds and herbivores.

What better way than skilled herders using livestock as tools of their trade? But that takes knowledge of the relationship between the herd and the smorgasbord of plants on a landscape. To set up the "first course" of a meal, a "booster phase" of ten to twenty minutes may be just right while one of thirty to forty minutes may be too long. Moreover, a herder must know which mix of plants works best as "appetizers" and "booster" phases to target grazing on the "first course" of a meal. The ability of the herder to understand such subtleties and to influence where and how long the flock enjoys various courses in a meal requires nuanced moves throughout the day. A rancher in the West told Michel, "On my ranch, I need four workers to make a daily survey and fix fences." With four full-time cowboys, why not use two of them for intensive herding? Replacing fences as babysitters with stockmanship and management-intensive grazing is an exciting opportunity.

At first glance, intensive herding may seem a costly imposition. However, herding unites two areas of growing interest and competence among ranchers in the United States: low-stress techniques for moving and settling animals, advocated by people like Bud Williams,[2] Steve Cote,[3] and Burt Smith,[4] and management-intensive grazing, advocated by people like Allan Savory[5] and Jim Gerrish.[6] Ranchers and farmers are learning to move and place livestock in landscapes in ways that minimize stress to

livestock and herders. They are also using management-intensive grazing, moving livestock at least once, if not several times, each day. That is
creating a mind frame that can accept moving and placing animals regularly throughout the day as part of a herded grazing circuit to enhance
health of animals and land. Even five years ago these ideas would have
been shocking to land managers, but given the interest in more intensive
management and the many now-recognized benefits of properly managed
grazing for soil, plants, domestic and wild animals, and people, they are
no longer outrageous.

Finally, herding is becoming ever more relevant in light of the recent
debate over how to manage wildlife. Herding could be used to manage grazing for sage grouse habitat improvement. People could design
grazing strategies that don't rely on fences, which pose a hazard to sage
grouse and are expensive to build and maintain. Such targeted grazing
could be used to improve range health, and to improve sage grouse habitat. Increasing annual and perennial forbs, and resulting insect populations, to improve brood-rearing habitat, providing residual nesting cover
for grouse, managing weeds, and improving livestock nutrition could all
be the objectives of stress-free stockmanship. Proper herding also could
deter predators of cattle or sheep, including reintroduced and opportunistic grey wolves in Wyoming, Montana, and Idaho — much of the heart
of the western sheep region.

Herders as "Ecological Doctors" Providing Ecosystem Services

Historically, many conservationists believed "grazing was bad for nature." But today, with more grounded experience, highlighted in books
such as *Gardeners of Eden* by Dan Dagget[7] and *Revolution on the Range* by
Courtney White,[8] some people are convinced that managed grazing can
preserve plant and animal biodiversity and landscape health. Conservationists, land managers, and people in urban areas are becoming aware
of targeted grazing to reduce weeds in cities, rangelands, and forests in
ways not known even a decade ago. Certainly US ranchers such as John
and Jocelyn Haskell have used stockmanship with cattle to increase the
abundance of nutritious shrubs, thus improving winter ranges for elk and
deer. In Namibia, holistic resource managers like Collin Boggs are using
stockmanship with cattle to improve watersheds. And in Australia farmers such as Bruce Maynard are using stress-free stockmanship to target
grazing of weeds with cattle and sheep.

In the absence of managed disturbances such as grazing, vegetation can
become dominated by a few unwanted species, weeds can encroach, and
wildfires can exacerbate the erosion of soil. Examples abound where ban-

ning grazing to "protect" nature was ruinous for maintaining habitat mosaics for wildlife. Just as clearly, grazing per se is not enough: positive environmental impacts depend on how grazing is managed, particularly on extensive rangelands with great diversity of soils and plants, as opposed to monoculture pastures of grass. Managing grazing requires know-how to integrate the dynamics of vegetation with the changing needs of the herd, within and among days and landscapes. By adjusting how a landscape is used during the course of a meal, a skilled herder can optimize forage value for the herd while conserving or restoring biodiversity.

In *A Sand County Almanac*, Aldo Leopold[9] wrote that while misuse of the ax, the cow, and the plow had devastated landscapes in many places in the United States, those same tools could be used to rejuvenate the very lands they had degraded. He appreciated the possibilities for people to use domestic animals to become what we propose to refer to as "ecological doctors": herders that practice intensive herding both for the proper feeding of the herd, the benefit of the land, and the well-being of people who use the products produced from the land. Young people in natural resource schools in the United States still read about and admire Aldo Leopold well over a half century after he died. So, too, do conservationists and land managers.

A skilled herder is analogous to an "ecological doctor" who at his finest has learned how to maintain the health of communities by providing ecological medicine in the form of ecosystem services. The herd in his hand is a living organism, a biological and ecological "instrument" for enhancing and maintaining the health of soil and water, plants, and the wild and domestic animals that depend on them for food — as well as providing ecosystem services for people. While scientists and environmentalists have discussed ecosystem services for decades, these services were popularized and their classifications formalized in the 2005 publication of the United Nations *Millennium Ecosystem Assessment* (MEA), a four-year study involving more than 1,300 scientists worldwide. They organized ecosystem services into four categories: *provisioning* (e.g., producing food and water), *regulating* (e.g., controlling climate and disease), *supporting* (e.g., nutrient cycling and pollinating crops), and *cultural* (e.g., spiritual and recreational benefits). Properly managed livestock can provide most of these ecosystem services.

World leaders are looking for ways to deal with global issues such as climate change, the role of carbon in those processes, and the increasing costs of fossil fuels. They often seek technological fixes, but they need to look beyond cars, coal-fired power plants, and big industry to local farming and grazing practices. Two-thirds of the Earth is rangeland, home to 2 billion people who depend on livestock at least partially for their livelihood. Thus, managing land for carbon sequestration and low fossil fuel inputs, even on a small scale, could have a big impact on people and the planet. In the United States, the cowboys and shepherds who moved herds in the nineteenth century did so to provide a service to people: meat and wool. In the process, they became the cattle and sheep ranchers of the twentieth century. Ranchers today have an opportunity to provide other kinds of services, ones not exclusively focused on meat but also on using livestock to generate ecosystem services.

GENERATING INTEREST, TRANSMITTING KNOW-HOW, CREATING OPPORTUNITIES

While there is great potential to use herding to manage landscapes in ways not remotely possible with fences, several issues must be addressed before young people in the United States will get interested in becoming herders as ecological doctors. First, few young people are aware of activities such as herding, let alone the broader concept of ecological doctors, and among ranchers who are cognizant the work is held in low esteem. Who wants a vocation as a herder? Most ranchers are not inclined to spend long hours working with animals in natural landscapes. Mostly people from other countries come to United States to work as shepherds, and they generally accept hard working conditions and low wages. Some of them had never before worked with sheep. Thus, in addition to lack of awareness and low regard for the occupation, there is no money in becoming a herder. Finally, there are few jobs in the profession. So, the critical questions are: Is it possible to raise awareness and esteem for herding practices and for herders to earn a decent wage? If so, who will train herders? Where will they be employed? A much broader issue pertains to the notion of ecological doctors. Can we create programs to train people as ecological doctors who care for the health of soil and plants, animals and people? What form might that take? Do young folks want to be ecological doctors?

Herding Schools for Young Americans?

Universities that train people to be stewards of land are filled with young folks who want to do good things to benefit water, soil, plants, animals, and ecosystems generally. . . . Unfortunately, they are not taught through hands-on experience to use domestic animals to care for the health of communities, but they could be. Sometimes activities such as herding—described as "old-fashioned"—come back in vogue as people's values change.

We need to create programs to train young people, not necessarily to obtain advanced degrees, but preferably to become ecological doctors who through their relationships with livestock and landscapes can work holistically with communities. It is worth noting that over a hundred years ago medical doctors were poorly paid, the profession was not held in high esteem, and the American Medical Association was little-known in the United States. Since then, programs were developed to train doctors, who united and convinced people we couldn't live without their services. They are now a major force in the United States.

In the United States, we have no formal schools to train herders. Universities have degrees in water, soil, plant, animal, fish and wildlife, and range sciences, as well as behavioral and landscape ecology, but no curricula train students holistically in all these disciplines. This collective knowledge is not integrated to create and maintain the health of rural and urban landscapes without costly inputs of fossil fuels, herbicides, and pesticides. Anyone interested in becoming an ecological doctor would have to acquire the skills on their own by attending schools and workshops and working on the job. Can a program be created to train herders, and at what costs? If so, how do we integrate training with opportunities for employment for ecological doctors? This is an opportunity to create programs to train ecological doctors.

France has four herding schools (chapters 12 and 13) that came into being from the early 1970s to the end of the 1990s thanks to requests by livestock farmers who lacked skilled herders. From then until now, many farmers counseled their children to quit farming and find more profitable and less demanding occupations in the city. Others encouraged their children to go to agricultural schools to get a farm operator diploma, which didn't include herding livestock on rangeland as part of the curriculum (chapter 1). In so doing, most of the remnant hired herders — some knowledgeable but aging, others younger but not as reliable — were not sufficiently motivated and trained to face the many changes in herding: larger flocks and herds to manage, grazing resources altered due to land fragmentation and forests expansion, environmental concerns and provisions, multiple usage in the mountainous areas.

During the past two decades, French guys and gals have become interested in herding as a profession, and these four schools receive roughly three hundred candidacy letters annually (chapter 12). The United States doesn't have such schools, but the same proportion of citizens would yield fifteen hundred young American candidates each year. What are the origins of all the young French folks interested in herding? Could there be similar interest in the United States, or do the youth of France differ so greatly in interests and values? At first glance, it seems clear that France as a part of Old Europe has little in common with the United States in agricultural secular traditions and know-how. France's diverse and delicate landscapes testify to this, especially in hilly and mountainous parts in the South such as Provence and the Pyrenees, where one can easily find herders and some US tourists in summer.

In fact, most young adult French males and females have become more or less conscientiously quite similar to their United States counterparts. French television, video games, and the internet shower every one of them with US songs, television series, and movies. Those media transmit a distillation, if not a caricature, of US social and material values. The majority of young people are spending a major amount of money to follow the most up-to-date fashions. Cell phones, social networks, video games, cars, and binge drinking have become essential components of social life. Is there any reason to think that some of these young people would be interested in herding sheep, goats, or cattle for a vocation? Incredibly, the answer is yes.

More than 80 percent of young adults who are applicants in French herding schools now come from cities. They discover the schools while browsing for jobs on the internet. Some also had a chance to meet and visit with a herder while hiking in the mountains. They are fed up with costly, noisy, polluted cities and suburbs. They are horrified with urban waste, especially food scraps. Generally, they've had cruel experiences in schools while earning diplomas that take them only to temporary jobs and unemployment. They are eager to be involved in a job that makes more sense than the one they've got. They are also searching for a better quality of life, with a view to raise a family. Most of them have read books like *The Man Who Planted Trees*, written by Jean Giono, a French writer also known in the United States for this story about one shepherd's long and successful singlehanded effort to rejuvenate a mountain in Provence.[10] Stories like these make some French youth dream of a life made up of endless starry skies, breathtaking mountain views, the sound of their heartbeats mixed with the musical bells of sheep returning at night to a shed built two or three centuries ago.

Their interest and awareness are enhanced because French herding schools, along with livestock farmers' unions and pastoral services, have made constant efforts to improve the image of the profession to reflect the ever-changing meaning and many skills required for the job. The possibilities are then presented to young urban adults through their favorite mass media, including webpages, web movies, television documentaries, and DVDs that illustrate the multiple challenges and opportunities of being a herder. As discussed in this book, the livestock farming profession and regional entities—including national parks and regional natural parks—have also greatly improved living conditions for herders. Most new and old-but-refurbished cabins can now accommodate the shepherd's wife and one to two children. Nearly all are equipped with solar panels that provide electricity, refrigeration, and hot water. Cell phone signals are easily received near or within most cabins.

The great majority of the young French folks who enroll in the herding schools have no personal or family experience with herding or animal husbandry. But increasingly some of them have a diploma and some primary experience in nature conservation. They are disappointed with the usual academic approaches in the ecological sciences concerned primarily with "theory" and with referencing and mapping the behaviors and habitats of plants, birds, and wild ungulates in wildland reserves. As applicants to herding schools, they hope to put their sensitivity and knowledge of natural systems into action through becoming a skillful and environmentally friendly herder.

Blending Hands-on and Scientific Knowledge to Create Job Opportunities

When seen by surprise on a high-definition television or on a cell phone streaming video, the herding occupation may appear an attractive alternative to someone feeling abused by "city lights" both in France and the United States. Of course this viewing leaves out the heat, cold, flies, and the smells of life and death. Such a preview is the first step in catching the attention of young adults. Then they need an opportunity to enter a learning process—not to go back to school full-time like any teen, but to blend hands-on experience in real-life situations with more scientific and formal knowledge, and with individual tutorship made by an experienced herder or farmer (details in chapters 12 and 13). Some young Americans, fed up with "solutions as usual" in this time of global economic and social despair, unemployment, and environmental crises, could find attractive such way of learning and partaking in an occupation with meaning.

We put here a hypothesis: as in France, there are herders in the United States with experiential knowledge and skills that can be used within an educational network. But, again as in France, this is a "hidden" knowledge, as practically nobody, including the herders themselves, discusses their know-how or links it with other knowledge. Why? First, they have to build it through a long and patient working relationship with herds on specific grazing lands. It is hard to explain, to share with somebody else, even sometimes with their nearest colleagues or family. Second, such knowledge gets rather radically away from conventional ways of thinking and acting in science and grazing management, with the many prescriptions for "adapted animal breed," "optimal stocking rate," "best forage quality," and so on. Third, there is not yet enough sense to discuss the art of herding in public arenas. Before writing this book, French scientists and livestock advisers with an interest in herding began an extensive search to find herders who would agree to discuss their knowledge. They did so, not to standardize and thus impoverish such knowledge, but to make it more comprehensible, thus more attractive and teachable. We hope this book will help people in the United States and other English-speaking countries get certain "keys" or initial pathways to initiate similar programs. We also hope this book will help some herders in the United States to develop an interest in becoming tutors for transmitting their know-how.

All the herders in France, and probably most in the United States, are deeply convinced that *"herding certainly cannot be learned from a paper board!"* Such know-how must come first from hands-on experience, and any scientist or engineer who would try to give them courses about "how to herd more skillfully" is an imprudent and arrogant person. Moreover, the majority of experienced herders are reluctant to accept knowledge and prescriptions that come directly from a lab or experiment station. They know well the degree to which agronomy and animal sciences have succeeded in disqualifying their own knowledge and practices as being too "subjective" (chapter 1).

From our experience, we may say that trainees and experienced herders become highly interested when scientists tell them about their own learning process: initial paradigms, controversies, methods, conditions, trials, errors, unexpected results, and paradigm changes (chapter 8). Scientists, too, have experiential knowledge, acquired step by step. To the degree that they conduct research to understand biological principles and processes, their work has generality across time and space. On the other hand, research to study practices deals with specific sets of conditions that vary uniquely according to peoples and landscapes, in which case scientists cannot pretend their conclusions are applicable to all sites and conditions. The circumstances — places, times, and human values — are an essential part of their research, so scientists must not focus on proving the generality of their results in biological science. They have to adopt the paradigms and research methods of anthropologists and ethnologists. They also must not pretend to be herders; they must make efforts to share their learning processes in a way that is similar to that of the herders. When the educational network is supposed to blend knowledge, the posture scientists adopt is a crucial point to consider.

Herding is a relationship between man and the animals in our care. Roy Kady, a Navajo shepherd and master weaver from Teec Nos Pos, Arizona, told Michel when he was invited to visit his farm, "You and I have something in common: our interest about how to live and work together with sheep and goats!"

BOOK CONTENT

Thirty-three authors of various origins and experiences contributed to this book: eleven salaried herders or farmer-herders; ten researchers; five pastoral engineers; five training officers in herding schools; and two managers of natural areas. Naturally, most authors are working in the South of France, near or within mountains and hilly areas (see Figure 1). We regret the absence of contributors from Corsica, where livestock farmers and herders make strong efforts to conserve and renew a living Mediterranean pastoral culture. We also regret the absence of managers from

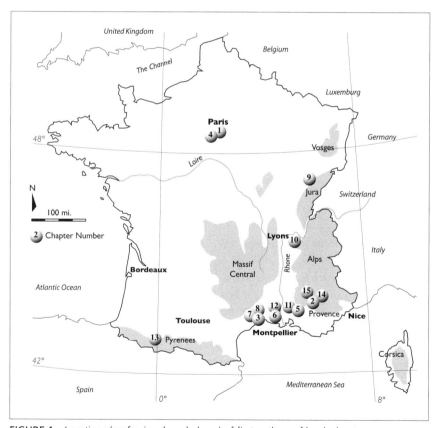

FIGURE 1 – Locations (professional workplaces) of first authors of book chapters.

the French National Forest Service, who have collective experiences of nearly thirty years with herders who have worked for them to defend forests against wildfires using targeted grazing management in the South of France.

The book is organized into six parts: "Shepherds in France: A Know-How to be Revalorized," "Herding Practices by Shepherds: Scientific Explorations," "Amazing Appetite of Herded Animals," "Shepherds and Nature Conservation," "Herding Schools," and "Herding Occupation as Seen from Inside."

Shepherds in France: A Know-How to be Revalorized. We chose to start the book with a chapter entrusted to Bernard Hubert, former scientific director of the French National Research Institute in Agronomy (INRA), regarding the successive changes of function and social value of the rangelands in France during the last two centuries. Rangelands are areas of predilection of the herders. Hubert reminds us how, within the context of agricultural modernization, agronomic research contributed to a loss of technical knowledge in animal husbandry, with disqualification of rangeland resources and therefore of herders' know-how. He pleads for voluntarily "subjective" research practices, where the sharing of knowledge between researchers and practitioners is essential.

The practitioners are herders, but who are they in reality? How many exist in France, how has their occupation changed during the last forty years, and what are their current working conditions? These issues are addressed in the second chapter, entrusted to Jean-Pierre Legeard. He is president of the French Pastoralism Association, which is affiliated with all the pastoral support services in France. We come to realize in this chapter why it is necessary to give their knowledge more consideration, especially when conceiving grazing contracts that include achieving biodiversity conservation goals on both public and private lands.

Herding Practices by Shepherds: Scientific Explorations. Four chapters are grouped here that link researchers, shepherds, and also some pastoral engineers. For the first time in science, researchers tried to understand how shepherds conceive and practice herding at the scale of a farm territory or high mountain range to utilize various forage resources while avoiding overgrazing and soil erosion.

Chapter 3 is written by Pierre Martinand, agroeconomist and animal production scientist. In the 1970s, Pierre was working for the French Ministry of Agriculture. He was responsible for promoting techniques of animal husbandry that substituted the capital for the workforce. He thus tried to understand why sheep farmers of the Southern Pre-Alps persisted in herding their flocks with shepherds. This practice turned out to be relevant, notably through its combination of use of cultivated lands with that of nearby rangelands. Critically, his findings collided with the deep disbelief of animal scientists at INRA, who were then occupied with publishing the first tables of feed values of cultivated forages and principles of feeding at the trough. Convinced that the only valuable results in animal science are non-circumstantial ones, they told Pierre, "We cannot publish your paper, since the herder is the one who determines the herd's [production] results."

The fourth and fifth chapters are dedicated to exploratory research ten years later on a high mountain summer pasture in the Alps. Jean-Pierre Deffontaines, geoagronomist of rural landscapes and agricultural practices, had met a shepherd, André Leroy, in the course of mountain hiking. They had corresponded for several years, and André agreed to work with the researchers to explain in detail his practices of herding and to help model them. In the chapter by Isabel Savini, the mountain pasture changes its face. It appears strategically structured by the shepherd at the beginning of the summer season, then tactically used with grazing circuits in the course of days and weeks. This know-how is experiential and quite technical, and at the same time respectful of the sheep and the pastoral area. The chapter by Elizabeth Lécrivain, animal behaviorist, continues to develop explanations of the previous chapter, and with the help of some meticulous drawings by André, illustrates how a shepherd is able to evaluate the relative quality of grazing areas by observing different forms taken by the herd (elongated, ovoid, etc.) in the course of a daily herding circuit. No doubt the herd as a whole is the biological entity maneuvered by a shepherd.

Agronomists and animal production scientists ignored the results of the last two chapters. The research procedures are not canonical, and the conclusions are perplexing compared with the simplicity of traditional scientific models dedicated to pastures. For example, the shepherd's knowledge of the terrain — if it's cup-shaped or convex and how that changes the stability of the herd and the time each animal dedicates to the selection and intake of the plants — reappraises the established scientific idea that states pastoral value is the function only of biomass, nutritive value, and the prehensibility of edible plants. Nonetheless, these works were promoted and developed by pastoral engineers as efficient tools for the practical management of high mountain pastures.

Chapter 6 takes us down to the plain, on the steppe of Crau near the Mediterranean Sea, a large area of uniform and flat space where transhumant shepherds have herded for centuries. We wanted this chapter, entrusted to pastoral engineer Rémi Dureau, to show that shepherds and the animals are the same on the plains as in high mountain pastures, thus the methods of herding are similar. Though physical, climatic, and vegetation cover conditions are much different, the shepherds' know-how imposes itself with the same rules of action, having apparently some general value.

Amazing Appetite of Herded Animals. Chapter 7 is a sharing of experiential knowledge between a shepherd and a goatherder about practicing herding. Though their conditions appear to be very different, with distinct landscapes and animal species, Michel, the researcher who organized and comments on this debate, discovers many common rules they use to optimize the appetite of a herd foraging on diversified pastures. The next chapter synthesizes over ten years of research led by Michel concerning sheep and goatherders practicing their skills in hills and mountain pastures. By adjusting the sequences of a half-day grazing circuit, which corresponds to a meal, a herder can optimize the feeding value of pasture by increasing the intake to twice that expected from the scientific models based on the nutritive values of individual forages. The keys to this unexpected success are numerous, but they can be explained in part as the food education of very young animals and subsequent interventions of the shepherd in the course of a meal to renew appetite in relation to less palatable plant species. Essentially a grazing place—fallow land, grassland, or bushy undergrowth—does not have any fixed value. Rather, the worth depends on the relationship between the herd and the herder as they make grazing circuits that utilize various plant communities. Each local feeding value depends on the order in which the shepherd will guide the herd in the course of a circuit.

Shepherds and Nature Conservation. Environmental policymakers in Europe, particularly those concerned about biodiversity and conservation of remarkable habitats of fauna and flora, appear recently interested in pastoral practices and shepherds' know-how. But how does that happen in practice? We entrust chapter 9 to Francis Muller, one of the managers of the French National Federation of the Natural Area Conservancies. Everywhere in France to some degree, even far north, conservancies have recruited shepherds or made contracts with them to help restore and maintain protected natural sites. The problem is that today these sites are located in regions where agriculture has become artificialized, where it is therefore difficult to find experienced stockbreeders and shepherds using natural forage resources, which are quite different from the more usual seeded meadows. Based on about ten years of experience, conservancies paint a picture in muted colors. Passing from a position of distrust to one of partnership can't be done in a day. Obstacles are numerous, and many depend on their capacity to mutually understand each other. Chapter 10 was thus entrusted to two people: Mathieu Erny, a salaried shepherd working for Rhône-Alpes Natural Area Conservancy, and François Salmon, his employer. They describe, besides their respective professional roles, what they judge to be the keys to success for herder-conservationist collaboration.

In these two chapters, the policies regarding nature and biodiversity appreciate and encourage the shepherds and their practices. But the situation for shepherds in France can differ greatly due to the fact that one of the elements of biodiversity is also a protected predator: the grey wolf. We entrusted researcher Marc Vincent to describe how the return of wolves to the French Alpine range is convulsing the practices and living conditions of shepherds. From this study, accomplished mostly in the Queyras Regional Natural Park during 2005 and 2006), one realizes the measures of herd protection recommended in France are not very efficient, nor especially humanly allowable. Due to the presence of guard dogs, areas used by the shepherds sometimes become risk zones for mountain hikers and village residents. Securing the herd in a night pen located near the shepherd's cabin hinders good pastoral management and alters mountain meadows and soils. More fundamentally, there is a big contradiction between a policy of encouraging pastoral practices for nature conservation and a policy of no regulation of the French population of wolves. In France, the strictly protected status encourages the wolf to develop a highly opportunistic feeding behavior, especially with respect to sheep and goats. The national policy of "nothing but high fences and guard dogs" discourages stockbreeders and shepherds from persisting in their occupation.

Herding Schools. In France there are four establishments that train shepherds and cow herders in one- to two-year programs. We entrust both chapters on this topic to the teachers in charge: Michelle Jallet, responsible for training at the Shepherds School Le Merle in Provence, and Pierre Gascouat, co-responsible for training at the agricultural high school of Oloron in the Pyrenees. Marie Labreveux, teacher in the training of Rhône-Alpes, cosigns the first chapter. These schools alternate sessions at school with herding in the field under the supervision of confirmed shepherds and farmers. In so doing, young trainees become immersed in the shepherds' culture and acquire the know-how to work on their own. This is a huge challenge for the training officers, whose trainees are different every year in terms of schooling and professional experience as well as personal expectations. Each year is thus a kind of social and pedagogic experiment in which training must also take place by exchanging points of view within cohorts of trainees' classes.

Herding Occupation as Seen from Inside. We wanted the shepherds to have the last word. These authors had not read the other chapters at the time each one wrote his or her chapter. This section of the book is not therefore about answers, validation, or criticisms of other writings.

We entrusted chapter 14 to Isabelle Baumont, a salaried shepherd who had provisionally interrupted her career herding animals in high mountains to get an MS degree in sociology at Paris Sorbonne University. For the first time in this book, she tackles the emotional part of the job and the discipline the occupation requires due to daily work with the herd in rigorous mountain conditions with all kinds of weather. Stories and analyses of the herders' jobs show how much harsher and more demanding the job actually is compared to what most young shepherds imagine at first. Isabelle also helps us understand that the physical and mental demands of herding allow the shepherd to establish intimate familiarity with the herd and to appreciate the mountain pasture as a true home — a space of freedom, but also sometimes a space of social isolation and imprisonment.

The final chapter was entrusted to Roger Minard, a salaried shepherd and vice president of the Provence and Southern Alps Shepherds and Cowherders Association. His chapter is based on a discussion that he organized with six of his colleagues of various ages and experiences. The conversation concerns the realities of the occupation as these professionals live it from day to day. The shepherds organized the chapter. They chose the topics to be addressed and their order of presentation, beginning with how they feel others — all the people who also use French public lands for other purposes — regard them. No nostalgia here, just frank talk, realism, and reflection.

Finally, we have to say that other experienced shepherds deeply wanted to contribute to our book, but not in written form. They invited Michel to take photos of their places during periods of the year when they were practicing herding. The photographs of Patrick Fabre, pastoral engineer, those of shepherds Guillaume Constant, Marie Labreveux and Roger Minard, as well as the front cover photo by Pierre Constant, supplemented Michel's photos. The shepherds then individually chose the photos that they considered the most representative of their job and working conditions. These photos are placed in different locations throughout the book to satisfy the visual appetite of the reader, as supplementary "visual stories" without words.

OUR ASPIRATIONS FOR THIS BOOK

With this book we hope to raise awareness of what's possible if people rely less on fences and grazing systems and more on rekindling our relationships with livestock and landscapes, linking soil and plants with herbivores and human beings. We want to celebrate this little-known but fascinating culture in France. We wish as well to underscore the idea that rigorous research in partnership with the gathering of local knowledge — researchers working together with practitioners — can lead to better results for understanding landscapes and our relationships with them than can either academic science or practice in isolation. We hope that, after reading in this book about shepherds' know-how, you will agree that we need to create programs to train young people as ecological doctors who, through their relationships with livestock and landscapes, can work holistically with communities of human beings.

Many young people may consider shepherding in the open range an unrewarding occupation, one that appears at first glance to have little in common with contemporary social issues and technological progress. That is certainly the case in industrialized countries like the United States and France, which have no living pastoralist culture. But it also may be the case for young people in African or Latin American countries, where they are trying to escape from centuries-long traditions, keeping their eyes on North American and European social and material values. We hope some of these young folks will read the book and be surprised to see that countries like ours are now encouraging more herders as ecological doctors working closely with researchers. They might then be interested in imagining and creating practices that link the health of soil and plants with animals and human beings, after seeing that as a critical issue for their own well-being and that of the planet.

NOTES

[1] Smith, M., 1918.
[2] http://stockmanship.com
[3] Cote, 2004.
[4] Smith, B.M. 1998.
[5] Savory, 1998.
[6] Gerrish, 2004.
[7] Dagget, 2005.
[8] White, 2008.
[9] Leopold, 1949.
[10] Giono, 1953.

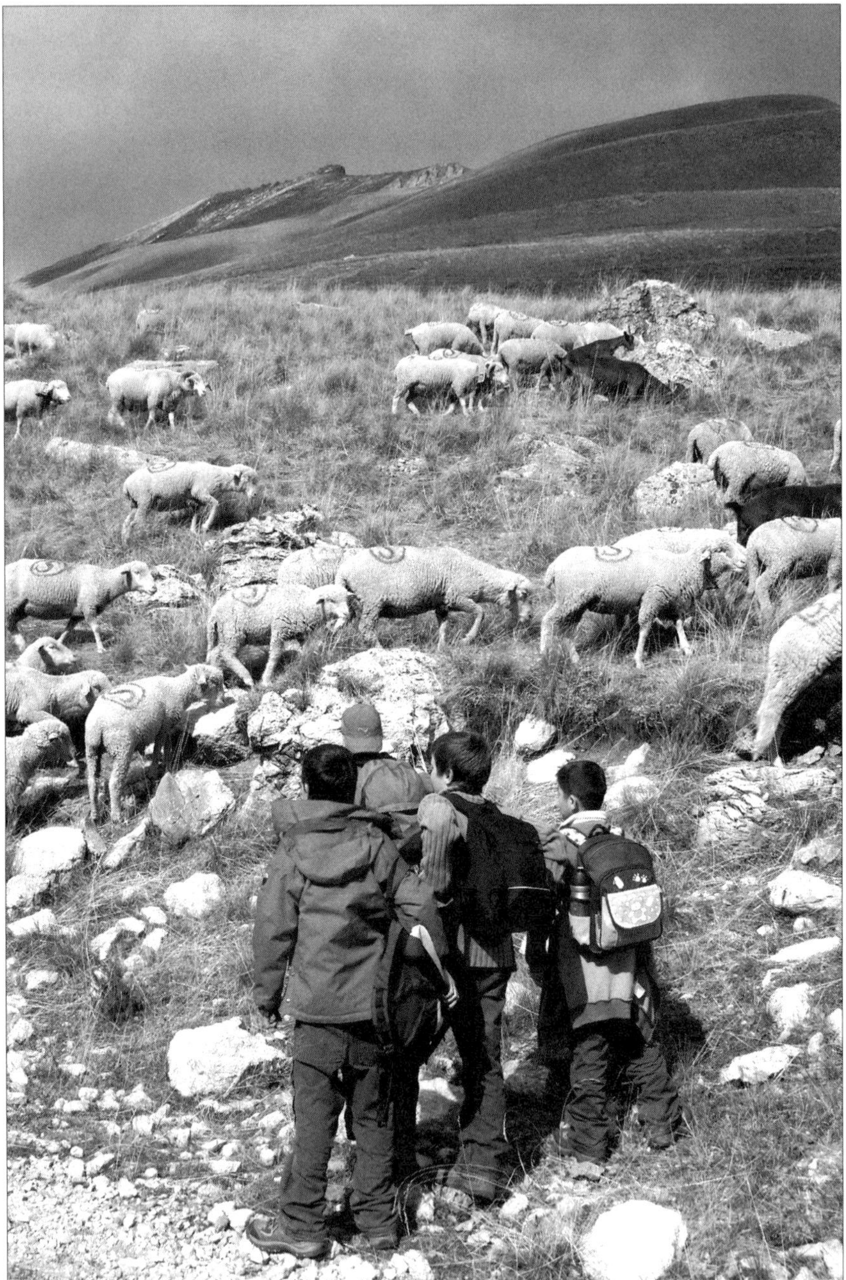

PATRICK FABRE

PART 1

Shepherds in France:

A Know-How to be Revalorized

CHAPTER 1

The Rangelands of Southern France:

Two Centuries of Radical Change

Bernard Hubert, Christian Deverre
& Michel Meuret

THE rural landscapes of southern France are widely admired. The French think highly of them, especially city-dwellers out for some fresh air over a weekend, as do tourists from other countries who like to spend their holidays in a rented country cottage with a view of hills against a mountain backdrop. Everyone delights in the clusters of villages and farms, small cultivated fields, roads bordered with low walls, hillsides bright with flowers, and groves of hardwoods and conifers. And when the sounds of nature are overlaid with the music of a flock of sheep with their bells, the effect is enchanting. A woman visiting from Wyoming once told us, "I was brought up near the Grand Tetons, and when it comes to landscapes, I'm not easily impressed . . . but I must admit, this is magnificent."

At first sight, it seems natural to think these landscapes have been here forever, or at least for centuries. They appear to be the outcome of a wealth of ancestral knowledge handed down within families by generations of peasants. Everything in sight looks serene, meticulously planned and laid out for the benefit of both nature and agriculture. But that is the picture as seen from the side of the road or the window of the rented country cottage.

A closer look, in the course of a walk up into the fringes of the woods, reveals that under the trees, the countryside is actually covered with ruins, including the tumbled remnants of stone walls and former roads hidden beneath thickets of brambles. Further on, the visitor finds himself in the midst of what was once upon a time an orchard with various kinds of fruit trees now gone to brush, having been left unpruned and unharvested for decades. Still further, he may notice, lying on the ground, some fragments of a plate, the remains of a pig feeding trough, or a rusty horseshoe. At this point, the visitor may sit down on a convenient rock and ask himself some questions. Who used to eat that fruit, who once fed those pigs, and who built those countless terrace retaining walls? When was this countryside, so peaceful at first glance, ravaged by war?

The visitor might think of asking the shepherd he met a short time previously at the head of his flock. He would know all about it. But, doubtless to the visitor's surprise, the shepherd would turn out to be someone who had recently moved to the region from a city, and while he would know a great deal about his sheep, he would know nothing about the local history (see chapters 2 and 12).

For that reason, we propose to describe the successive upheavals that have affected these rural landscapes, primarily as a result of changes in the uses of the rangelands and the consequences of those changes for farmers' and herders' array of skills. We shall begin by defining what we mean by "rangelands" in the European sense (i.e., lands traditionally devoted to pastoral husbandry, mainly shepherding). Within the period of our study, namely the past two centuries, we shall describe three periods that have led French society as a whole, including farmers, to radically different conclusions about the value of those lands. Initially, they were an integral aspect of mixed farming production systems, but they were subsequently marginalized by the widespread adoption of what are known as "rational" agricultural techniques. Since the 1990s they have attracted renewed social and political interest because of their environmental values. To conclude, we shall review the way agronomic research has accompanied, or even helped bring about, those upheavals, and we shall recommend new research practices that are both holistic and deliberately "subjective" in analyzing issues associated with rangelands and their resources.

LANDS "IN BETWEEN"

Rangelands are rural areas that agronomists and geographers designated with the term *saltus* as long ago as Roman times.[1] This ancient categorization differentiates them from *ager* (cultivated lands) on the one hand, and *silva* (forested lands) on the other. Rangelands comprise all uncultivated agricultural lands bearing natural vegetation that are commonly used as pasture for herbivores, including cattle, sheep, goats, horses, and donkeys. That is why the term "rangelands" as used in France refers to areas with a highly diverse vegetation cover, frequently including herbs, shrubs, and trees, which are not subjected either to agricultural operations (such as tillage, seeding, or fertilization) or to planned forest management activities (such as planting, thinning, and pruning).

In these "in-between" lands, the main impact on plant dynamics is produced by grazing livestock. On rangelands, in contrast to cultivated grasslands, a farmer manages his flock or herd to ensure that the animals are adequately fed while simultaneously seeing to it that the land's forage resources will be renewed and available for future seasons or years. In some situations, the farmer may supplement the effect of grazing with controlled burning or by cutting and shredding brush that is too dense for other control methods.

The perceived value of rangelands depends on their technical, economic, or social functions, which for the most part are associated with the land in light of objectives that are broader in scope than any associated with pastoral husbandry. Originally, rangelands were the main source of organic matter inputs (manure fertilizer) to farmland, conveyed there by livestock. They were subsequently abandoned by farm operators, especially those who specialized in field crops, as they became irrelevant when inorganic fertilizers came into general use. Now the pendulum has swung back around as the rangelands' role in biodiversity conservation or the preservation of landscapes, deemed to be outstanding, is coming to be recognized. Farmers have frequently found that their views on the value of rangelands have shifted, not that the characteristics of the land have changed in any way, but because the aims and productive processes of their animal husbandry operations have changed over time within an evolving social context.

RANGELANDS AS AN INTEGRAL PART
OF MIXED FARMING SYSTEMS

Until the second half of the nineteenth century, every part of rural France, including the mountainous Mediterranean regions of the South, was "full," inhabited by a dense, growing population.[2] Farmers, including livestock producers, were already caught up in market relationships, but their production systems, which covered most of their families' needs, functioned and perpetuated themselves using local resources almost exclusively. Farming systems were based on a sociospatial organizing principle that may be thought of as "domestic coordination"[3] within which peasants carried on a variety of activities, depending on seasons and occasions, which sometimes entailed periods of absence from the family home.

The countryside was thus used for complementary purposes involving several components, including not only cropland and rangeland but also woodland, depending on the location, legal status, and productive potential of the land in question and the technology available. The result was that every local community was a rather fine-grained, contrasting mosaic of cultivated fields, fallow lands, seminatural swards, scrublands, and areas of woodland, the latter in some cases the scene of logging operations. Both the rangelands, whether tree-covered or open, and the woodlands were major sources of energy and fertility exports: woodcutting (coppicing in the cases of oak and beech, in many cases with subsequent assarting and crop production for two to three years), gathering aromatic and medicinal plants, gathering small shrubs for firewood and compost, and pasturing animals during the day followed by their enclosure overnight on cultivated land.[4] At that time, the main function of sheep-raising in southern France was not wool or meat production but manure production: sheep manure was essential for maintaining fertility in two-year cereal crop rotation systems designed primarily to produce food for home consumption. Flocks of sheep consisted mainly of wethers (castrated males, or *moutons* in French, which has become our English word "mutton") that were not slaughtered until after their fourth or fifth annual shearing. Rangelands thus functioned as a fertility reserve within a heavily labor-intensive local system. They contributed to biological reproduction of the farming system while themselves becoming progressively transformed as a result of the cyclical recurrence of their various uses: scrubland opened up, coppice growth was reduced, erosion affected the most fragile soils, and vegetation dynamics were reoriented to expand shrub and small tree cover.

From the standpoint of the farmers and herders, whose aim was to produce manure, rangelands were regarded as particularly valuable when they provided herds with what nowadays would be called "coarse" feed (i.e., plants rich in low-digestibility fiber). The practice of herding, which can still be observed in many parts of the world today, frequently consisted of taking the animals around long closed loops in the course of the daily grazing circuit, with their rest periods (when they ruminated and dropped their dung) organized to coincide with times when the herd was on prospective arable land or in its immediate vicinity. Areas of rangeland with more nutritious plants or crop residue were used only when the herd included lactating dams and their offspring. At other times, areas with coarser vegetation were adequate for adult animals to maintain themselves and for replacement animals to grow satisfactorily.

The daily movement of the herd created a direct link between the rangeland, with its store of fertilizing substances, and the arable land, where families grew produce for home consumption or sale. As population pressures increased, herders took their herds further afield, thereby jeopardizing the system's performance owing to the increased energy expenditure needed to travel the longer distances. In some cases, plots of arable land were also relocated further away in an effort to utilize the remaining rangeland resources. When the resources of scrubland and undergrowth failed, herders began cutting foliage from the forest canopy. Beginning in the mid-nineteenth century, the government reacted by enacting new regulations and laws prohibiting any herding in woodland. Thus the public interest was adduced as justification for the abrupt denial of local rights of access to and use of resources previously managed within peasant communities through specific local rules and standards.

The herders were usually younger sons of peasant families. By custom they did not marry, which not only prevented them from inheriting the family property but also denied them decision-making power with respect to that property. Yet their herding skills were recognized as a professional asset highly valued and deemed worth handing down from generation to generation. Those skills were transmitted by "old herders" to "young herders" within family groups, and everywhere there were families renowned for their "good herders" who "knew the animals." But the knowledge was not formally codified in any way, and for that very reason could not be taught to third parties. It was transmitted essentially through a learning process based on guidance and support provided by one herder to another and through on-the-job training absorbed day after day in an ongoing interaction among herder, his animals, and the land where they grazed.

RANGELANDS MARGINALIZED BY THE RATIONALIZATION OF AGRICULTURE
Responding to Market Forces

In the second half of the nineteenth century and throughout the twentieth, France's rural areas were subject to a new economic regime. Urban areas were becoming demographically predominant, and, more important, means of transport and transport systems were being developed: national, colonial, and international food markets were coming into existence, and a burgeoning agri-food industrial sector, both upstream and downstream, had appeared. "Market coordination" was putting its stamp on agricultural production systems, leading to both regional and local specialization.[5] The market determined not only which areas were most suitable for various types of crop but, within communities and individual farms, which plots of land possessed the greatest economic potential for profitable market production, thanks to the adoption of "modern technology." The implementation and effectiveness of that technology were themselves the outcome of progress in the fields of transportation and the movement of goods (fertilizers, imported food products, and fossil fuels). As the land could now be fertilized with off-farm resources, farmers no longer had to keep livestock nor have neighbors who did. Stock-raising became an area of specialization in its own right, dedicated entirely to the commercial production of meat or milk and demanding for its animals, selected expressly for those purposes, an "enriched diet" consisting of cultivated grassland, silages, fodder corn, high-protein oilseed meal, and industrial feed mixes.

An Altered Landscape

In the new situation, with labor and capital concentrated on arable land and stock-raising having become specialized, rangelands served no purpose, so they were abandoned or planted with trees. In France, reforestation took place in the context of a government policy aimed at encouraging landowners to plant trees on their properties voluntarily. As a result, softwoods were planted on many properties with little regard for geographic or economic consistency. In some cases reforestation was carried out on isolated postage stamp–sized plots of land (some less than three acres in extent), thinning or pruning operations were seldom conducted by absentee owners, and timber harvesting was frequently difficult due to the small areas and inaccessibility of the forested areas. Conversely, there were instances of ambitious land acquisition strategies by large corporations (insurance companies, banks and the like) that bought large stretches of land and planted it all with softwoods, with the result that entire valleys were made uninhabitable. Some rangelands were thus converted to forest. The landscape became more coarse-grained, until ultimately a clear-cut division became discernible, with cultivated fields in the valley bottoms and the slopes left lying fallow and becoming progressively covered with trees, either because of reforestation or simply as a result of natural expansion. The process was dynamic and fast-moving (forest cover expanded by 30–40 percent over a period of thirty years), producing a homogenous landscape from what once were remote fields, natural grasslands, and steeply sloping terrain that now was also left largely or entirely unmanaged. Visible human activities were now confined to valley bottoms, with the forest fringe close by, accentuating the impression of a closed landscape.[6]

While the remaining rangelands were no longer used for farming or logging, they were by no means deserted: they were ideal for hunting (a popular activity in France, and one commonly practiced by peasants) and nature-oriented recreational activities pursued by city-dwellers and country folk alike (walking, gathering, contemplation, sports). The habits and customs, local rights and usages that had governed relationships among individuals, collective entities, and local renewable resources had in a sense given way to a new dichotomy. On the one hand, there were now incentives for the appropriation of productive farmland, in the form either of loans aimed at facilitating the purchase of land and owner-occupancy or of legislation on tenant farming (farm leasing) designed to benefit persons who cultivated the land.[7] On the other hand, public assets (hunting, recreational activities, and the like) were emerging in areas for which there was progressively less demand in terms of ownership. The issues of land tenure had thus become simplified: in the case of arable land, farmers had priority with individual management, while in the case of other land, multi-use became the common rule, with no identifiable management or collective regulatory mechanisms at all, apart from the self-enforced regulations of hunting associations in some cases.

The lack of regulation on extensive areas of land left to the dynamics of brush proliferation and reforestation has inevitably been a factor in the rapid degradation of landscapes and land use in the Mediterranean hinterland. Witness the wildfires that break out there every summer, which become front-page news when they devastate hundreds or thousands of acres in a few hours, defying the efforts of even the most up-to-date fire-fighting technology.[8]

A Break in Livestock Production Knowledge and Techniques

In the context of agricultural modernization, virtually all farmers have come to regard rangelands as worthless.[9] They now keep only new, high-performance animal genotypes, which require a standardized, nutrient-rich diet for meat or milk production. More important still, the new rules on feeding livestock taught to young students in schools of agriculture call for optimization of animals' daily ration by adjusting their feed supply to meet demand. How is this to be applied to animals grazing on rangeland? It is impossible to estimate their energy demand reliably, as they are constantly moving and subject to temperature variations, substantial ones on occasion, with the result that their energy demand may vary by a factor of more than 50 percent. And determining forage supply is an exceedingly uncertain business because the animals are constantly sorting through a wide assortment of plants, most of them edible but some more palatable than others, and consequently predictable intake is highly variable. The solution recommended by livestock sector support services is thus to keep a "productive" herd indoors, or on forage crops under the conditions for which ration optimization was designed, based on feed value tables.[10]

What has become of herders in an age dominated by calculated feed ration optimization? Most of them have been discarded like so many obsolete tools, now that herding has become a byword for an activity that is not economically viable, except in the case of long-range transhumance in which flocks of sheep are shifted up and down between lowland plains and high mountain pastures. As regards rangelands in hilly regions, the dominant technical recommendation is to "save time [and money, in the form of the herder's wages] by putting up fences" (see chapter 2), which also should enable the farmer to optimize grazing by adjusting stocking density, as with cultivated pasture management. Herders, whether family members or year-round farm employees, must either build fences or monitor grassland rations. In the latter case, they are still using their skills to some extent by setting daily boundaries to provide fresh grass on an area determined on the basis of the height and maturity of the forage. As a veterinarian put it, "For [goat] farmers today, herding on rangeland is not something to be taken seriously. Whereas fencing the herd in to graze a known plant species, moving the wire a few inches every day, ah, that's much more high-tech, more rational."[11]

In this context, farming, too, has become a different occupation. The farmer is no longer a peasant engaged in a variety of activities but a specialized producer, a "farm operator," whose performance is assessed on the basis of energy efficiency and technical and economic criteria. A change of that order could not have come about by itself. It has been the result of a sustained nation-wide effort aimed at adapting and designing agricultural technologies, underpinned by a full range of expertise and services under the sponsorship of the Ministry of Agriculture: publicly funded agronomic research, technical support, and vocational training (initial, continuing, and higher). Other factors contributed, including vigorous mutualization through cooperatives, close relations with product suppliers, and agriculture sector marketing processes, even though these are still essentially based on the family farm model.

In the course of a single generation (between 1960 and 1990), modernization produced an "epistemic break" in the area of knowledge about the world of living things (domestic animals, crops, and natural resources). On the one hand, crop farmers, livestock breeders, foresters, and the like were in the habit of working partly by following the example of their predecessors and partly by trying out, on a case-by-case basis, new solutions appropriate in terms of their historical, geographic, social, and economic conditions. On the other hand, scientists, distancing themselves from the practical realities of agriculture and natural resources, were concentrating on laboratory work, focusing on increasingly specialized projects in the field of biology, and applying state-of-the-art techniques and high-performance instruments. Scientific teams produced reams of new knowledge, most of it "fundamental" (i.e., regarded as independent of any local context), and their findings were disseminated by agricultural development services. Farmers could take advantage of them only insofar as they approached the industrial high-tech model, which draws a clear distinction between the knowledge and skills of designers and users. One obvious example is the genetic improvement of breeds of livestock[12] and crop plants. This new split in knowledge applied to the field of livestock feeding and nutrition as well: the only feeds worth considering were those listed in feed value tables based on research at experimental stations using standardized forages and animals. Plants that grew on rangelands were thus no longer usable: being so numerous and complex, no feeding experiments were devoted to them, and consequently they were not listed in the tables. It was easier and, more important, safer for farmers to keep animals and use feeds that were as close to the standard models as possible than obstinately continue to rely on their local natural resources.

In France, the industrialization of agriculture inevitably impacted rural societies. Between 1954 and 1992 agricultural production grew by 250 percent, farm labor productivity increased tenfold, and the farm population declined to a quarter of its former size. Early in the 1950s the country had 3 million peasants, most of them possessing a stock of empirical knowledge acquired from their fathers and their peers; by the 1990s, this total had shrunk to 600,000 "farm operators," trained in over 100 agricultural vocational schools and/or closely advised by specialized technicians. Information was now transmitted in accord with a linear model based on the "popularizable" component of scientific and technical knowledge (i.e., the knowledge deemed transmissible). The transmission process also relied on adopting new technologies linked to the acceptance of recommendations derived from "decision support tools," such as computer and software for planning of diets and/or feeding strategies for animals at the farm.

THE REHABILITATION OF RANGELANDS FOR ENVIRONMENTAL PURPOSES AND NEW USES FOR THEM
Production Objectives Exceeded and Unanticipated Adverse Effects

In western Europe, production models based on market coordination and the industrial model of a division of knowledge and labor, heavily supported by public funding, had achieved "success" by the 1970s. The result was the appearance and growth of structural surpluses of unsalable agricultural products, and hence increasingly ferocious international competition. As the cost of trade wars and surplus stock management came to weigh progressively more heavily in the public finance crisis, the European Union's leaders began to reconsider the issue of public support for agriculture product development. This political reorientation, confirmed by the first reform of the Common Agricultural Policy (CAP) in 1992, was accentuated in 2003 in a further reform implemented under the pressure of the World Trade Organization's determination to eliminate all public support for agricultural production.

By the early 1990s, the legitimacy of industrial agriculture had begun to wane, and some opinion leaders took advantage of the opportunity to emphasize the harmful effects of its practices and territorial specialization: the artificialization and pollution of productive farmland and the abandonment of extensive areas of rural land resulted in degraded landscapes, reduced biodiversity, and increased fire hazards. In response to these charges, EU leaders began to redirect some agricultural funding toward incentive measures aimed at encouraging farmers to "adopt or maintain more environment-friendly practices."[13] These incentive measures, in the form of voluntary contracts between the French government and farmers who undertook to modify their practices, hardened considerably in 2003, gradually becoming prerequisites for eligibility for other forms of public support, in accord with the principle of cross compliance.[14]

Many rural areas had been emptied of farmers as a result of the previous policy, and land restoration became the subject of publicly funded incentives aimed at rediscovering new regional forms of "civic coordination,"[15] including in particular a new agropastoral equilibrium within which rangelands would acquire new social values and livestock owners would assume new functions.[16] Progressively larger numbers of stakeholders came to participate in this effort to design a form of "sustainable rural area development," including not only government agencies responsible for agriculture and the environment but also associations of naturalists or consumers, local authorities, new residents of rural areas, and even agri-food firms in search of positive brand images for their products. All these and others combined forces to bring pressure to bear on farmers.

When seen with fresh eyes, whether by persons from literary or, as was increasingly the case, scientific backgrounds, these areas were perceived as an essential component of "healthy, balanced landscapes," reservoirs of rare or endangered species, and matrices of biodiversity. This might be described as a vision of a countryside that was ideally to be "renaturalized," "restored to its wild condition," "ecologized," in stark contrast to a vision of an agricultural countryside to be "managed" by means of land consolidation, the removal of banks and hedges, drainage, irrigation and the like, with orderly fields planted in field crops and factory farming— "reduced to a lowest common denominator."

Thus the issues that arise relate to the reconquest and management of these areas, which have been abandoned for several decades now after centuries of intensive utilization. What is the best way to take control of the dynamics of plant communities that will ultimately homogenize these rangelands as they progressively evolve into forests, "closing them off" and making them more vulnerable to wildfire? What can be done to direct the course of their evolution, preserve endangered animal or plant habitats, and achieve a satisfactory measure of biodiversity at various scales? What is the most effective way to take poorly maintained woodlots, with little or no productive function, and make them more attractive and reintegrate them into the landscape? What is the most practical approach to reconstitute a finer-grained landscape instead of one comprised of nothing but forest and cropland? There is no question of re-creating the mosaic landscapes that resulted from old uses long since vanished, but rather establishing an "assemblage" of varied, functional ecosystems, deemed indispensable for the sustainability of life on earth. This is a recommendation supported by the Millennium Ecosystem Assessment, which introduces a number of new concepts for the world of agriculture, including "ecosystem services."[17]

The Rise of Environmental Concerns and Environmental Provisions in Agricultural Policies

To establish this new policy, much is expected of the remaining farmers, many of whom still own these lands even if they do not use them. The farmers' function of producing tradable goods as their sole means of earning a living is increasingly questioned. Consistent with a vision of rural areas no longer exclusively devoted to market production, regional entities (regional natural parks, regional charters, Natura 2000 sites*) are shaping new legislative and regulatory instruments in the name of the public interest and new public goods (biodiversity, air quality, soil conservation). An array of general measures have been introduced based on contractual incentives for individuals, such as agri-environmental measures (AEMs) and local operations, which are implemented at the level of a specific area. These measures have been funded jointly by France and

---

* Sites having priority status for the conservation of outstanding ecological habitats and their species, pursuant to the European Union's Habitats Directive, issued in 1992, the year of the Rio Earth Summit (Pinton et al., 2006).

the EU since the 1992 reform of the CAP, which made AEMs compulsory. They commit farmers' groups and other rural stakeholders, such as local communities or naturalists' associations in charge of managing outstanding natural areas, to participate in defining and applying agricultural practices that take environmental values into account.

Since 2003, when the CAP was last reformed, commitment to "good agricultural and environmental conditions" is a prerequisite for eligibility for public funding for commercial agricultural production in any form. The process is thus becoming more extensive, as it addresses all areas included in the category of "ordinary nature," such as riverbanks in a plain where cereals are grown. Incentives, contracts, and penalties are becoming the tools used to induce farmers to assume their environmental responsibilities. This may be termed the "ecologization of European agriculture."[18]

Thanks to these contractual incentives, domestic herbivores are being allowed out of their barns and cultivated pastures and turned out to graze nearby rangelands with increasing frequency. For farmers, this contributes to more effective control of undesirable plant dynamics,* such as excessive colonization by brush species or forest encroachment, or homogenization of natural dry swards by broadleaved grass cover. Areas have priority either because of their biodiversity and wildlife habitat or because they are at risk of wildfire. As a rule, contracts cover individual parcels of land for a term of five years; the farmer is required to document his/her ownership of the land or right to use it. For every parcel or group of parcels used to pasture a herd, the aim is to design or adjust a "targeted grazing" schedule to achieve more effective control of undesirable plant dynamics.[19]

But Where is the Knowledge to Implement the Environmental Provisions?

Despite rewards that may be fairly substantial (from $30 to nearly $270/ acre/year, depending on the region and how serious the issues are on a particular parcel of land), farmers have been unenthusiastic. Most of them, in fact, have reacted with some bewilderment. Formerly they had been advised to feed their livestock indoors or on cultivated grasslands with standard approved feeds. Now, suddenly, they are supposed to turn them out to graze what they consider unknown territory, since virtually none of the standard reference works on livestock feeding deals with

---

* See also: Council Directive 92/43/EEC of May 21, 1992, on the conservation of natural habitats and of wild fauna and flora: http://eur-lex.europa.eu/LexUriServ/LexUriServ.do?uri=CELEX:31992L0043:EN: html.

rangelands and the memory of the way such lands were formerly used was lost after about thirty years. What sort of edible forage plants grow up there? What quantities are available; how much feeding value do they have, if any; and will they be adequate to enable the animals to survive, and more importantly, to grow and perform satisfactorily? The wealth of technical literature on animal husbandry affords no answer to any of these questions, having been entirely dedicated for the past thirty years to feed regimes based on cultivated forage crops, cereals, soybeans, and crop by-products. There are a few scattered scientific studies on grazing on rangelands, but they tend to discuss matters that are rather strange for farmers accustomed to the industrial livestock production model: functionality of combinations of grazing areas, social behavior within herds, effects of associations of plant toxins on ingestion, and the like.

Since the technical recommendations and references were no longer available from the usual sites, farmers, their technical support structures, and natural environment managers decided to look to "nonconformist" farmers who had persisted in using rangelands, and thus had been largely marginalized during the preceding period, plus a few experienced herders. Those farmers proved a surprise: in contrast to their preconceived image, many of them had genetically improved breeds of livestock with herd performance records similar to those observed for animals fed on cultivated forage. They fine-tuned their use of rangelands in terms of grazing schedules, alternating or combining them with cultivated grasslands, and periods of grazing on rangelands did not coincide with declines in herd performance.[20] Some of the herders had well-stocked empirical repositories of information obtained from their constant, repeated observations of the evolving relationship between the animals and the resources of the area where they grazed.[21]

For twenty years, there has been a research and development effort in France aimed at taking the practical know-how of these farmers and herders, now considered experts, and making it intelligible and teachable, while a further aim has been to assess their performance in feeding their herds and renewing rangeland resources.[22] In the case of a shepherd who grazes his flock on rangeland, that know-how is expressed in structuring the area into grazing "quarters" and "sectors" (see chapter 4), and subsequently the design of "grazing circuits" to promote feeding synergy between sectors that are grazed successively in the course of a meal (see also chapters 7 and 8 on the MENU model).[23] Confronted with the heterogeneous nature of a stretch of rangeland, herders do not attempt to identify the few high-quality homogeneous sectors for the herd's meals. On the contrary, understanding that a sequence of very different resources has a useful effect on the animals' appetite serves as an incentive to use a variety of grazing areas. This practice stands in contrast to feeding models based on the feeding trough or cultivated grasslands: instead of minimizing the animals' selective behavior, herders seek to use the predictable expression of that behavior as a tool to control of their herds' feed selection and grazing locations in the course of each day, which enables them to regulate the impact of grazing on target plant populations that are desirable to control because of their colonizing tendencies. This is so important it may be the subject of contract specifications.

A problem remains: the CAP measures relating to the environment refer to the persons in charge of farming operations, and contracts must be concluded with them. But farmers, especially younger ones and those who employ "a good herder" in particular, frequently delegate the responsibility of managing the herd on rangeland to the herder himself. These farmers are busy with a host of other farm activities and have lost much of the practical pastoral know-how their parents possessed. The herders possess it now, and the successful execution of contracts depends on them. It thus seems timely to involve herders in the task of designing environmental measures and grazing contracts, but there is no way of doing that without upgrading of the status of hired herders (see chapter 2).

CONCLUSION: A PLEA FOR "SUBJECTIVE" RESEARCH PRACTICES

As often as not, scientific research has not so much anticipated great economic and social changes in the world of agriculture as it has accompanied them. Sometimes it has formalized indigenous know-how rather than actually "inventing" new practices. The great agronomists of the eighteenth and nineteenth centuries developed theories about the principles of organic fertilizers when European agriculture had already resulted in demographic expansion, and they based their analyses on rational comparison of the performance results obtained by existing production systems.[24] Paradoxically, the advent of organic chemistry, the transport revolution, and the rise of market relations made organic fertilizers irrelevant for agricultural production and generated a preference for inorganic fertilizers instead.

In the twentieth century, on the other hand, there is no denying that agronomic research developed the scientific and technological bases for impressive animal and crop productivity gains resulting from genetic improvements. These gains have enabled many agricultural sectors to respond quickly and satisfactorily to the spread of the market economy.[25] There also have been some resounding failures, when technological support has proved inadequate to overcome both traditional practices and the hazards of weather conditions. Thus a number of "green revolutions" and "improved breeds," sold by the Western world to the developing countries, have not survived a straightforward technology transfer, unaccompanied by either a voluntary support policy or any consideration of preexisting local knowledge. The result has been the marginalization of part of the planet and the identification of so-called difficult zones or less-favored areas in Europe, such as rangelands, where farmers found they qualify for assistance on the grounds of their "natural handicaps."*

Given the ability today to manipulate genotypes and predict animal and plant behavior and the massive use of synthetic products in farming, soilless agricultural production, fully controlled and totally independent of local conditions, is quite feasible. At the same time, as a result of social and political change, farmers in Europe are mandated to carry out new missions: redeploy into abandoned rural areas, develop "environmentally friendly" practices there, minimize negative impacts, and maximize positive ones, especially regarding the conservation or enhancement of biodiversity. At first, knowledge of modern agronomy seemed to have no effective response to this process of change. But experimental science soon rallied in the face of these new "social demands." Efforts are now underway to evaluate animal welfare under extensive husbandry conditions; to bring hardy herbivorous species back into fashion, owing to their ability to thrive on rugged terrain under adverse weather conditions; and to formulate feed additives that will enable animals to digest some rangeland forage more efficiently. But few research projects have really attempted to address this change in the nature of research objects:[†] for example, by studying herd grazing behavior with a view to enlisting the animals' behavioral abilities as allies in the challenge of attaining these new goals, or by encouraging the ability of existing animals, regardless of breed, to learn to balance their diets at pasture instead of trying to reactivate costly, uncertain genetic programs. Might it not be more imaginative to reconsider certain excessively artificial husbandry and feeding methods in an effort to avoid undesirable systemic effects, such as emergent diseases, greenhouse gas emissions, and the like, instead of trying to treat these effects using an end-of-pipe approach?

---

* Areas marginalized as a result of agricultural modernization thus qualify for compensation under the CAP, thanks to the introduction of "Compensation for natural handicaps" legislation.

† A research object is an intellectual construct developed by the investigator. It is much more narrowly circumscribed than a research theme. It comprises a scientific issue set within a theoretical framework, together with a procedural approach by means of which hypotheses can be tested. The term "object" leads to a determination of what precisely is to be investigated and an assessment of the feasibility of the research; thus an investigator may perceive that his/her research object is too broad and poorly demarcated, and consequently not manageable, or, conversely, is too small and concerned with a relatively trivial issue that will yield to common sense.

Might not the new orientation of Europe's "ecologized" agricultural policy afford a good opportunity to break with the century-old tradition of compartmentalized agronomic research, with its obsessive focus on "objectivity"? Scientists might participate fully in the emergence of new compromises in the relationships between agriculture and society and ask original questions, not only about the technical feasibility of new projects but also about their desirability and compatibility with local societies.

It is becoming necessary and urgent to take a fresh look at technical farming activities, owing to new thinking about land values.[26] In just over a century, France has gone from a diversified array of local rights to national regulations imposed in the name of the general interest to EU or international commitments that apply worldwide, such as conventions aimed at reducing the erosion of biodiversity or providing support for adaptation to climate change. Societies have changed, but so have natural environments, even though they have retained their own dynamics, albeit under the influence of human activities. Rural areas, once characterized by a broad range of human activities aimed at producing resources essential for life, first became extremely simplified under the impact of a few high-performance technical models and are now beginning to rediscover the benefits of functional diversity, which underpins the great ecological balances of an Earth heavily dominated by the human species. This should provide an incentive for the decompartmentalization of scientific disciplines, with a new emphasis on interdisciplinary initiatives involving the natural sciences, technology, and the social sciences.[27]

Research of this kind might aim at immediate practical relevance for all parties concerned: farmers, environment managers, and political decision-makers.[28] In particular, to address the concerns outlined in the present work, it should devise methodologies structured in accordance with three points of view: 1) input from farmers and herders about their working environments and the reasons for their activities; 2) modeling of observed situational processes; and 3) the findings of analytic experimentation. For example, in the area of feeding on rangelands, one research theme worth pursuing is related to the action of "steering the ingestion of less palatable resources."[29] The act of rationing the herd would be considered from both a biological standpoint (ingestion process) and an organizational standpoint (inducing the herd to ingest). By observing the ingestion process at temporal and spatial scales perceptible to the herders, the scientist would maintain consistency with their own input. This would lead him to focus on a new research object: the grazing circuit and its effects on the kinetics of the herd's daily meals, as the grazing circuit is the process that herders have to design and manage. Investigation of this research object would raise issues relating to the spatial analysis of territorial dynamics (geography and landscape ecology) and to the understanding of external, or circumstantial, appetite factors (animal nutrition).

New research objects of this kind have emerged from interdisciplinary research initiatives. These are deliberately "subjective," as they are bound up with the active participants, both the scientist and the farmer or herder.[30] Information on these research objects makes it possible to identify issues that might well have been neglected with traditional objective approaches, such as ethical considerations relating to animal husbandry, management of the performance of a herd as a whole, or collective or individual social values in the use of rangelands.

If, in only fifty years, knowledge about the living world has moved from the countryside into the laboratory, may it not be time to take stock of forms of knowledge proving to be complementary and bring them together? Otherwise, we may be surprised to find that a gap has developed between increasingly daring inventions on the one hand and, on the other hand, farmers who are progressively disassociated from their production, seen as mere users, and not enthusiastic ones at that! May it not be urgent to develop new spaces within which scientists and farmers can interact before the last practical knowledge has been lost, leaving nothing but principles and recipes that are specific to discrete problems? The present work, dealing as it does with shepherds' practices, should contribute to that aim.

NOTES

[1] Kuhnholtz-Lordat, 1944; Dion, 1991.
[2] Young, 1909.
[3] Boltanski and Thévenot, 1991.
[4] Hubert, 1991a.
[5] Juillard, 1976; Weber, 1976.
[6] Eychenne, 2006; Brossier et al., 2008.
[7] Deverre, 2005.
[8] Hubert et al., 1993.
[9] Joffre et al., 1991; Chabert et al., 2002.
[10] Leroy, 1943; Jarrige, 1978.
[11] Meuret, 2006.
[12] Vissac, 2002; Micoud, 2003.
[13] Buller, 1995.
[14] Deverre and de Sainte Marie, 2008.
[15] Boltanski and Thévenot, op. cit.
[16] Deverre and Hubert, 1994.
[17] UNESCO, 2005.
[18] Deverre and de Sainte Marie, op. cit.
[19] Léger et al., 1999; Launchbaugh, 2006.
[20] Meuret et al., 1995.
[21] Ravis-Giordani, 1983; Landais and Deffontaines, 1988.
[22] Hubert, 1991b; Landais, 1993; Institut de l'Élevage, 1999; Guérin et al., 2001.
[23] Meuret, 1993.
[24] Young, op. cit.
[25] Polanyi, 1944.
[26] Thompson, 1995.
[27] Hubert et al., 2012.
[28] Osty, 1993.
[29] Meuret, 1993.
[30] Albaladejo et al., 2009; Provenza et al., 2013.

CHAPTER 2

Shepherding in France Today:

An Overview

Jean-Pierre Legeard, Michel Meuret, Patrick Fabre,
& Jean-Michel Gascoin

WHAT IS A SHEPHERD?
More Than Just a Guardian

The word "shepherd" is a very old one, and generally speaking its meaning is unambiguous: a shepherd is a person who herds a flock of sheep. It is the English counterpart of the French term *berger*, the etymology of which goes back to the twelfth-century word *bergier*, a guardian, from the Vulgar Latin *berbicarius*, itself derived from *berbex*, a ewe. Literary references to shepherds and their skills are found from antiquity. They appear in allegories in the Bible: "As a shepherd cares for his herd in the day when he is among his scattered sheep, so I will care for my sheep and will deliver them from all the places to which they were scattered on a cloudy and gloomy day."[1] In France, the earliest practical work on the subject is *Treatise on the State, Science and Practice of the Herding and Tending of Ewes and Woolly Beasts*, written in 1379 at the order of the King Charles V of France by a self-taught shepherd who had gone to live in Paris.[2] A work entitled *Instructions for Shepherds* was subsequently published in 1794 by a professor at the Museum of Natural History: "A knowledgeable, conscientious shepherd in charge of a large flock is kept almost constantly busy, tending them carefully during the day, penning them at night, feeding them during the winter, caring for them, and treating their diseases. Consequently, shepherds can command good wages in regions where sheep are kept; they are well paid, if they know their work and perform it assiduously."[3]

We learn from these early texts that shepherds' occupation was not restricted to ensuring that the sheep "had plenty to eat." Their occupation was more comprehensive: keeping track of their charges' general condition and behavior, identifying and treating illnesses, and organizing grazing in a way that manages the resources of the pasture to its best advantage. Additional tasks might include milking the ewes and making cheeses. A shepherd, then, should enjoy living close to the flock and should develop empathy with the ewes, learning how to interpret their attitudes and understand their habits, thereby becoming their "skillful guide."[4] Only shepherds who have acquired a "passion for their animals," "an instinctive affinity for the flock and mountain pastures," are regarded by their fellows as good herders.[5] While the basic role of guardian is still part of the job, as the continued use of the stick helps to remind us, the herder's work is rapidly growing more diverse. Tasks now include maintaining grazing land facilities, rehabilitating environmental resources, coexisting with hikers, and protecting the flock from predators. Accordingly, some herders reputedly now prefer to refer to themselves as "high mountain pasture technicians."[6] This increase in responsibilities and tasks brings up the issue of the need for a skills rating system for herders, which we shall address at the end of this chapter.

In France, not so very long ago, "the shepherd" was frequently either the family's youngest boy, who was set to herding the flock if he was not to be taught any other trade; a foundling whose work with the sheep made it worthwhile to provide him with board and lodging; or an immigrant with no family from a part of the world that had long enjoyed a reputation as a source of competent herders, such as Italy or Spain. In France, as in many other countries, these individuals "did stints" as herders for one or more flock owners as long as their age and health allowed. In order for a man to upgrade his status from hired herder to sheep farmer, it was — and is to this day — necessary for him to acquire a flock and own some farmland.

A person who becomes a livestock farmer, however, may still continue to herd his flock. We thus find farmers who herd their own flocks, professional herders who do not own sheep themselves, and a broad range of intermediate situations. Consequently, it is difficult to arrive at a fully satisfactory definition of the term "shepherd." The authors prefer to use the original definition of a shepherd as "a person whose occupation is herding a flock of sheep." Accordingly, persons whose herding is confined to fenced areas will not be considered here. On the other hand, our discussion will extend to "goatherders." In view of the subject of this book, however, persons who tend herds of cattle will not be included. Such persons should properly be termed "cowherders," although in some parts of the French and Swiss Alps the term *berger* is used to denote a person who herds any kind of livestock.

Eleven Categories of Shepherds and Goatherders

In France, there are many different categories of shepherds and goatherders. In Figure 1 we present a simple breakdown of four different types of herders: "Farmer who herds his/her own flock" (FH), "landless farmer-herder" (LFH), "hired herder" (HH) and "assistant herder" (AH). This is followed by a further distinction: "sedentary" (s) or "transhumant" (t). A sedentary herder is a year-round user of grazing land located in the vicinity of a single dwelling and its shed(s). A transhumant herder (for the purposes of the present discussion) is one who shifts his dwelling over one or more seasons to keep the whole or part of an individually owned or collective flock on pasture. Transhumance is not the same as nomadism, as the shift is usually carried out as a single operation. Transhumance may be local (over a distance of a few miles) or over long distances, involving shifts of up to two hundred miles or more ("long-range transhumance"). This may involve the use of both high mountain pastures during the summer ("summer transhumance") and lowland or foothill pastures during the winter ("winter transhumance"). Some sheep farmers in the Alps or the Pyrenees who shift their flocks locally and live in the uplands all year round prefer not to be called transhumant, in order to differentiate themselves from their counterparts whose permanent homes are elsewhere and who move their flocks up to mountain pastures only on a seasonal basis.

Applying our terminology, a sheep farmer who herds his/her own flock may be either sedentary (FH_s) or transhumant (FH_t). A member of the former category is likely to be the owner of a small or medium-sized flock (consisting of perhaps two hundred to four hundred breeding ewes) who also supplements his income with other activities, such as cereal cropping or a bed and breakfast on his farm. The same applies to goatherders, especially those who obtain a high-value-added product from their flocks in the form of farm cheeses (approximately forty to seventy goats). As a rule, their pastures are managed as fenced areas on arable land, permanent grassland, or rangeland. Where the resources afforded by such pastures are inadequate or too seasonal, the farmer minimizes hay consumption by taking the animals out and herding them. When his own resources are exhausted, he may seek permission to use municipal land, land belonging to neighbors who do not keep livestock, or even public or private woodlands. Herding of this kind also often makes use of land owned by people who have become city-dwellers and may not even be aware of their rural property. In practice, few transhumant sheep farmers devote their summers exclusively to herding their own flocks because they must harvest hay during that season, and it is economi-

The Eleven Types of Herders

Herding jobs come in many forms, from hired hands to flock owners. As the researchers sought to understand herders—and take a census—an alphabet soup of abbreviations soon evolved. Take a moment to understand the following; it will help you gain a better understanding of the shepherd's many roles.

The four main types...

FH	farmer who herds his own herd
LFH	landless sheep farmer-herder
HH	hired herder
AH	assistant herder

Divided by mobility...

s	sedentary; uses the same dwelling and surrounding land for pasture year-round
t	transhumant; travels with his flock and changes dwellings as he herds them

Divided by how employed...

d	directly employed by the farmer
i	indirectly employed by a number of transhumant farmers
p	permanently employed
s	seasonally employed
M	employed by municipalities

For example, $HH_t Mds$ indicates a herder who is directly hired by a municipality, who travels with his flock, and who is employed seasonally. LFH_t indicates a herder who owns his own flock, but does not own or lease the land he uses to graze his flock, and travels with his herd.

cally advantageous to join forces with other producers to hire a seasonal herder, as legislation in force in France since 1972 expressly encourages collective organizations.

Landless sheep farmers-herders, referred to by the term *herbassier* in Provence, are declining in numbers. A person in this category owns a flock of sheep that provides him/her with enough income to live on. However, for reasons related to the cost of land, and in some cases for ethical reasons as well,[7] they neither own nor lease the land on which they graze their flocks. They are in effect all transhumant (LFH_t), and their mode of husbandry resembles nomadism. It is a precarious way of life that tends to be regarded rather dismissively in France. However, some of these farmer-herders have managed to develop relationships of mutual

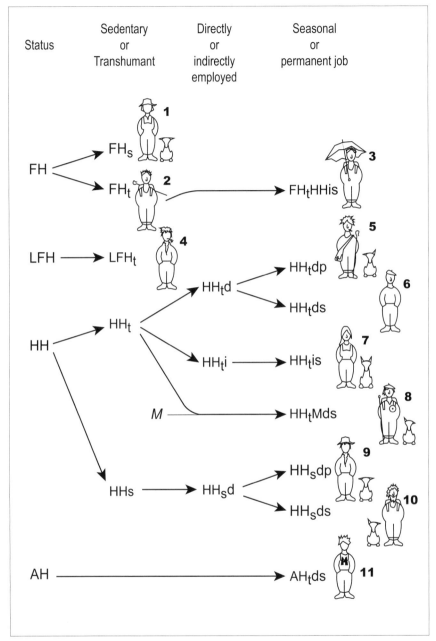

FIGURE 1 – Simplified typology of the eleven categories of persons whose occupation is herding flocks of sheep and goats, identified on the basis of four discrimination criteria (see the text for a detailed explanation of the codes).

confidence with landowners, both private and public. At the same time, they are subject to a social disability: in a country that lacks a nomadic cultural tradition, it is not unusual for them to be excluded from marriage and family life, given their permanent uncertainty about where they will be living and under what conditions, especially in the winter.[8]

Hired herders (HH) are still numerous, but a number of distinctions should be made. The herder may be hired by a sheep farmer who may be either transhumant (HH_t) or sedentary (HH_s). Either way, the herder may be either directly employed by the farmer (HH_td or HH_sd), or indirectly employed by a number of transhumant farmers (HH_ti) who have formed a "breeders' grazing trust." If he is directly employed, his job may be either permanent (HH_tdp or HH_sdp) or seasonal (HH_tds or HH_sds). All indirectly employed herders work on a seasonal basis for a breeders' grazing trust (HH_tis). In addition, some hired herders work for municipalities (M), especially municipalities that operate ski resorts, where it is essential to keep the grass nibbled short during the summer in order to avert the risk of avalanches. A herder of this kind is ordinarily in charge of a flock consisting of sheep owned by a number of transhumant farmers (HH_tMds).

Lastly, our typology would be incomplete if we were to overlook the recent phenomenon of "assistant herders." "These persons, who are employed thanks to joint funding provided by the French government and the European Union, protect flocks from predators. They are employed on a seasonal basis by individual transhumant sheep farmers or by a breeders' grazing trust (AH_tds). As a rule, full-time hired herders tend not to regard them as real colleagues, as their tasks are ordinarily limited to the management of electrified night pens, where they keep watch over the flock with the assistance of guard dogs (see chapter 11). Herders in the Savoie region have suggested renaming assistant herders "prevention auxiliaries."[9]

At this stage, our typology does not take into account any changes in status that may occur in the course of a year in order to avoid an even greater degree of diversity. To take a single example, a sheep farmer (FH_t) not infrequently spends his summers working as a hired herder indirectly employed by a breeders' grazing trust (FH_tHHis) of which he is a member, with his own ewes being part of the trust's flock. There are other cases as well, such as a hired herder who in the summer is indirectly employed by a breeders' grazing trust (HH_tis) and during the rest of the year is directly employed by a sheep farmer.

The eleven categories of herders we have just identified do not take into account changes in status that may occur in the course of a year.

In view of our definition, we have not included persons whose occupation — in some cases their sole occupation — consists in milking the animals and making cheese. The inclusion of assistant herders is arguably questionable, as those persons contribute only a specific fraction of flock-herding activities.

THE PERILOUS TASK OF DETERMINING NUMBERS OF HERDERS

How many herders are working in France at the present time? What is the origin, age, sex, family status, and skill level of each? Unfortunately, we cannot answer these questions.

Both the National Bureau of Statistics and the Income Tax Administration in France count sheep farmers, including those whose only occupation is farming and those who hold other jobs, but neither agency notes whether a sheep farmer engages in herding. In statistics on seasonal employment in the agricultural sector, shepherds are included in the "seasonal agricultural workers" category, where they account for only a microscopic fraction of the total, given the vast numbers of seasonal employees recruited to work in the market gardening, fruit production, and grape-growing sectors. By way of illustration, in 2007 there were nearly twenty thousand seasonal agricultural workers in the southeastern department of Vaucluse (population 550,000) alone. Among them all, they were maybe only fifty or one hundred seasonal herders. While herders sometimes sign on with the French National Employment Agency, they seldom list their shepherding activities, as most of them are looking for job opportunities outside the summer herding season. During that season, herders tend to find employment through traditional hiring practices, which in most cases are outside conventional bureaucratic channels. Perhaps the greatest difficulty in counting the hired herder population is its shifting nature. From year to year, between one summer herding season and the next, the hired herder population is characterized by a high replacement rate, even though some situations remain stable over periods of ten years or more. Once the summer season is over, hired herders leave the department, or even the region, in search of employment in other economic sectors until the following year.

Pastoral Surveys

For nearly forty years, the pastoral mode of husbandry and the places it is practiced, especially in mountain regions, have been the subject of investigation in France. Two regional administrations, Provence-Alpes-Côte d'Azur (PACA) and Rhône-Alpes (RA), have prepared pastoral atlases,[10]

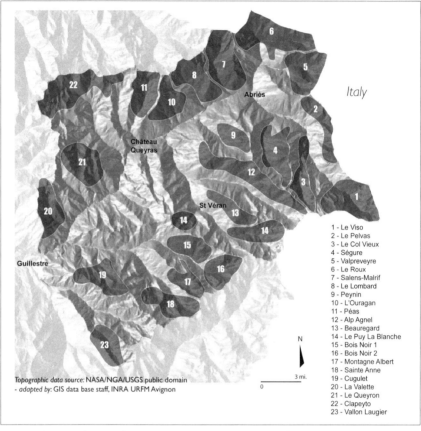

1 - Le Viso
2 - Le Pelvas
3 - Le Col Vieux
4 - Ségure
5 - Valpreveyre
6 - Le Roux
7 - Salens-Malrif
8 - Le Lombard
9 - Peynin
10 - L'Ouragan
11 - Péas
12 - Alp Agnel
13 - Beauregard
14 - Le Puy La Blanche
15 - Bois Noir 1
16 - Bois Noir 2
17 - Montagne Albert
18 - Sainte Anne
19 - Cugulet
20 - La Valette
21 - Le Queyron
22 - Clapeyto
23 - Vallon Laugier

Topographic data source: NASA/NGA/USGS public domain
- adapted by: GIS data base staff, INRA URFM Avignon

FIGURE 2 – Map of pastoral units located within the perimeter of the Queyras Regional Natural Park (period 2002–2005). Source: Queyras Regional Nature Park, supplemented and updated on the basis of surveys conducted by Vincent (2011).

which have been published by the Statistical Services Branch of the Ministry of Agriculture.[11] Specific surveys on shepherds were conducted between 1995 and 1997 with the assistance of CERPAM (the Pastoral Service Bureau for the Provence-Alpes-Côte d'Azur Region).[12] In the Pyrenees, which extend through a number of regional administrations, a pastoral survey was conducted in 1999; since then, thanks to the advent of new computer-based tools, a specialized Geographic Information System has been developed and is freely accessible on the internet, making data relating to summer range in those mountains available.[13] However, only data on summer range under collective management have been mapped at the site as yet.[14] In the same year (1999), Corsica undertook a census of its extensive mountain rangeland, where the tradition of transhumance is still very much alive.[15] Lastly, the five French national parks and fourteen regional natural parks (RNPs) in which pastoralism is practiced, mainly in the form of shepherding, regularly conduct censuses of herders working in an area totaling 7.45 million acres.

The main objective of pastoral surveys has been to identify "pastoral units" (PUs), since in the general agricultural census such areas are not differentiated as a rule (for an example, see the PUs of the Queyras Regional Natural Park, Figure 2). The definition of PUs and the several categories of PUs date from the first national surveys conducted in individual municipalities in 1972.[16] Those surveys were originally restricted to summer range, defined as "high-altitude areas that are used for less than four months per year." Since 1999, they have been extended to include "mid-altitude and low-altitude rangeland that is used for much of the year, including winter." In some instances, PUs that straddle more than one municipality have escaped municipality-based surveys. The definition of a PU may be slightly different in different regions, but for our purpose the following definition will serve: "A PU is any area used exclusively as pasture (except permanent grasslands and farmed land), ordinarily on a seasonal basis owing to soil and climate conditions; it constitutes an uninterrupted geographic unit equal to or greater than 25 acres in area, which is grazed by a single flock or a single group of flocks herded by a single manager."

PU mapping databases contain information relating to such aspects as area, type and size of flock or herd (cattle, sheep, goats, mixed livestock, etc.), type of landowner, type of manager (e.g., breeders' grazing trust), season(s) when used, and type and condition of facilities, including the shepherds' cabin(s). A number of them also provide detailed information on the status of the flock manager and his mode of husbandry, including: sheep producer, hired herder; permanent, half-time or occasional herding; and flock left to graze freely or within fenced areas.

Unfortunately, this wealth of data does not yield a reliable count of the numbers of working herders, much less a breakdown in accordance with our eleven categories, for several reasons. In the first place, it is frequently difficult for shepherds or goatherders in the farmer-herder category to comply with their legal obligation to declare to the governmental authorities the total area they use for herding (a task that is much simpler in the case of fenced areas). Livestock farmers are required, every year, to indicate on a land survey map—now, indeed, on an aerial photograph—the exact boundaries of the areas they use for grazing purposes, which confers eligibility for agricultural support payments. All herders are careful to remain within the area that they are entitled to use, and they do not encroach on land owned by neighboring livestock farmers. But it is unrealistic in many instances to require a herder to identify all the boundaries of the areas grazed by his/her flocks with a margin of error of no more than a few yards, indicating the number of days of use. For that reason, in the context of a number of "local agri-environmental operations" (see chapter 1), the practice of herding was initially criticized by governmental authorities as being "too imprecise."[17] Another major source of difficulty in conducting a census is that the summer range herder population can be counted only during the summer. Consequently, unless the Pastoral Service Bureau commits substantial effort and expense, any statistical survey featuring direct contact runs up against the isolation and access conditions that characterize high-altitude pastures and the herders who tend their flocks there.[18] It might be feasible to count the numbers of shepherds' cabins, which in France are permanent structures, but a single cabin may be used by a number of herders, each of whom may be single or accompanied by his or her spouse, apprentice herders, or even assistant herders camping out in tents. Furthermore, a single herder may use a number of cabins successively in the course of a single season, where the cabins are located in different sections of the summer range. Another consideration is that on the one hand, a PU may sometimes be managed by a succession of different herders, while on the other hand, two PUs, or even two flocks, may be managed over one or more seasons by a single herder. Finally, on mid-altitude rangeland, fences have come to be widely used, and consequently all fenced PUs must now be subtracted from the total.

Our estimates, offered by way of a rough indication with no suggestion they be extrapolated to indicate the number of working herders, indicate approximately 1,200 PUs grazed by flocks of sheep, wholly or partly tended by herders, in Provence and the Alpine arc from the department of Var northward to those of Savoie and Haute-Savoie. In the same area, but taking only high mountain pasture into consideration, Landrot arrived at a figure of 922 PUs.[19] The task of making an accurate count is even more difficult in the case of mountain pastures grazed by mixed flocks or herds (Pyrenees and Corsica). Our own conclusion, based on somewhat disparate data, is that that mountain rangeland comprises approximately 2,000 PUs grazed primarily by flocks of sheep tended by herders, in most cases with a number of farmers (FH_t) herding a single collective flock in turn; this is the case in the department of Pyrénées-Atlantiques in particular. After adding data from other regions, not necessarily relating to mountain rangeland (Massif Central, Jura, Burgundy, Vosges, Pays de Loire, and Lorraine), from natural parks for the most part, we arrive at an estimated total of approximately 3,600 PUs grazed primarily by flocks of sheep or goats, wholly or partly tended by herders, in mountainous terrain, foothills, and lowland areas.

Confronted with the difficult task of determining numbers of shepherds, CERPAM conducted postal surveys in the PACA and RA regions in 1995 and 1996, sending questionnaires to all identified summer range managers (i.e., sheep farmers).[20] Each set of forms also contained three questionnaires to be completed by shepherds; these were left unsealed for the sake of transparency, and the task of distributing them was left to the farmer. The return rate was 18 percent for sheep farmers. For shepherds, the response rate is unknown: thirty herders returned questionnaires, but there is no way of knowing how many received one from their employers in the first place. As we shall see later, these responses, limited in number as they were, were revealing none the less.

Enter Ministries and the National Assembly

In 2001, the "Interministerial Group on Pastoralism" was established in France with a mandate to examine the situation of pastoralism and to formulate proposals aimed at encouraging that activity, "confronted as it is with competing interests or species."[21] Two years later, a commission of inquiry made up of members of the National Assembly undertook another investigation on "the presence of wolves in France as a factor in the practice of pastoralism."[22]

The National Assembly commission concluded that "in the southern Alps . . . herders are present on 80 percent of all high mountain pasture areas" and that "there are between 700 and 750 hired herders in France." Comparing these figures with our estimate of 3,600 PUs for the country, and assuming that the total number of herders should be increased by approximately 40 percent to account for herders who do not work for wages, especially in Pyrénées-Atlantiques, where it is usual for farmers to take turns herding a collective flock,[23] this would mean that every herder was in charge of nearly three PUs in the course of a year. This figure seems far too high. Rather, it is likely that the ministerial sources counted only hired herders recorded by the French administration. Here we have additional evidence that taking a census of the herder population in France is beset with pitfalls, in contrast to the relative simplicity of obtaining data on numbers of livestock producers, acreages, and numbers of livestock broken down by species. Another fact that is confirmed by the Interministerial Group's findings is that "pastoralism" in the present-day context is no longer synonymous with "flocks of sheep tended by herders" because herding as an occupation has become increasingly diversified and pastoral practices (including the use of fences) increasingly "rationalized" in the course of the past thirty years.

HERDERS CONFRONTED WITH PUBLIC POLICIES

The transformation of the French countryside under the combined impacts of economic, agricultural, environmental, and land-use planning policies was discussed in chapter 1. Here we present an overview of the main consequences of that transformation on herders' activities over approximately the past forty years.

Three French Legal Instruments with Collective Implications

The modernization of pastoralism in France began in January 1972, following the enactment of Law No. 72-12 "concerning the enhancement of pastoral husbandry in regions having economies based on mountain resources." The law provided for three supplementary statutory instruments "tailored" to address the situation.[24] These, with successive amendments introduced in the years that followed, have had a major impact on the pastoral community and are relevant to this day, especially regarding herder recruitment and the work performed by herders:

1. Under a multi-year grazing agreement (MGA), a landowner may grant a livestock farmer, or a group of livestock farmers, not free disposal of his land and its products, but solely the right to use it as a grazing place during a specified period of the year, for a minimum of five years. This enhanced security of tenure gives the farmer an incentive to make improvements (such as the introduction of watering troughs, sorting pens, catch pens, and the like). Such agreements also occur in the western United States.

2. A breeders' grazing trust (BGT) gives livestock producers an incentive to use rangeland collectively for grazing purposes by providing them with an appropriate legal structure. A BGT that secures French government approval qualifies for financial support for capital expenditures (such as the construction or renovation of cabins, sorting pens, catch pens, and the like), and for payments under agri-environmental contracts. This enables livestock farmers to offer seasonal herders good wages and provide them with improved living and working conditions. These trusts, too, are occurring in the United States with some major successes, although the logistics of setting up these collective units is very large and may involve more than twenty permittees and thousands of animals.

3. A land tenure grazing trust (LTGT) constitutes a reliable, long-term solution to the complex problem of land fragmentation (in Provence, it is not unusual for a flock and its herder to traverse the properties of more than twenty landowners in the course of a single day). This legal instrument affords a means of mustering all

municipally or privately owned properties within a specified perimeter and, with the support of the French government and under
its control, consolidating them into a single entity for management
and development purposes for a period of twenty to thirty years.
Majority rule prevails: where a majority of landowners whose aggregate holdings constitute more than half the land area involved
are in favor of establishing a LTGT, landowners who are opposed
may be compelled to join. The LTGT's board of directors and chair-
person decide matters relating to land rental and development in
areas of pastoral husbandry, logging, or tourist facilities. Proceeds
from rentals and costs are distributed among the landowners in
proportion to the size of their respective holdings.

An assessment from 2005 found nine hundred approved BGTs for
France as a whole.[25] MGAs have also been widely adopted, even though
casual verbal rental agreements or rental on an auction basis remain common in some regions. LTGTs, in contrast, have been less popular: in 2004
there were approximately five hundred of these trusts covering a total of
375,000 acres. Private landowners and municipalities have been reluctant
to commit to a term of twenty to thirty years. As a result, it is common for
a herder to tend his/her flock on a patchwork of properties where one or
two owners refuse to allow sheep or herder to set foot on their land, even
though they have long since ceased to use it for any purpose.

The Impact of Agricultural and Environmental Policies

A Time Of Diversification in Agricultural Development Models

During an initial period, extending approximately from 1970 to 1985, the
objective of development in the livestock production sector was to reintegrate rangeland resources into the so-called modernization process; previously they had been largely neglected in favor of cultivated grasslands and
forage crops, which afforded much greater potential in terms of intensive
production. Until the 1970s, rangeland was regarded as extraneous to that
process, owing to its uncertain legal status, its often rugged terrain not
suitable for heavy farm machinery, and the diversity and variability of the
forage plants it produced, the value of which was for the most part unknown. As we shall see in the introduction to chapter 3, herders' work was,
from the standpoint of agronomic research and agricultural development,
an opportunistic gathering that afforded little scope for livestock feeding
rationalization paradigms.

FIGURE 3 – A poster designed and distributed in 1986 by the Pastoral Service Bureau for the Provence-Alpes-Côte d'Azur Region (CERPAM): "Save time: put fences on rangeland!"

Beginning in the 1970s, however, a new initiative with an economic rationale was launched in southeastern France to use arable land and rangeland in tandem to reduce production costs. In that context, herding was deemed worthy of interest: its mobility meant a variety of natural resources could be utilized with few inputs (grassy summer range, woodland range, barrens, abandoned former farmland, the scrublands known as *maquis* and *garrigue*, and the steppe of Crau). The initial task was to modernize the facilities available for herding livestock on these various types of rangeland: fences, cabins, watering points, access roads, sorting and catch pens, and the like (see Figure 3). The next step was to encourage the rehabilitation of grazing resources (brush clearing, thinning, sodseeding with forage species, and so on) in areas that had been abandoned as a result of rural depopulation. During the same period, functional analyses of the practical knowledge of farmers and herders were produced, covering both those who pastured their flocks in fenced areas[26] and those who herded them on open rangeland.[27] Herders came to be seen in a new light in which they were perceived as capable of empirically conceived but technically advanced management based on forethought and flexibility, and governed by rules largely unintelligible to anyone but the herders themselves.[28]

A Time of Multiple-Use Management on a Partnership Basis

Toward the end of the preceding period, scientists and agricultural agents came to see the technical capabilities of sheep farmers, goat farmers, and herders in a new light, but they were still assumed to be "the managers of flocks and resources," in sole command on the rangeland where their animals grazed. But it soon became clear that herding entailed nearly constant negotiation with a host of other users of that same land, all legitimate and no less important in economic and social terms. Their activities included logging, hunting, gathering, recreational activities, tourism, and nature conservation. One goatherder working under a brush-clearing contract with the National Forests Authority (NFA) said ruefully, "Herding on public land is not always a simple matter!"[29]

At that point, policymakers decided it was not appropriate to obtain priority for herding activities on rangeland; rather, herding should be integrated into the broader framework of land-use management. The technical sophistication that some Pastoral Service Bureaus had acquired during the preceding period helped give operational content to the concept of "multiple-use land management," which had previously been the subject of full-scale trials at a number of experimental sites. The forests of southeastern France, for example, with their high incidence of wildfires, were an ideal testing ground for a management operation aimed expressly at using flocks of sheep to clear brush, before summer, from areas that were to serve as fuelbreaks.[30] In that case, livestock farmers and herders were compelled to enter into a negotiated management agreement that met the fairly stringent terms of both forest managers and firefighters. Once the concept had proved its worth in that demanding context, it was extended to other types of sensitive natural environments. As a result, a number of farmers and herders have now become important partners with national parks, regional natural parks, wildlife or vegetation conservation areas or reserves, and NFA lands designated for new management actions. Even so, the multiple-use concept has its limitations, in particular when shepherds and their flocks must adapt to share their range with protected predator species such as wolves or bears (see chapter 11), groups of hikers accompanied by dogs, or any other users who may not always react appropriately to herding activities (see chapter 15).

A Time of Agri-Environmental Policies and Techniques

The beginning of the 1990s saw the welcome advent of the European agri-environmental policy. However, as Hubert et al. noted in the preceding chapter, that policy was concerned primarily with agricultural activities other than herding, polluting activities in particular. It was designed "to compensate farmers for additional costs incurred as a result of environmental constraints." From that standpoint, herding activities, which for the most part were already recognized as being environmentally beneficial (brush clearing, diversification of grassy areas, and the like), did not warrant priority. However, the various regional Pastoral Service Bureaus were able to use the policy to legitimize the practices of livestock farmers who used sensitive natural environments. This was the origin of measures on landscape protection, fire control, and the effort to combat rural depopulation,[31] which provided compensation for alterations to or consolidation of existing herding practices.

There remained the problem of differentiating among those practices and identifying their respective impacts on qualitative aspects of the environment, if only because of the importance of using public funds judiciously. This proved easy enough in areas subject to the risk of forest fires, for diagnostic capabilities had been developed a short time previously. The case was somewhat different in other areas, owing to lack of knowledge, especially with respect to performance assessment indicators. Consequently, the main instruments developed were "input-based" contracts stipulating users' obligations (e.g., requiring strict observance of pasturing dates, specifying stocking density limits for particular areas, the production of invoices proving that work had been done using prescribed complementary machinery, and the like). The agencies responsible for assessing agricultural practices and products had no difficulty in ascertaining whether these contracts had been properly executed.

Livestock farmers and herders thus found they were being enlisted to pursue objectives that were in many instances somewhat difficult to grasp, such as a requirement to "promote biodiversity." Yes, but what kind of biodiversity? While farmers reaped financial benefits that were sometimes quite substantial (from €20 to nearly €180 per acre per year [US$26–240], depending on the region, the nature of the issue involved, and the constraints imposed), most herders were no better paid than before, and many of them were not pleased at being abruptly required to comply with new instructions issued by persons who knew little about herding. One herder, whose competence was unquestioned, hired for a summer transhumance in the Massif Central (volcanic region in the center of France), said to us: "Just to give you an idea, they have 450 acres of land, they own it. On those 450 acres, they expect me to pasture my sheep on 35 acres, including a strip that's 50 feet wide and 1.8 miles long. And I'm not allowed to step outside that strip on either side. And I have to just walk my sheep along it, so that there won't be too much erosion. So I explained to them that the more bunched up the sheep, the greater the erosion. And then I gave up even trying to explain."[32]

These "input-based" contracts were not only irrelevant but, more importantly, highly infantilizing for farmers and herders alike. More recently, some have proposed that in certain cases they should be replaced by "output-based" contracts in the Alps.[33] Specifications would be an integral part of every contract, containing realistic, clearly specified output objectives over a five-year period, in which the contractor has full discretion to decide on his technical inputs and adjust them on a case-by-case basis. The purpose is to engage the responsibility of farmers in their capacity as producers not only of lambs or cheeses, but also of local environmental resources. The herder would become a technical comanager and as such would qualify for part of the funding, as is already the case with those employed by some farmers.[34] The level of support should be commensurate with the issues involved, but in France this is still something of a gamble in view of the uncertain future of agricultural policy and the lack of funding for environmental policy. More fundamentally, the object is also to promote a dialogue among some farmers and their herders on the implications of this kind of pastoral management. As one herder put it to us, "For a farmer, agri-environmental measures are perceived as a constraint that qualifies him for more agricultural subsidies, whereas for many of us herders, they may represent extra work, but they are part of a kind of 'pastoral ethic.'"

THE NEED TO REDEFINE AND RECOGNIZE
THE SKILLS OF HIRED SHEPHERDS

In France, a consensus is gradually emerging on the need to formally acknowledge the practical skills and professionalism of hired shepherds and to recognize the activity as a craft in its own right, allowing it to shed its aura of nostalgia and folklore. However, this consensus raises a number of unresolved issues relating to communication, pay scales, working conditions, and a national status defining a social setting.

Do Herders Belong in a Museum or Primary Schools?

For the past twenty years or so, transhumant sheep farmers, herders, and their flocks have filled the streets of a number of towns during the Festival of Transhumance, which is held at the summer solstice every year.[35] There are thousands of spectators; as often as not, there are more spectators than sheep. Herding dog competitions are also successful events, popular with both herders and dog fanciers. Bookshop shelves are full of lavishly illustrated books about shepherds, mainly in the regional or nature sections. Some authors have boldly set out to explode the shepherd myth by painting a realistic picture of the conditions under which herders live while grazing the flocks in the plains or hills,[36] taking them through long-range transhumance to high mountain pastures[37] and spending the summer there with them.[38] This interest in sheep and herding exists because France is now heavily urbanized, and French people continue to feel nostalgic about their rural traditions, especially those involving open-air activities. Tour operators who offer mountain hiking holiday packages frequently include a visit to an authentic shepherd's cabin as part of the program. Many herders find this annoying, as they have no desire to be put on display as living museum exhibits.

Partly as a reaction to this, there have been a number of recent initiatives aimed at informing the public and local representatives that herding is still a living occupation, one that is essential for conservation of the economic, cultural, and environmental aspects of mountain heritage. Since 1997, an organization known as the Association de la Maison de la Transhumance based in the department of Bouches-du-Rhône (where there are more transhumant flocks of sheep than in any other part of France) has been working to facilitate contact among sheep farmers, scientists, experts, and local representatives. The association's Interpretation Center on Mediterranean Pastoral Cultures has produced numerous books, films, traveling exhibitions, and other events, and in addition it has contributed to the Euro-Mediterranean pastoralism network.[39] It is active in the Pastoralism Centers Network, which comprises seven centers in France, with

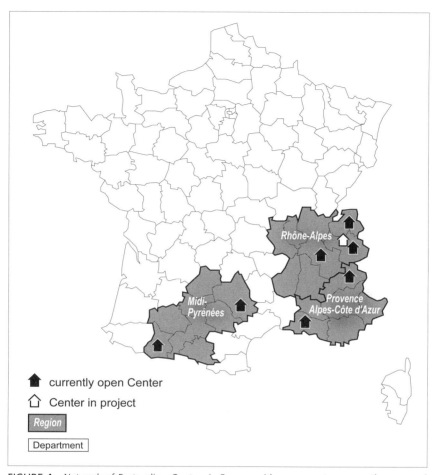

FIGURE 4 – Network of Pastoralism Centers in France, with seven centers currently open and one more to come. In addition, two other centers have been established, one in Spain and the other in Italy. 2013 update: Patrick Fabre.

one more to come (Figure 4). The aim is to create a network covering the Mediterranean area. One center has been established in Spain and another in Italy. The network aspires to heighten awareness among the general public and to muster support for the sheep production sector by serving as a multidisciplinary watch service for herding practices.[40]

A similar approach, seeking to provide information rooted in reality rather than nostalgia, has been adopted by the Pastoral Service Bureaus of Savoie and Haute-Savoie in the northern Alps. They work in partnership with their counterparts in Switzerland and in the departments of the Ain and the Jura, and with the support of the Ministry of National Education and various agricultural associations. Beginning in 2001, these bodies have joined forces to pursue an initiative entitled "A Herder at My School."[41] This educational activity has been highly successful, with more than a thousand children between the ages of five and twelve participating each year. Groups of herders, who are paid for their contributions, consult with teachers to determine what messages should be presented to the children. One message deemed to warrant priority was, "Being a herder is a career choice!"

Lastly, it is increasingly common to find notices at the starting points of hiking trails in mountain regions informing users that high mountain pastures are also the place where herders work. Hikers are asked to behave appropriately: for example, not to allow their dogs to stray, not to use a herder's cabin as a picnic site, and not to badger herders with questions about what the weather is going to be like over the weekend.[42]

"Can't Find Good Herders Anymore!"

In France, demand for shepherds currently exceeds supply,[43] and sheep farmers frequently complain it is difficult to "find a good herder" who can endure the frequently solitary life high on a mountain summer pasture, provide the flock with basic care, and do his work conscientiously. There are many tales of herders who have abruptly abandoned the summer range where they were tending their flocks, or who have been dismissed in mid-season for gross negligence.[44] This was one reason why CERPAM conducted a series of in-depth surveys of sheep farmers and herders in the PACA region. The initial surveys were qualitative,[45] the later ones quantitative.[46] A further objective of these surveys was to contribute to the task of relaunching the educational project originated by the Merle Herders School (see chapter 12). Similar in origin (i.e., in response to a request from farmers) was an equally large-scale, long-term (1990–1998) project carried out in the three departments of the western Pyrenees. The outcome has been a specialized training program leading to certification as a qualified "Pluriactive [multiple job holding] sheep/cow herder."[47]

The results of the CERPAM surveys may be summarized as follows. In 1995, a large majority of sheep farmers employed relatively young seasonal herders (most of them between the ages of twenty-five and forty-five, with three quarters of them in the twenty-five to thirty-five age bracket), nearly all male, and city-dwellers. In one case out of every two, the previous experience of herders from an urban background was rated "good" by the farmers (i.e., the herders had worked more than three summer transhumance seasons); only one out of five were herding a flock on summer pasture for the first time. For herders from a rural background, eight out of ten were described by the farmers as having good herding experience. One persistent feature, which is increasingly prominent today, is a lack of stability in the work relations between herders and farmers: only a third of the herders had been employed for three years or more by the same farmer, and half of them were being employed for the first time. On the whole, despite the complaints that gave rise to the surveys, the farmers declared themselves satisfied with more than three quarters of their herders and willing to continue to employ them to herd their flocks on their summer range. Regarding seasonal hired herders from urban backgrounds in particular, however, employers said they had been satisfied with their work in no more than one case out of two, giving such reasons as total lack of motivation or conscientiousness. Cases of this kind were not common (one in six), but there were enough to make farmers uneasy.

Working Conditions and Rates of Pay

Newly employed hired herders are almost always alone with their sheep on the summer range, even in their first season; the only exceptions are trainees attending a shepherding school. In the Alps, most of them are in charge of a flock of between 800 and 1,500 breeding ewes. Note that a flock of 1,500 breeding ewes represents, when the ewes are pregnant, a capital asset of approximately €300,000 (US$400,000). Once they have acquired some experience, they may find themselves herding anywhere from 1,500 to 2,800 ewes, depending on the range.[48] In the western Pyrenees, in contrast, the situation is considerably different: the herder is required to look after a flock of 150 to 300 dairy sheep and to make and deliver cheese. This kind of work is markedly more collective in nature because that region is characterized by a different pastoral culture, and because the sheep producers' home farms are located in much closer proximity to the mountain summer pastures.[49] In the Alps, most herders have to make their own supply arrangements, although quite often nowadays at the beginning of the season the employer will have the herder taken up to the mountain pasture by helicopter, along with salt for the sheep, nonperishable food supplies, and firewood. On occasion in the Alps, and almost invariably in the Pyrenees, herders are resupplied on a regular basis by the farmers, hired assistants, or even their spouses, family members, or passing friends.

During the past few years, the basic facilities available at summer range sites (e.g., cabin, water supply, photovoltaic equipment) have become much more satisfactory thanks to the efforts of Pastoral Service Bureaus, national parks, RNPs, and other regional bodies. This is not uniformly the case, however; some herders still have to make do with cramped cabins in poor repair, with no running water or electricity, that are poorly insulated

MICHEL MEURET / INRA

PHOTO 1 – The four-year-old son of a hired herder, "on vacation" with his father (the herder) and mother on summer range in the Alps.

and consequently cold and damp in inclement weather. Working facilities (e.g., sorting and catch pens, communication equipment) were seldom available in the Southern Alps at the time of the CERPAM surveys in 1995. Today, most of high pasture mountain range has partial cell phone coverage. Some progress has been made with working facilities as well, including the use of helicopters to ferry supplies and equipment in at the beginning of the season, or, in the Pyrenees, to fly sheep's-milk cheese out during the season.

In areas where living conditions are still primitive, a herder cannot very well bring a spouse along to share his or her life of inconvenience and discomfort unless the spouse is also a herder (see also chapter 14). Consequently, approximately half of all herders are single and childless. That is why herding is effectively subject to an age-limit: many shepherds give it up when they turn forty.[50] Old, unmarried herders are becoming a rare phenomenon, and a new trend is appearing, partly as a result of the availability of more comfortable accommodations: increasingly, we find herders who are accompanied on the job by their spouses and children during the summer school vacation (see Photo 1).

In France, herders are not covered by a national convention governing their employment and wages, in contrast to most other occupational groups. In some departments, however, collective agreements have been signed between farmers' unions and farm employee unions, with herders explicitly included. Virtually all hired herders are paid by the month. As a rule, they are not paid less than the official French minimum wage (Salaire Minimum Interprofessionnel de Croissance, or SMIC), the net amount of which is €1,122 (US$1,480) per month in 2013. However, we have found that there are exceptions involving substantial disparities in some instances, and these frequently appear to be unrelated to a herder's experience. They range from half-time wages for full-time work, offset by "pocket money" or payment in kind (food and drink), to net pay of up to €1,700 per month (US$2,200). In 2010, we learned of cases of herders who were not only paid net wages of the order of €1,500, but also received a "long-service allowance" of €300 per month (US$400) from their employers in recognition of years of satisfactory work on the same summer range for the same farmer or group of farmers.

This may sound like reasonable pay, but many herders regard it as inadequate. The CERPAM surveys indicate that those who are dissatisfied tend to be younger herders (in the twenty-six to thirty-five age bracket) who have had a good deal of experience (five to ten years). The chairman of the Hautes-Alpes Shepherds and Cowherders Association recently stated, "We have the responsibilities of surgeons, we never have a moment's respite . . . and we are paid laborers' wages." He went on to say, "In the course of a season, we work the equivalent of 300 or 340 hours a month."[51] This is a problem, as in France the minimum wage is calculated on the basis of 152 working hours per month, approximately half the number of hours actually worked by most herders. In the eyes of the labor inspection authorities, persons who employ herders—like many others who employ seasonal workers—are unquestionably breaking the law. To comply with the law, they would have to hire two herders, one working mornings and the other evenings, with a replacement to work weekends. In addition, herders are not supposed to put in more than the number of hours an employee may be required to work in France, as a rule forty-eight hours per week. But just try putting a herder in charge of a flock with instructions to stop working as soon as he has done his legal number of hours! As a skilled professional, he would laugh.

We shall not attempt to resolve the difficult issue of pay here. We conclude from our interviews with herders that the key to a solution would be a wage greater than or equal to the full-time French minimum wage rate. All employers should pay approximately the same wage, supplemented by more than a token slice of any future agri-environmental contract, plus adequate accommodation and working conditions and relations of mutual confidence between herders and their employers. We believe most skilled hired herders would find these terms satisfactory.

A Prospective Qualification: "Skilled Shepherd"

The Interministerial Group on Pastoralism has looked into the status of hired shepherds and/or cowherders and concluded that "the relevant legislation needs to be amended or overhauled."[52] The group's first proposal concerns the preparation of a draft national agreement protocol to be used as a basis for negotiating collective employment conventions and agreements covering individual regions or departments. The protocol would prescribe hired herders' working conditions and minimum safeguards, and it would be accompanied by a standard work contract. However, the Ministry of Agriculture's Employment Service Branch has pointed out that a precondition for such a protocol would be an agreement between one or more union organizations representing employees on the one hand and employers on the other. At the present time, herders in France have no nationwide craft union.

The Interministerial Group also suggested developing a rating scale identifying different competence levels for hired herders, with the idea that the higher an individual's rating, the greater the degree of responsibility he would be qualified to assume. This would make it feasible not only to rank and clarify the various tasks assigned to herders, but, even more importantly, to provide a herder with better prospects for recognition and career advancement, in contrast to the present situation, where a herder's chances for promotion depend on nothing more tangible than his reputation among employers and other herders. The lowest rating would be a "working herder" whose work is limited to keeping watch and herding the flock and milking dairy ewes; in practice, many novice herders perform those tasks. The highest rating would be a "highly skilled herder," whose duties include contributing to range management in partnership with other stakeholders, as is the case with herders who participate in such matters as forest fire prevention (see chapter 12, Figure 1).

Most herders would fall into the intermediate category of "skilled herder." We interpret this to mean what sheep farmers today call a "good herder," but of course every farmer judges on the basis of his/her own standards, and consequently a herder's reputation rests on word-of-mouth comments, which inevitably tend to be subjective. In order to offer his services as a "skilled herder" in the job market, an individual would have to (1) have taken formal training courses at the beginning of his/her career, or skills upgrading courses at a later stage (in either case the training would be attested by a diploma from a shepherding school); (2) have had several years of practical herding experience; (3) be involved in effective rangeland resource renewal management; and (4) be involved in the input adjustment process required under agri-environmental contracts (see previously). According to the Interministerial Group, a herder would be required to possess this level of competence in order to qualify for employment herding a collective flock.

CONCLUSION

Why are they still out there with their flocks, these farmers and shepherds? It is a fair question in view of the fact that sheep production, and pastoral sheep production in particular, especially where transhumance is involved, is having some difficulty fitting into a society that tends to regard it as a quaint relic of the country's cultural heritage.[53] The socio-economic conditions characterizing that type of sheep production have evolved considerably over the past few decades. In France, as in other countries, sheep farmers have been confronted with falling lamb prices, owing to imports: half of all the lamb meat consumed in France today is imported, mainly from the United Kingdom and Ireland. To be sure, the type of production just described receives European agricultural support, which accounts for over half producers' net income. That support is vital to them, but at the same time it tends to make them feel their occupation is meaningless. Lastly, while the industry unquestionably has assets, including the excellent image enjoyed by its products compared to those available from other forms of livestock production, factory farming in particular, it has not yet succeeded in turning those assets into economic returns. Accordingly, farmers are increasingly inclined to reduce their production costs, including the cost of employing a herder, and hired herders have declined considerably in numbers in the past fifty years, especially in the lamb production sector. The situation is somewhat better in the dairy sheep and goat production sectors, especially for farmers who make local cheeses marketed under a controlled-origin brand. All the others are confronted head-on with the high-volume, low-priced products of factory farming, which in some cases are sold with the help of advertising featuring illustrations of herders, even though, as a rule, the sheep have been fed nothing but cultivated forage and concentrates.

Some observers, including the authors as members of the Association Française de Pastoralisme, remain optimistic. We have faith in the ability of pastoral sheep farmers and herders to adapt and innovate, as they have shown themselves capable of doing many a time in the past. Most shepherds are perhaps not *born* such, but they have chosen their occupation out of conviction. Similarly, herders and farmers take their flocks of sheep or goats out to pasture, or entrust them to the care of herders, for reasons that have as much to do with ethics and identity as with economic or ecological considerations. They are turning local resources to account, finding satisfaction in a meaningful activity,[54] achieving a harmonious family life and experiencing personal pleasure.[55] However, it would be futile to believe that their "passion for their animals" alone can enable them to hold their own in a context of globalized trade in goods and services, rapid change in the uses and functions of land in France, and insecure employment and working conditions.

The main challenge is securing recognition of the full diversity of pastoralism, with its array of concomitant functions,[56] including its role in preserving the biodiversity produced by "ordinary nature" on rangeland.[57] That is the function that warrants the most generous funding, for it is now deemed essential by many observers, including scientists, elected representatives, and nature managers. It also would be constructive to discard the concept of "environmental constraints," which originally referred to polluting intensive agricultural practices. In the case of pastoralism, in contrast, it would be more to the point to devise "environmental resource production contracts" with legal force, analogous to food production contracts. This would not merely be playing with words, as a change of that magnitude would have momentous consequences, especially for herders. At that stage, it would be crucial for shepherds formally certified as "skilled" to be invited to participate in discussions and negotiations relating to ecologically relevant and technically feasible actions—which would vary from one grazing section to another and one grazing season to another—that could be implemented in the context of shepherding activities. Not to adopt this course would be tantamount to reinforcing the concept of the herder as merely one of a number of factors, possessing no unique knowledge or practical skills. But if herders themselves are to be persuaded to endorse this scheme, in tandem with farmers, a number of major issues remain to be resolved. People must recognize the multiple functions expected from professional herder. Herders also need more security of employment, both during the summer range season and during the rest of the year. Actions are needed to enhance awareness of the technical, teachable aspect of the work and the frequently impressive flock performance results that are characteristic of herding practices (the present collective book purports to be a contribution to that endeavor). Lastly, actions are needed to rectify the common image of the herder as a marginal individual estranged from society, with his head in the stars and his heart devoted exclusively to his sheep and his dog.

NOTES

[1] Ezekiel 34: 12 (Biblegateway, American Standard Version).

[2] Jehan de Brie, 1541.

[3] Citoyen Daubenton, 1794.

[4] Landais and Deffontaines, 1988.

[5] Mallen, 1995; Lassalle, 2007.

[6] SEA Savoie et Haute-Savoie, 2001.

[7] Leroy and Gaubert, 2000.

[8] Benarous and Sourd, 2002.

[9] SEA Savoie et Haute-Savoie, op. cit.

[10] Ernoult and Favier, 1997; Ernoult et al., 1999.

[11] Landrot, 1999.

[12] Legeard, 1996, 1999 and 2003.

[13] Roucolle and Plainecassagne, 2003.

[14] APEM, 2007.

[15] Dubost, 2000.

[16] Martinand, 1991.

[17] Meuret and Chabert, 1999.

[18] Legeard, 1996.

[19] Landrot, op. cit.

[20] Legeard, 1996, 1999, and 2003.

[21] MAPAR, 2002.

[22] Estrosi and Spagnou, 2003.

[23] Lassalle, 2007.

[24] Landrot, op. cit.; Charbonnier, 2012.

[25] Dodier, 2005.

[26] Guérin and Bellon, 1990.

[27] Landais and Deffontaines, 1988.

[28] Landais, 1993.

[29] Faure, 1990.

[30] Etienne et al., 1990; Etienne et al., 2002.

[31] Lavoux et al., 1999.

[32] Meuret and Léger, 2001.

[33] Mestelan et al., 2007.

[34] Mallen, op. cit.

[35] Duclos, 1994.

[36] Brisebarre, 1978; Roux et al., 2011; Blond, 2012.

[37] Doisneau, 1999.

[38] Bodin and Bardiau, 1997; Caraguel et al., 2011.

[39] Fabre et al., 2002.

[40] Fabre, 2004.

[41] SEA Haute-Savoie, 2007.

[42] SEA Savoie et Haute-Savoie, op. cit.

[43] MAPAR, op. cit.

[44] Legeard, 1996.

[45] Mallen, op. cit.

[46] Legeard, 1996.

[47] Lassalle, 1998.

[48] Legeard, 1996.

[49] Lassalle, 2007.

[50] Legeard, 1996.

[51] Estrosi and Spagnou, op. cit.

[52] MAPAR, op. cit.

[53] Fabre, 2002.

[54] Eychenne, 2006.

[55] Meuret, 2006.

[56] Moneyron et al., 1995; Suaci Alpes du Nord, 2007.

[57] Alphandéry and Billaud, 1996a.

PART 2

Herding Practices by Shepherds

Scientific Explorations

CHAPTER 3

Shepherding on a Farm with Diverse Pastures:

A First Insight

Pierre Martinand & François Millo

FORTY YEARS LATER: LOOKING BACK AT THE RESEARCH
Pierre Martinand

*I*N *the early 1970s, a colleague from New Zealand came to France to visit sheep farms in the Southern Prealps. At the end of the day, he pointed to a shepherd with his flock and asked me, "What does he do?" I answered, "I don't know. All I know is that the day there are no more herders in southeastern France, there won't be any more sheep."*

At the time, I was a young agricultural economist and animal scientist working for the Ministry of Agriculture in a department in charge of studying and implementing animal production policy. Our goal was to modernize animal production through genetic improvement, forage crop intensification, and modernization of facilities and equipment. The small team I was on in Montpellier was in charge of the sheep meat industry. Like everyone else, I had been asked to improve the productivity of livestock farms by replacing labor-intensive techniques such as herding with capital-intensive techniques: for instance, by promoting grazing within fenced areas on rangeland.

I had carried out technical economic surveys of hundreds of sheep farms that all devoted daily time to herding their flocks. Some of the farms did not have full-time herders; in that case, the farmer and his spouse would herd the flocks several hours every day. The practice was considered archaic and strongly resisted agricultural modernization. It was in fact its resistance that prompted me, as an industry expert, to try and better understand it.

Adapted from: Martinand P., Millo F., 1979. Différenciation du territoire des exploitations ovines des Préalpes du sud en fonction de l'utilisation pastorale. *In*: Molénat G., Jarrige R. (coord). *Utilisation par les ruminants des pâturages d'altitude et parcours méditerranéens*. Éd. INRA, Versailles: 397-407.

It was clear that, in conducting the herder surveys, it would not be possible to use our usual methods to assess a pasture value, which consists of recording the consumable biomass and the flock's grazing time for each grazing sector. At the time, a new approach was emerging amongst some research groups. It was inspired by the ethology of wild ungulates and had been adapted for observing domestic animal grazing. This new approach nevertheless was not consistent with my own hypotheses, since the ethologist's model proposed that animals fed themselves better on their own than when they were herded. I therefore based my work on ethologists' observation methods, but not on their model. This led to the manuscript written in 1979, which is presented in this chapter.

It was interesting to note animal scientists' reactions to such research at the time. In 1978, I presented my research at a conference for the Animal Production Department at INRA. It would be an understatement to say that most attendees found the research rather unorthodox and impossible to reproduce. Robert Jarrige, then department head and coeditor of the conference proceedings, wrote me the following: "We cannot publish your paper, since the herder is the one who determines the herd's results." I replied, "If they know how to achieve the results they want, they know more than we do, and that's a good reason to study their methods!" My paper was published, but it was the last one I wrote in an animal science book.

As a result of our research on shepherds' practices, we were soon able to provide assistance to sheep farmers throughout southeastern France. At that time (late seventies and eighties), most of the younger sheep farmers in southeastern France were quickly and happily modernizing animal production (see chapters 1 and 2). Sometimes they even discarded their own knowledge as herders in mixing the diversity of resources and using the complementarities within rangeland resources and between rangeland and parcels of cultivated resources. Our methods for planning the right sequence of areas for grazing livestock enable farmers in southeastern France to better utilize the diversity of grazing resources, considering the development of incentives to fence pastures. These and other pioneering results also resulted in agronomists', landscape ecologists', and economists' taking into account practices linked to specific grazing areas within a farm setting and making them legitimate research objects, in addition to understanding and modeling the reasoning behind them, their processes, and their outcomes.

Southeastern France has many areas of rangeland, and the heterogeneity of the region's stock-farming land, which is one of its essential characteristics, is also displayed—indeed, to an even greater extent—by the rangeland. This diversity results more from past use of the land, as gardens, cropland, and hay meadows, and to a lesser extent current land use, than from local differences in the soil and climate (see Photos 1 and 2).[1]

PIERRE MARTINAND

PHOTO 1 – A portion of the study area in early spring of 1978.

PIERRE MARTINAND

PHOTO 2 – In the seventies, the landscape was a mosaic of rangeland and cultivated parcels. This diversity results more from past use of the land as gardens, cropland, and hay meadows, and to a lesser extent from current land use, than from local differences in the soil and climate.

In the majority of French Mediterranean sheep farms, current differences in land use result primarily from shepherds' management of flock grazing. Herding, often considered somewhat summarily as a practice that involves "living off the land," in fact requires the herder to constantly adjust stocking density to available forage resources. Different types of rangeland and grassland are thus subjected to extremely variable seasonal stocking rates depending on the state of vegetation. This in turn can induce changes in vegetation.

To better understand the underlying causes of local variations in stocking rates, we developed ways to analyze the overall operation of sheep farms where flocks were herded. We carried out three surveys in 1972, 1975, and 1976–1977 in the sector of the Southern Prealps between Digne, Draguignan, and Nice. We first described the principal activities of the region's sheep farms in time and space, without emphasizing any one farm in particular. To do this, we surveyed 140 farms, virtually all those with more than one hundred ewes. We thus demonstrated the importance of average stocking rate for ground use, particularly in the area devoted to growing crops on each farm.[2]

Between the fall of 1977 and the summer of 1978, we studied a subsample of sheep farms and improved our understanding of the technical aspects of farm operation—especially shepherds' practices—through frequent observations in situ. However, the duration of our study was not sufficient to furnish multiple series of homogeneous, comprehensive recordings. In this chapter, therefore, we use two examples to simply propose a few elements of a framework of analysis and several comments on farm organization and its impact on changes in the vegetation.

THE FARMS STUDIED

We studied five sheep farms located in the Prealps, between Digne and Verdon, a region that Raoul Blanchard called the Bloc de Majastres.[3] There we chose farmers who made significant use of the rangelands, whose farms were representative of the diversity of the region's sheep farms, and who agreed to frequent visits (i.e., once or twice per week) (see Table 1).

All the farms are family-run. The father does most of the herding, and the son and temporary help are responsible for other farm work and lambing.

We collected the following information:
- Questionnaire (family, property, livestock farming system)
- Identification of all land in use on a land tenure map, including those parcels of land owned by the farmer
- Financial statistics
- Flock performance
- Quantity of feed (forage and grains) produced and distributed
- Observation of herding practices
- Base map of landscape units

The methodology of our daily grazing pattern observations was based on behavioral studies of sheep in high mountain pastures.[4]

TABLE 1: The Five Sheep Farms Studied between 1977 and 1978

Farm number	1	2	3	4	5
Farmed surface area (acreage)	25	62	62	49	74
Total surface area (acreage) - including summer range - not including summer range	6,178	2,718	1,853	988	198
Number of ewes	600	550	320	200	350
Principal lambing season	March	March	Oct.-Nov.	Oct.-Nov.	Oct.-Nov.
Number of workers	2.5	2.5	2	2	2
Altitude of the farmstead (ft)	3,773	3,445	2,461	2,461	3,117

Over the course of a grazing circuit, or the planned route taken by the herder and his sheep, we noted the following at regular intervals (twenty to thirty minutes):
- Flock outline on a map
- Flock activities (grazing, travel, etc.)
- Actions taken by the herder and his dogs
- Weather conditions
- Plant cover

It was not possible to carry out observations as frequently as originally planned (i.e., one to two days a week between November and March, a period during which only Farms 1, 2, and 3 used the rangelands). Nevertheless, for all five farms, we either observed or were able to reconstruct, together with the individual herders, the sequence of farming and grazing operations occurring in the various land parcels in 1977 and 1978. In summarizing the data, we identified three concepts to differentiate one piece of land from another. These concepts are based on the period of use and intensity of human activity on the land: a) quarters; b) sectors and grazing circuits; and c) parcels of land.

GRAZING QUARTERS AND SECTORS

On all five farms, the annual grazing schedule determines the layout of grazing quarters, each of which includes a rest area for the flock. No one quarter is used regularly throughout the entire grazing season. Some quarters are used during the grass-growing seasons in the spring and fall, while others are used in the summer and winter. Farms 1, 3, and 4 keep one area, generally at a higher altitude than the rest, for summer pasture; this zone includes one or more bed grounds for the flocks. Farms 1, 2, and 3 have "transition zones," which are used before and after the summer and contain a shed or other rest areas. On Farm 5, only one shed is used to access pasture.

The existence of one or several distinct quarters seems to depend on the average stocking rate of the total surface area used by the farm. Our surveys of 140 farms indicate that, under a threshold of 0.2 to 0.4 ewes per acre, a minimum of two rest areas, and therefore two quarters, are used. The following two examples are on both sides of this threshold.

Farm no. 3

This farm has relatively uniform elevation (see Figure 1), and since its various grazing quarters have similar sun and wind exposure, the annual growth rate of grasses is fairly comparable throughout.

The principal lambing season and the "catch-up" lambing session in the spring take place in Lambing Sheds 1 and 2. Hay is stored in these sheds, which are located near the farmhouse. In the fall, as the lambing season approaches, the ewes are led into these sheds, from which they are turned out to graze primarily in Sector Ia. During this time, the rest of the flock grazes on Quarter II, especially Sector IIb. To reach Quarter II, they start out from Shed 3, which is old and small. On sunny winter days, the entire flock is led out either to the meadows near the sheds (Sector Ib), or to the oak undergrowth (Ic), which is the highest sector on the farm.

In the spring, the entire flock, including the lambs born in February and March, graze on the rangelands and meadows located above the lambing sheds (Sector Ib), where supplementary feed is also provided. The flock is then moved into Shed 3 to graze on Quarter II, usually on Sector IIa, which is rested in autumn.

For several years now, Quarter III has been used for part of the summer. It comprises two former plantations of black pine (*Pinus Nigra* Arnold), which together account for ninety-nine acres. However, these conifers have gradually spread over hundreds of acres. The forage resources of Quarter III are therefore relatively limited. Although the flock is kept in the same quarter for the night, and despite the difficulty of herding a flock in a wooded area, the herder comes every day to manage the flock's grazing circuit.

There are two categories of land on this farm, as far as the herders are concerned:
- Land accessed from each of the flock's three bed grounds (or *couchade*, as the farmers and herders call these areas), which, by analogy with

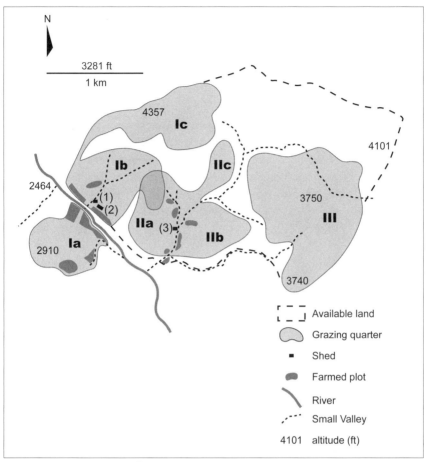

FIGURE 1 - Farm 3 (320 ewes for 1,853 acres).

the terms defined for high mountain pasture,[5] we will refer to as "grazing quarters."

- Land grazed over several days, which will be referred to as "grazing sectors." Within each of these sectors, the herder plans a specific route for the flock; this is known as the "grazing circuit." This circuit may be split into two phases if the flock returns to the shed to rest halfway through the day. The term "standard circuit" (*circuit-type*) is used to refer to all the circuits followed within one particular sector. Herders refer to each sector by the word "circuit," together with a place name.

Within a grazing quarter, a herder delimits several distinct grazing sectors and uses them alternately. His daily choice of a particular standard circuit depends on three considerations:

- The flock's behavior: sheep tend to seek out new, tender grass and neglect areas they have recently traveled through.
- Weather conditions: soil type and availability of shelter in the various sectors play a role in deciding which sectors are better in wet or windy conditions.
- Management of forage resources: The circuits used in Sectors Ib and IIa overlap and are those most often used in the spring. These sectors have vegetation with consistently good feeding value each year. They have the highest proportions of property owned by the farmer and recently-abandoned fields (lavender crop until 1968). Sectors IIb and IIc, on the other hand, are little used, especially in the fall, when they are taken over by dry grasses and shrubs. The last crop fields were abandoned around 1920.

The organization of grazing lands into quarters, sectors, and circuits also affects farmed land. The meadows in Sectors Ia and IIb, which are not grazed in the winter or spring, are the first to be cut and then grazed intensively in the fall. The meadows in Sectors Ib and IIa are heavily grazed in early spring to encourage vegetation regrowth. They are cut in the summer for hay and can only be used for grazing again in late fall, and some plots are not even cut every year.

Farm no. 5

There are two sheds on this farm: Shed 1, which is older and centrally located (Figure 2), is used during the main lambing season in the fall and through December 1; and Shed 2, which is newer, is located in the village and used for the end of the fall lambing season and for the catch-up lambing season in the spring. In Shed 2, the flock is managed in confinement, which is why the grazing area of this farm is used as a single quarter (I). From late June to early October, the flock is under the care of another sheep farmer from the village, who leads the sheep into Ubaye, a mountain range located about fifty miles away. The flock of around 350 ewes is therefore not grazed on the farm for about a third of the year.

In the winter, the ewes, having lambed in the fall, are taken to Shed 1 after drying off. As soon as the vegetation begins to grow again, the ewes are run in the meadows in Sector Ia and receive supplementary hay and oats for flushing purposes.

Every morning, starting on May 15 (i.e., at the beginning of gestation), the main flock is led into one of three sectors on a rotational basis (Ib, Ic, and Id). In the afternoon, it is herded over a smaller area consisting of meadows in Sector Ia. High grazing pressure in the meadows is either

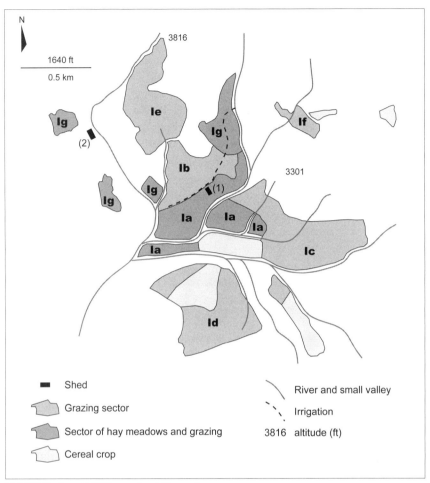

FIGURE 2 - Farm 5 (350 ewes for 198 acres).

to encourage vegetation regrowth early in the season or can simply be considered the first grazing period, depending on the time of year. Most of these meadows can be irrigated and then cut for hay. The exact date of cutting depends on when they were grazed. During the first two weeks of June, the furthest sectors (Ie and If) are used almost exclusively and without leading the flock back to the shed at midday.

Starting on September 15, as the lambing season approaches, the ewes are brought into Shed 1. Lambing usually takes place outside during the day, in the pastures surrounding the shed in Sector Ia. Once the number of ewes having lambed and those at the end of gestation is sufficient to constitute a flock, these animals are led alternatively into one of three sectors (Ib, Ic, or Id) in the morning and into the meadows in the afternoon.

Of the meadows available, there are 1) those located the furthest away, which were not grazed in the spring (Sector Ig) and must therefore be grazed thoroughly before winter in order for the vegetation to grow back the following spring; and 2) the meadows in Sector Ia, which may be grazed in two or three installments.

After December 1, only the ewes that will be lambing in the spring are kept in Shed 1. When the weather allows, these ewes are turned out onto rangelands, particularly in distant sectors (Ie and If). These sectors, which are consistently taken over by dry grasses and shrubs, are thus "cleaned up" every two or three years through grazing, as well as through prescribed burning on dry days in February or March.

These annual grazing schedules roughly define two utilization patterns for both meadows and rangelands:

Meadows

- Meadows in Sector Ig are cut two to four times a year, whenever there is significant forage biomass. Grazing is simply a means of utilizing fall aftermath when it is difficult to make hay as the days grow shorter.
- The meadows in Sector Ia are mainly used for grazing at various times of the year, with stocking density varying according to the vegetation's state of growth. In this case, hay appears to be more important in maintaining the meadow than as forage to be harvested. Some meadows are cut only every two to three years, or not at all.

Little fertilizer is applied to the meadows. Specifically, very little nitrogen is given, and the meadows are not very productive, with the average harvest being around one ton of hay per acre.

Rangelands

- The rangelands in Sectors Ie and If are used during two brief grazing periods, when forage biomass is substantial but partially dry. These are set aside as "reserve" areas, thus preventing the using up of grazing lands during periods of slow grass growth. This type of management results in ungrazed plants gradually dominating the area, even with high stocking density.
- The rangelands in Sectors Ib, Ic, and Id are used more regularly, with frequent grazing and variable stocking density. This appears to extend the period of high-quality forages and stabilize the mix of vegetation.

The average stocking rate is approximately 1.4 ewes per acre. This takes into account the fact that a) the flock is absent from the rangelands in the summer, b) part of the flock is sent to graze on other land in the fall, and c) the feeding requirements of the flock vary from season to season. This stocking rate, which is relatively high for the region, is achieved through more frequent use of rationed grazing and, more importantly, through a significant proportion of farmed pasture. The producer has cleared thirty acres to make way for farmed pastures and is planning to clear more land in Sector Ic with a view to discontinuing the practice of sending ewes to other land in the fall. This sheep farmer is, in our opinion, typical of producers in the process of switching from a herding-based system to a pasture-based system and will soon no longer need a herder.

GRAZING CIRCUITS

The grazing circuits a herder chooses provide the flock with diverse forage resources over a single day and over an entire season. Just how does a herder go about this?

Let's take as an example a grazing circuit designed on Farm 3. This circuit was followed on a fall day in Sector IIb (see Figure 1). The flock ate a variety of forages, including meadow grasses, in a single meal, with different grazing behaviors (see Figure 3 and Table 2).

The circuit took six hours to cover, including about five hours of grazing. During phases of grazing activity, the stocking density varied by a factor of 1 (phases 5 and 7 on steep slopes) to 40 (phase 9 on alfalfa meadows). The areas of the most intensive use were (in decreasing order): alfalfa meadows (phase 9), dry grasses and shrubs (phase 4), abandoned crop fields (phase 3), and old, eroded land (phase 6). Until the flock reached the alfalfa, the herder intervened just four times (see Figure 3). The first time, the herder oriented the flock's direction (*biais*). The next two times he stopped the flock as it reached the edge of the area of dry grasses and shrubs (phase 4). The fourth time, which required the longest action, the herder slowed and redirected the flock's travel in phase 7 as it made its way down the eroded slopes. On the alfalfa meadows, the herder allowed just one strip of grass to be grazed by setting his dogs as boundaries for the sheep. The rest of the time the herder placed himself a relatively long way off, and usually towards the tail end of the flock. We were struck by the cohesion of the flock and the homogeneity of its activity.

This farm's ewes apparently have been trained to a pace of activity and to the exploration of this area such that the herder does not have to intervene frequently to adjust the circuit to the circumstances and his objectives. However, the herder appears to use an empirical method of

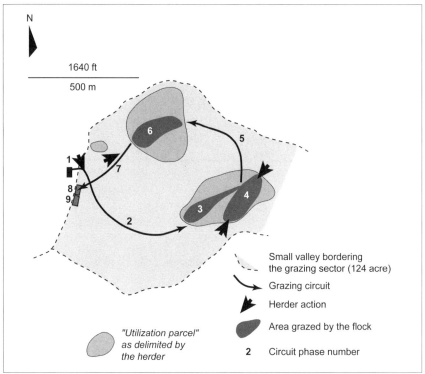

FIGURE 3 - Grazing circuit covered on November 08, 1977 in Sector IIb, Farm 3.

adjusting the quantitative and qualitative aspects of the flock's diet, by varying the area occupied by the flock and its speed of travel along the grazing circuit. Goïc uses the term "speed of exploration" to mean the area covered per unit of time, which is linked to the quantity of grass consumed.[6] This criterion is easy to assess visually.

In addition to direct observations of grazing circuits for the five farms, we also reconstructed all the grazing circuits and sectors used in the various seasons and depending on the number of ewes in a flock. This was done through surveys of herders, using base maps. For example, on Farm 3, the grazing circuit within Sector IIb, presented previously, was used seventy times between August 25 and November 25, 1977, with a flock whose numbers decreased from 300 to 150 ewes. The same circuit was used ten times between May 15 and July 1, 1978, with the entire flock, including the lambs born in the spring. These numbers correspond to an average frequency of three days out of four in the fall and one day out of five in the spring.

During periods of grass growth, herders adapt how frequently they use certain sectors to their flock's rate of consumption and to the development

TABLE 2: Major Phases of the Grazing Circuit

Phases	Time (GMT+2)	"Landscapes" within the sector	Flock activity (%) T = travel G = grazing		Duration of grazing activity (min)	Surface area occupied by the 185 ewes (acres)
			T	G		
1	11:15 a.m.	Leaving the shed	0	salt	0	-
2	11:25 a.m.– 12:00 p.m.	Eroded slopes and pine trees	100	0	0	0.7
3	12:00–12:30 p.m.	Crop fields abandoned around 1920	20	80	24	1.0
4	12:30–2:00 p.m.	Dry grasses and shrubs	0	100	90	2.0
5	2:00–2:20 p.m.	Steep slopes and pine trees	90	10	2	4.9
6	2:20–4:20 p.m.	Eroded former cropland	10	90	108	5.9
7	4:20–4:45 p.m.	Eroded slopes	80	20	5	3.7
8	4:45–5:15 p.m.	Orchard grass meadows	0	100	30	2.7
9	5:15–5:45 p.m.	Alfalfa meadows	0	100	30	0.5
10	6:00 p.m.	Return to the shed	100	0	0	-

stage of reference forage species. When vegetation growth slows or stops, herders seek to preserve high-quality parcels of land while meeting their flocks' need to seek out new grass compared to that grazed the day before. When interviewed, herders never referred to the availability of grass over the course of a grazing season, or to surface area. Instead, in designing their grazing circuits, they appeared to choose a succession of land types that differed in terms of both nature (former cropland, grasslands overrun by pine trees, etc.) and the flock's capacity to utilize the land.

By analogy with parcels of cropland that undergo homogeneous human intervention, we decided, together with the herders, to call the different land types they used "utilization parcels." The herders then had no problem providing specific drawings of all their utilization parcels on base maps, each of them characterized by plant species that could be grazed under certain conditions.

CONCLUSION

The information collected on sheep grazing management by herders of the Southern Prealps sheep farms demonstrates the great variety of grazing land utilization patterns available to them. These diverse techniques enable herders to adapt to new situations involving variations in available area, natural environment, and the socioeconomic strategy of producers. In each situation, it is possible to look for improvements taking into account working conditions and the renewal or improvement of forage resources.

Experiments being conducted on reference farms and research stations, which aim at expressing the full forage potential of rangelands by using fenced areas without herders, involve considerably higher stocking rates with a minimal amount of work. In our opinion, however, it is equally important to analyze the practices of producers and herders in other situations, as these may be improved without doing away with herding.

Indeed, despite the major demographic fall in the number of people working on farms in the areas where sheep farms are most prevalent, and where producers have low capacity for investment, herded grazing often represents the most flexible and productive way of exploiting the diversity of pastoral resources. This is all the more true as land has in many cases become more or less abandoned by its owners. This means that livestock farmers can run their animals without a lease on large surface areas of land that cannot be farmed by the land owners. Using the land in this way restores a traditional right from the Middle Ages of animals, farmers, and their herders to use rangeland for grazing (in French: *droit de parcours*).

NOTES

[1] Blanchemain, 1979; Thiault, 1979.
[2] Thepot, 1977.
[3] Blanchard, 1945.
[4] Favre, 1976.
[5] Favre, op. cit.
[6] Goïc, 1977.

Taking Advantage of an Experienced Herder's Knowledge to Design Summer Range Management Tools

Isabelle Savini, Étienne Landais, Pascal Thinon & Jean-Pierre Deffontaines

THE research presented in this chapter was conducted as part of a collaboration that began in 1987 between the Science for Action and Development Department of the INRA Versailles-Grignon Research Centre and an experienced shepherd by the name of André Leroy (see Photo 1). Each summer, Leroy herds flocks of 1,000 to 1,500 sheep belonging to local sheep farmers in the French Southern Alps.

Initially, research in the field was carried out merely to support a broader research project to develop and illustrate several methods for studying the practices of various agriculture sector stakeholders to aid their decision-making.[1] A detailed study of André Leroy's herding practices[2] led to an innovative interdisciplinary collaboration.[3] Because the document was considered particularly useful as educational material, a documentary was also made in collaboration with prestigious French university École Normale Supérieure de Saint-Cloud.[4] Thanks to support from the Ministry of Agriculture, the film was widely distributed to agricultural teaching establishments and is used in herder internships organized by the Association of Employees for the Promotion of Agricultural Progress in the Hautes-Alpes department.

Adapted from: Savini I., Landais E., Thinon P., Deffontaines J-P., 1993. "L'organisation de l'espace pastoral : des concepts et des représentations construits à dire d'expert dans une perspective de modélisation." *In*: Landais E. (coord.) Pratiques d'Élevage Extensif: identifier, modéliser, évaluer. Études *et Recherches sur les Systèmes Agraires et le Développement*, 27: 137–60.

MICHEL MEURET / INRA

PHOTO 1 – The herder André Leroy and his dogs are both watching the herd on the Saut-du-Laire high mountain pasture (August 2007).

The fieldwork on Leroy attracted interest from local and regional development organizations, particularly CERPAM [the Pastoral Service Bureau for the Provence-Alpes-Côte d'Azur Region]. Research continued in collaboration with multiple partners with the objective of applying results to high mountain pasture management. First and foremost was the Parc National des Écrins. This national park's management expressed the desire to "contribute to maintaining grazing activities in the park while controlling impact on the environment." Specifically, this meant helping improve mountain pasture management (particularly through funds for herding facilities) and setting out the specifications for grazing that would preserve natural resources and the landscape, with a view to drawing up summer range grazing contracts.*

With this in mind, research involving André Leroy, who now herds a flock on the Saut-du-Laire experimental mountain pasture (the municipality of Orcières in the Hautes-Alpes) changed direction. One of our major goals was to use Leroy's expert knowledge to develop support tools for grazing management assessment and to design alternative manage-

---

* Research on this topic has been pursued and expanded since this study (1987–1993). CERPAM and the Parc National des Écrins have since come out with the following publication in 2006: Bonet R., Della Vedova M., Quiblier M., *Diagnostic pastoral en alpages. CERPAM* Ed., Coll. Techniques pastorales, Manosque: 125 p.

ment methods taking into account new constraints, such as complying with environmental regulations and developing tourism. This ongoing research has produced a number of concepts and graphical representations of the gradual formalization of expert knowledge. Several of these are given here as examples. They illustrate a unique approach, which is distinct from classic pastoral assessment based on the inventory and evaluation of forage resources that we consider impractical for management.

UNDERSTANDING HERDERS

We used the principle of *indisciplinarité* in studying André Leroy's practices.[5] This approach attempts to overcome conventional scientific disciplinary codes and barriers. To do so, we deliberately abandoned the methods commonly used in the human and natural sciences. Experience has shown that developing points of view specific to a particular discipline without taking into account the perspective of stakeholders is not effective in assisting decision-making. In this case, researchers instead reconstructed the herder's applied perspective. This perspective takes into account the overall functioning of a grazing system. It was developed to manage the interrelations apparent to the herder among grazing areas, forage, and the flock. Although the method is based on the recording of a person's statements, it is different from those used in the social sciences in that the objective is to form a practical model (for pasture management) from the knowledge of an expert, rather than to collect ethnological information. Specifically, this method involves translating expert knowledge into rules and references that have to obey content and form requirements, are reliable, and can be used as a model for others. The desired result is necessarily a blend of an expert shepherd's knowledge and scientific knowledge.

André Leroy transferred his knowledge through dialogue (part of which was recorded, either in the field or in a room) as well as written and visual material (maps, diagrams, photographs, and films). The last was essential, given the importance of space-related information. We used an iterative approach to formalize his knowledge. We first drew up a document based on Leroy's dialogue and diagrams, pointing out to him areas that needed clarification. The contradictions and imprecise information in André Leroy's statements were identified by systematic comparison with researchers' observations in the field, where his actions and the ensuing results were recorded using notes, maps, photographs, and films. Questions put to Leroy included observations that had not been explained in his dialogue and discrepancies between Leroy's planned results or intentions and the actual outcome. We communicated with Leroy until the information conveyed on paper was satisfactory to both parties. Mutual satisfaction was achieved once a new concept about a process or a practice was accepted and effectively used by both parties, with no ambiguity.

As our work advanced, concept definitions gradually emerged from Leroy's statements, and graphic images were refined. We did not limit ourselves to collecting expert knowledge; we also helped develop this experiential knowledge by imposing formal constraints and, unavoidably, by interweaving our own scientific knowledge. Throughout the process, we relied on our own references and mental categories and proposed formulations and images that were not necessarily identical to Leroy's. While he rejected a number of them, he adopted those which appeared useful. Yet other proposed formulations and images were modified before being accepted. Thus, the exchange of information was not one-way, but rather a blend of knowledge.

Basic information about the management of the Saut-du-Laire high mountain pasture was obtained from André Leroy's written records of his daily grazing circuits. If necessary, we asked André to supplement his writings with verbal comments. He drew these records, each for a half-day, on 1:10,000 base maps (see Map 1). The basic unit in these records is the "behavioral phase," during which the herder considers the flock's activity to be uniform. Our focus on an expert's description of the flock's behavior distinguishes this from other works,[6] which instead relied on instantaneous scans to describe the flock's behavior as the percentage of animals involved in each basic activity: grazing, travel, and rest. Each behavioral phase identified by André Leroy, described in detail at a later point, is associated with a particular time (start time, end time), space (the area used by the flock during the phase is delimited on the base map by a closed contour line), and food (the herder assigns an empirical grade to the phase that assesses its quantitative contribution to the flock's intake). This grade is expressed as a percentage of the quantity of green forage eaten compared to a "standard diet," which is equivalent to a half-day of grazing described as "satisfactory" by Leroy. The sum of the grades assigned to the various behavior episodes within one grazing sequence (morning or afternoon) may differ from 100 percent. This reflects Leroy's overall assessment of the sequence's effectiveness in terms of intake level.

These numerical and graphical data are entered into a geographic information system (GIS) computer database using ArcInfo software. This tool makes it possible to combine various layers of information and to produce new images for high mountain pasture management, for instance, as "reports" achieved by overlaying all of the daily maps of the season. In addition, information obtained from the herder can be compared with information from other sources.

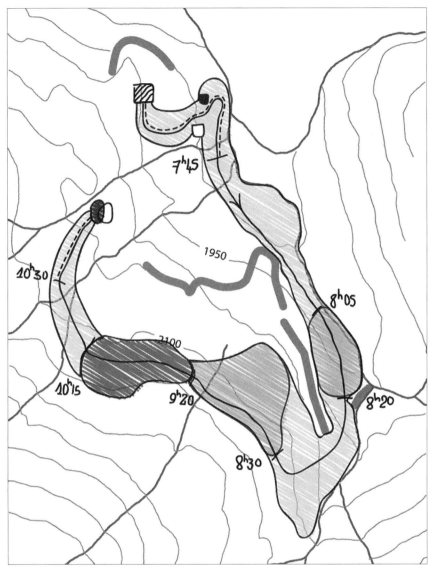

MAP 1: Example of notes taken by André Leroy. Morning circuit on July 22, 1991, on the Saut-du-Laire high mountain pasture.

THREE BASIC CONCEPTS

To describe the utilization of "a mountain" (herders' expression for a summer grazing place or grazing allotment), André Leroy uses three main concepts: sector, quarter, and circuit. Of these terms, only "quarter" is commonly used by other local herders and sheep farmers, though "sector" and "circuit" are both familiar concepts. These concepts simply

MICHEL MEURET / INRA

PHOTO 2 – During a morning circuit, André Leroy is staying in front of the flock while leading it to a very steep grazing sector with fresh grass (Saut-du-Laire pasture, August 2007).

emerge from the practice and are considered obvious facts in the eyes of herders. (Scientists and engineers specialized in rangeland grazing do not use these concepts, or perhaps they simply disregard them due to their ordinariness.) The novelty resides in recognizing the usefulness of these empirical notions for management purposes, and André Leroy's rigorous conceptualization and explanation of what have become to him "intuitive concepts" as part of a clearly applied approach to grazing systems.

For the sake of clarity, we will first present the concepts of "sector" and "quarter," which are used to mentally partition grazing land. This will facilitate readers' understanding of the "circuit" concept, which describes the use of that land by a herded flock of sheep (see Photo 2). This choice is arguable: the spatial distribution of grazing land as proposed by Leroy is not a priori but functional, and it is linked to the rules that govern the design of a grazing circuit. A herder considers the various sectors of a mountain based on what he knows or believes about the spatial and feeding behavior of his flock. We could have started out by talking about animal behavior. However, animal behavior is not independent of the physical characteristics of mountain pasture, and it is difficult to analyze behavior without discussing the network of sectors on a given piece of land.

The concept of pastoral land organization takes into account this complexity. We use this expression to refer to the manner in which herders organize (mentally) and use (in practice) grazing land, with the perception/ action duality being indissociable in practical thinking. People consider the land they use based on their prior experience with it, and they use it according to the way they perceive it.

Sector

A sector is a subdivision of grazing land that forms a physical whole and that determines a flock's spatial and feeding behavior. Changes in behavior occur as the flock moves from one sector to another. Among the various spatial scales that could be used to link flock behavior to pasture characteristics,[7] the sector is particularly useful for studying herding practice on mountain pasture. André Leroy's definition of a sector is, according to the former scientific director of the National Institute for Rural Studies in Mountain Areas (INERM), "perfectly suited to pastoral management. The 'sector' is as close as you can get to the much sought-after base unit of grazing land, and it makes it possible to reconcile the scientific approach with an operational one."[8] This is therefore one of the more striking innovations contributed by André Leroy.

The division of land into sectors is mainly based on geomorphologic features. Any given mountain area naturally has a number of obstacles, including fast-flowing streams, ravines, and rocky ridges (see Map 2 in the color insert), which block the way for animals and constrain their travel (see also chapter 5). As long as accessibility, vegetation, and area are useful for grazing, the "compartments" created by such obstacles are considered sectors or groups of sectors, depending on their size and degree of uniformity (see Map 3 in the color insert). As the entire flock must be able to spread out over an individual sector, the minimum area of a sector is related to flock size.

In practice, sector boundaries represent a compromise between exactness, which would require delineating a large number of sectors, and efficiency, which keeps that number within reasonable limits. The resulting network of sectors must be sufficiently simple and intelligent for memorization and utility. Usually, there are between fifteen and twenty sectors in a quarter (see the following sections), depending on the size of the mountain. The traditional place-names given to the areas on a particular mountain, largely defined by ancient pastoral practices, form the basis for division into sectors.

Various characteristics likely to influence flock behavior are used to describe each sector: altitude, sun exposure, landforms (e.g., relief, slope), terrain (e.g., stoniness, visibility), soil conditions, type and abundance of vegetation, surface area, accessibility, and location in relation to other sectors and other "fixed points" (see the section on flock behavior later in this chapter). The attractiveness or unattractiveness of a sector for a flock plays an important role, as we will see later on.

Quarter

A quarter is a group of sectors that are grazed over the same period during the summer, generally from the same flock's natural nighttime rest area (*couchade*). All the sectors in a given quarter have similar altitude, which determines when the grass grows and therefore when an area can be grazed. Quarters are usually quite distinct from each other and are easily recognized by local sheep farmers. They are the physical result of a utilization schedule for the mountainside that often goes back a long time. This functional dividing of a mountain area explains the location of certain facilities, including shepherds' cabins, catch pens, and drinking troughs. In most cases, the herder uses a different cabin each time the flock moves from one quarter to another.

Mountains are usually divided into two or three quarters:

- Spring quarter, also known as the July quarter. This quarter is the lowest in altitude, where the snow melts first and where grass becomes available the earliest.
- Summer quarter, also known as the August quarter. This quarter is highest in altitude, where the snow falls first and remains longest.
- Fall quarter, also known as the September quarter. This can also refer to the July quarter, as taking the flock through the same quarter twice can enable the herder to take advantage of grass regrowth, which is extremely variable from year to year.

For a given high mountain pasture, there are more or less set dates for changing quarters, just as there are to reach the mountain pasture at the beginning of the season (generally at the very end of June), and also to return to the plains (generally at the very beginning of October), with just a few days' variation. The flock is thus on each quarter for a foreseeable period of time, regardless of the weather and state of vegetation. The herder is responsible for keeping the flock on the land and finding it enough to eat throughout the season in a good or bad year.

Circuits and Standard Circuits

A grazing circuit is an itinerary or route followed by the flock over the course of a day; it runs through a number of sectors within a quarter. The circuit begins every morning from a given quarter's nighttime rest area, where it again returns in the evening, except on days when the flock travels from one rest area to another, either within a single quarter, or when it moves from one quarter to another.

The flock does not follow a different grazing circuit every day. The herder may take the flock around the same circuit several days in a row, in order to have the sheep gradually graze all the forage available on the various sectors visited. If the flock visits the same group of sectors in the same order several days in a row, the succession of behavioral sequences is consistent. The "standard circuit" concept refers to the interlinked sequence of sectors visited, activities, and the area taken up by the group of sectors (see Map 4 in the color insert). Much has been written on the utilization of grazing areas via a regular route.[9] In Corsica, for instance, the local terms *invistita* and *rughjone*, as reported by Ravis-Giordani in 1983, refer to the grazing circuit (or standard circuit) and the area covered by that circuit, respectively.

The herder and his flock can cover the entire high mountain pasture with a small number of standard circuits (i.e., ten to fifteen) on average. For example, in 1991 André Leroy's flock followed twelve different standard circuits to cover the Saut-du-Laire mountain pasture. Because of the constraints related to the flock's movement across the pasture and the utilization schedules for the various sectors, the layout of standard circuits is more or less fixed. The routes vary little from year to year, with herders adopting or rediscovering the same solutions as their predecessors. The development of certain facilities, such as footbridges, pens, and cabins, are designed to introduce more flexibility into the system by mitigating these constraints.

FLOCK BEHAVIOR: PACE AND DIRECTION

Animal behavior is the main factor to examine when attempting to understand the management of a pastoral system. There is one main invariant: the cycle of rest-rumination and foraging phases over the course of twenty-four hours. This basic model sets the pace for the flock's daily activities and motivates its spontaneous travel. The practical conditions of this travel, including physical direction, speed, and schedule, depend on the grazing area's physical characteristics, particularly the spatial distribution of the vegetation, resting areas, and watering points. The herders' own term, "direction" (*biais*), which involves the flock's processing of all these factors, results from the interactions between time and space.

Pattern of Flock Activity

The daily activity cycle of a flock while grazing summer pasture is typically made up of four periods: a nocturnal rest period and two diurnal periods of activity separated by a midday rest period.[10] The consistent pattern of diurnal activity makes it possible to distinguish various phases within each activity period: 1) the flock awakens and leaves the night-time rest area; 2) the flock gets going as the sheep stretch their legs and their appetite quickens with the first rays of sunlight; 3) the flock travels towards the major grazing zones, where it will eat most of its meal; 4) the flock enters its primary feeding phase; and 5) toward the end of the morning the flock gradually comes together to rest for several hours. The afternoon routine is similar to the morning and ends with the flock return-ing to its nighttime rest area and "supper." The hourly schedule adjusts gradually with the season as the days shorten and changes occur in the vegetation and weather conditions.

The phases described previously approximately correspond to the "be-havioral phases" identified by Leroy. The "primary feeding phase" is often split into several episodes of varying importance, in accordance with many observations made in science. These "episodes" are separated by move-ment that boosts the flock's appetite (see also chapters 7 and 8 on the MENU model). The activity types that define behavioral phases can be identified by observing the flock directly. This involves a qualitative assessment of several criteria including prevailing individual behaviors, flock pattern, and changes in that pattern. Such an assessment can be repeated, after a few learning sessions, and the activity types thus observed are the following:

- Stationary, or "peaceful," grazing: the sheep are virtually immobile as they graze and are facing all different directions. The few individual movements have no impact on the whole. This activity involves pri-marily "intense grazing," during which the sheep take rapid inges-tive bites. There are two variants of stationary grazing; these are less intense and are observed either just before or just after the diurnal rest period, or during the animals' "supper" just before they bed down for the night.
- Grazing-travel: intense grazing and slow movement of the sheep in the same direction. This activity is often encouraged by the herder, who slows travel speed.
- Travel-grazing: traveling that allows for some episodic grazing
- Travel
- Rest-Rumination, diurnal or nocturnal
- "Puttering": a disturbed behavior characterized by lack of coordina-tion of individual activity and dominated by movement in all direc-tions. The flock in this case is said to have no direction (biais) (see next section).

Spatial Regularity

Some of the flock's activities are associated with specific areas. Their regular occurrence at the same times of day is observable spatially as the flock travels from one location to another, according to a number of "fixed points."

The natural nighttime rest area (or night pen, as the case may be) is the central "fixed point" for the flock. The rest areas, where the flock comes together and stops to ruminate at midday, or the hottest time of day, are also fixed points. Like the nighttime rest areas, but to a lesser extent, the locations of the midday rest areas (*chôme*) are a feature of the mountain itself: the flock will only stay there and return later if it likes the location. Nighttime and midday rest areas thus become virtually fixed points.

Other fixed points that determine the itinerary of a given grazing circuit are watering points, "salt licks" (i.e., flat stones the herder uses daily to provide the flock with salt) and catch pens, where the sheep are periodically counted, treated, and sorted. "Compulsory passages" for gaining access to certain areas, which are often found near obstacles like streams, ravines, and rocky ridges (see Map 3 in the color insert), are also considered fixed points.

Direction (*Biais*)

Like many other shepherds, André Leroy uses the word *biais*, or "direction," to refer to most flock behavior information useful for high mountain pasture management. "Direction" means the spatial behavior the flock exhibits in a given place at a given time, and more specifically the corresponding physical direction it faces and pace of travel it chooses. This concept derives from the behavioral uniformity of large sheep flocks. According to André, "'Direction' really means the flock's behavior. When the flock chooses its direction, the herder sees 1,000 sheep all spread out or come together, peacefully and in unison. It's a beautiful thing to see. Every ewe knows exactly where the flock is headed."

Flock behavior is predictable so long as the characteristics of a particular flock are known, including size, make-up, genetic type, and condition of the sheep; the herding style they are used to; and their familiarity with the grazing area. Per André, "'Direction' also depends on the mountain itself. It is the result of the animals' activity pattern, their habits, their peculiarities, as well as the characteristics of the mountain, including relief, slope, exposure, vegetation, and the location of nighttime and midday rest areas." It is essential to be familiar with the flock's activity pattern and with what Leroy calls the "habits and peculiarities" of the flock, which determine its feeding and spatial behavior. These can refer to the sheep's food preferences, their taste for "new, clean grass," their methods for composing a varied meal by changing locations and therefore vegetation several times over the course of a half-day, and their tendency to graze "on the way up" a hillside, following the slope.

Some of these rules have greater weight than others, and given the right circumstances, govern the flock's major spontaneous movements. For instance, on sunny, warm summer days, the flock continually seeks to climb higher, as if in search of cooler air, but also to find tender new grass: "Only bad weather makes them come down." Being familiar with these rules allows herders to predict flock behavior, which is why herders often speak of the "direction" of one mountain or another. It would appear possible, therefore, to model graphically the major movements that characterize the "direction" observed on a given mountain.

Points of Attraction and Preferred Trails

Just like watering points in dry pastoral regions,[11] points of attraction are mountain areas that clearly and durably attract the flock. Left on its own, the flock will necessarily seek these areas. They are primarily found at high elevations, located near mountain peaks and ridges. Sheep will spontaneously go to these places, the size of which depends on the general shape of the mountain (see Figure 1).

The sheep's attraction to these high-altitude areas is greatest toward the end of the day. These are the areas where the sheep find their favorite nighttime resting places, often located on projecting ledges with an open view. Other areas can also be a source of attraction if they represent abundant and/or high-quality vegetation.

A given area's force of attraction depends on its location relative to the flock, and it is all the more powerful as the flock approaches it. It can nonetheless remain quite strong at a great distance, even across the entire mountain pasture. The approximate boundaries of an area associated with

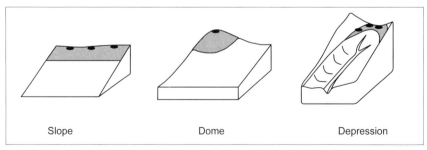

| Slope | Dome | Depression |

FIGURE 1: Location and features of high-altitude points of attraction, according to the general shape of the mountain (● possible nighttime resting areas for the flock).

a point of attraction are known to the expert, based on the herder's observations of his flock. This can result in original graphic representations (see Map 5 in the color insert) which indicates the "night points of attraction" of the Saut-du-Laire pasture and their respective surrounding areas of attraction. The force of a point of attraction, and therefore of a sector, is relative and may be compared with that of the other sectors within the pasture. The most powerful one prevails and determines the flock's *biais*. What is more, the force of attraction varies according to date and time:

- Based on a twenty-four-hour cycle with "night points of attraction" and "grazing points of attraction," the latter areas are found in various sectors with particularly palatable vegetation, which entice the flock to seek out these areas around mealtimes. Because the snow-bed grasses in the high-altitude sectors are especially attractive to sheep, these sectors often comprise both night points of attraction and grazing points of attraction. In such cases, their force of attraction is a permanent factor with which the herder must deal.

- Based on a seasonal cycle, the pull of the grazing points of attraction varies according to the stage of development and condition of vegetation. The pull of night points of attraction also varies. "At the end of the summer, the sheep start making their way down voluntarily, maybe because there is no longer much new grass, even at the top of the mountain."

Depending on the overall terrain of the mountain, and the location of obstacles and points of attraction, the flock adopts a direction, spontaneously following a number of preferred trails (see Map 6 in the color insert). The herder himself is more or less obliged to use these trails when planning a grazing circuit. Over time, said André, this organization of space becomes concrete: "For those who know how to spot it, the flock's direction is inscribed in the mountainside in the form of a vast number of small natural paths [*drailles*] made by sheep that have passed that way repeatedly. These paths show how the flock closes up at bottlenecks where all the sheep must walk in the same track."

ORGANIZING CIRCUITS AND SCHEDULING GRAZING

As we have seen, it is possible to predict in part the behavior exhibited by a flock at a given moment. Weather is the remaining major factor of uncertainty. As long as the herder takes into account the weather and has sectors that are both sheltered from the elements and easily accessible to the flock on days of inclement weather, the herder can effectively prepare a tentative plan of his season on summer range, which will be implemented in the form of a succession of grazing circuits.

The herder's main objective in designing such a plan is to "make sure the flock eats its fill day after day." He also has to maintain the flock on mountain pasture throughout the summer, which requires effective management of the available forage resources. Given these constraints, the herder has limited scope in designing grazing circuits, especially since he has practically no say in the decisions made as to flock size or the date set for the flock's departure for or return from summer pasture. These decisions are made by the farmers, who own the sheep.

Herding the Flock Based on "Direction"

Despite herders' limited latitude, they exhibit very different herding styles in high mountain pastures.[12] This diversity is observable in the subtlety of a given herding strategy, the amount of initiative allowed the flock, the exactness and authority of the actions of the herder and his dog, and in the overall quality of human-animal relationships. These are important aspects for various reasons. They play a crucial role in establishing the grazing environment, maintaining the well-being of the sheep, and also are likely to influence animal performance. They also determine the herder's control over the flock and his ability to make the flock follow a previously established grazing circuit. For the purposes of illustration, we will limit ourselves to presenting just one rule that André Leroy considers extremely important: the use of *biais*.

The herder's anticipation of the flock's direction, based on his knowledge of the previously mentioned rules, is an important part of flock management: "A good herder is actually able to put himself in his sheep's hooves, so to speak, and figure out what it is they want to do." This understanding of the flock is not gratuitous, as it is very useful in flock management. A good herder tries to follow the flock's natural direction as much as possible so as not to counter it. The more he respects the sheep, the easier and more peaceful the entire process, and the more the sheep get out of their time grazing. For the herder, a grazing circuit consists of alternating between controlling and giving into the flock's direction (see Figure 2). He should intervene only if the flock's natural direction deviates from the grazing circuit chosen. The better the circuit has been designed, the less the herder will have to intervene. One could say that the art of herding consists in providing the right direction for the flock and designing the best plan of utilization of resources with the least intervention required. "With a good herder, you should have the impression that he's doing nothing but following the flock!"

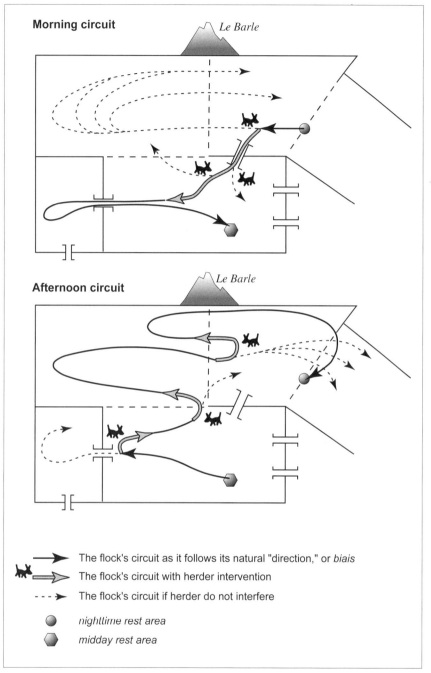

FIGURE 2: Grazing circuit followed on September 1, 1987, by the flock herded by André Leroy on the Vieille Selle high mountain pasture (municipality of Réallon).

Mountain Forage Management
The Art of Herding: Assessing and Adjusting

When a herder comes up with a mountain grazing schedule, which involves a succession of circuits to be taken daily, he must evaluate the amount of time the flock will spend in each sector and how many times it can graze each sector, taking into account the type of activity of the flock. For example, in Sector X, the herder knows that the flock will be able to graze intensely for about two hours for five or six days in a row.

In practice, grazing never goes quite according to plan for various reasons: stormy weather, a broken leg that forces the entire flock back down to the pen, the early drying-up of a stock watering point, etc. The herder must adjust his plan and constantly reassess the available forage resources and number of days of grazing left. He retains a certain amount of flexibility, since he can usually accelerate or slow the flock's movement, deciding to abandon a standard circuit or instead keep the flock on it a few more days, even if that means grazing the forage to a maximum.

The art of herding lies in the herder's ability to correctly assess the number of grazing days remaining. Assessing availability of forage and the sheep's potential consumption of it is difficult and subjective. It requires years of experience on the same mountain, but this is not always available to herders for reasons of professional mobility. In addition to any experience, the herder may rely on many indicators such as the condition of vegetation (stage of development, height, color, extent of grazing by the flock, etc.). Once the flock is on site, the herder looks especially at its behavior, because the way sheep eat provides the most reliable information on what to expect on a given sector.

Rules for Forage Management

André Leroy has provided a number of principles for grazing management. The following rules may be drawn from these principles.

Utilization Schedule

Two rules apply to the order in which the various sectors should be used:
- The first rule is that the order in which the sectors to graze at the beginning of season (i.e., July) should, to the extent possible, respect differences in vegetation growth. By the same token, the sectors whose vegetation is acceptable for the longest period of time should be set aside for the end of the grazing season.
- The second rule is related to the uncertainty of weather conditions. Inclement weather makes a number of passages dangerous, greatly reduces visibility, and causes mountain streams to swell and rocks

to fall. It is therefore important to have the flock first graze, weather permitting, the sectors that are the most distant, the most difficult to access, and the hardest to negotiate in high winds, rain, or snow, and to save the sectors providing the most shelter and the easiest to access until the end of the grazing season.

Different types of graphical representations make it possible to visualize the layout of a high mountain pasture and grazing schedule for that pasture. Figures 3 and 4 include: a) a symbolic representation of the functional division of the land into quarters and sectors, with details on the combination of the various sectors within successive sets of standard grazing circuits, and b) an analytical diagram based on a grazing schedule. This type of seasonal-schedule diagram is useful in that it includes information

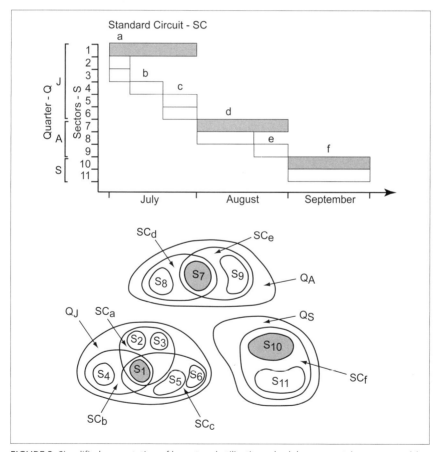

FIGURE 3: Simplified presentation of layout and utilization schedule: a mountain area comprising three distinct quarters (shaded area: sectors with one nighttime resting place).

105

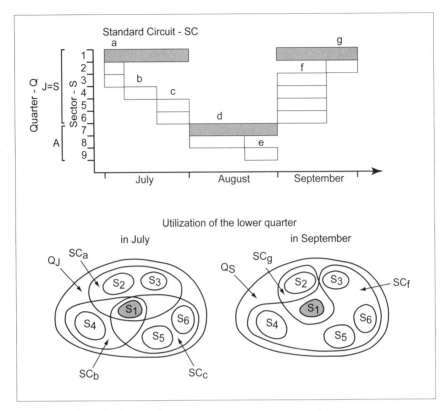

FIGURE 4: Organization and utilization schedule for a mountain with only two quarters (no separate September quarter).

at day-scale (Figure 5). Map 7 (see color insert) represents the mountain utilization schedule and is complementary to the previous map; it accounts for spatial aspects, which are absolutely essential in terms of management. One of the advantages of these two types of representations is that they can be produced quickly based on a simple survey.

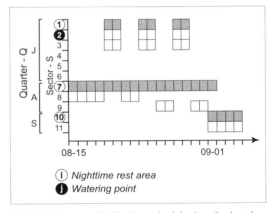

FIGURE 5: Seasonal utilization schedule described at day-scale. Example of a mountain area in which the August quarter lacks a watering point beginning in mid-August (variant of Figure 3). The flock must come down the mountain every three days to drink in Sector 2 of the July quarter, which requires it to go through Sector 3 and to rest for the night in Sector 1; it follows the same itinerary in reverse order the following day. Changing quarters on September 1.

Encouraging Intensive Grazing

Intensive grazing (i.e., stationary grazing and grazing-travel) allows the flock to use the sectors with the best resources, qualitatively and quantitatively, in the best conditions. It minimizes travel, wandering, and wastage while favoring forage intake. It is in the herder's interest to encourage the development of this type of behavior through his actions and forage management. The herder will lead the flock onto only those sectors that he considers the flock is ready to graze intensively. Once there, he will attempt to slow the flock down as much as possible. Finally, as soon as they begin to show disinterest and to move about, he will allow the flock to continue on its route, in order to keep from wasting forage.

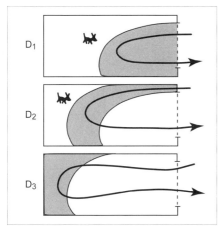

FIGURE 6: A flock's gradual exploration of a new sector (shaded area: zone of fresh forage grazed each day).

Choosing Rationed Grazing

This new rule may be considered a corollary to the last one. It involves herding the flock in such a way as to gradually explore a given area, so that the sheep find "new, tender grass every day." For this reason, André Leroy prevents his flock from straightaway traveling across an entire sector (Figure 6). He also rigorously manages the flock's grazing activity so that it resembles rationed grazing as implemented in some intensive production systems. According to him, rationing is a general principle that economizes forage by minimizing wastage. Left on their own, sheep will quickly travel across the entire area available to them, feeding on only the most palatable vegetation while trampling and dunging on the entire area. Rationed grazing has other advantages, according to André:

> Rationing means that sheep get more regular meals from one day to the next. If the herder allows the sheep to roam free, when they get to a new quarter, they splurge the first few days and survive on a meager diet many days after that. Sheep are happy to find new grass. They'll settle down and calmly start eating. That means that they're more likely, later on, to graze already-visited areas, because a sheep eats better on a full stomach than on an empty stomach. It maintains their interest—when all the good stuff has been eaten, the sheep want to move about constantly.

They know exactly which areas they have already grazed and which areas have fresh grass. That facilitates herding the flock and designing grazing circuits.

Map 8 (see color insert), which was produced using GIS, vividly illustrates the gradual process of exploration of the mountain pasture. The size of the juxtaposed plots of fresh forage, or the new zones that are explored from one day to the next, provide information on the abundance of vegetation: "The less dense the grass, the greater surface area must be provided to the flock, that is, if you want it to stop and graze quietly." This requires a compromise, taking into account the overall availability of resources. In periods of scarcity, the plots of fresh grass become progressively less numerous and even disappear.

MODELING PROSPECTS

Using André Leroy's expert knowledge as a model makes it possible to develop tools for representing a posteriori or for simulating a priori high mountain pasture management as a succession of daily circuits. The next step is to conduct an overall assessment of management based on diverse criteria. We are at the beginning of this designing period, which will rely on the formalization of rules that govern the relationships among a number of management entities (e.g., sectors and circuits) that result from the herder's practice. Most of these objects have been presented in this chapter, and we have highlighted a few rules to take into account.

One of the goals in modeling such knowledge is to create a tool for developing criteria and methods for evaluating and comparing various management solutions, whether already implemented or obtained through simulation. Our plan is to produce a high mountain pasture management model that is not finalized *a priori*. That model must be usable by scientists and local managers when they have to deal with a range of different issues, even if it means entering additional information into the database and using assessment criteria to compare management alternatives.

The criteria should allow for a comparison of the extent to which utilization rules are respected, such as utilization of the flock's "direction," the minimization of distances traveled, or the availability of a patch of fresh forage each day (see Map 8 in color insert).

The assessment criteria can also lead to the adoption of other points of view. For instance, perhaps it would be possible to use such a model to inform decisions relating to the restructuring of "pastoral units" following the establishment of a land tenure grazing trust (see chapter 2) or the extension of rangelands on privately owned former farmland. It could also be used to set up new management methods that take into account new utilization constraints, such as agri-environmental measures (protection of rare plants and nesting areas, and limitation of food competition with wild ungulates, which imply statutory fencing off of certain areas), regulation of traffic in tourist or hunting sites, and so on.

At this point, we can only present a few representations of the database that provide a basic idea of opportunities provided by GIS. Map 9 illustrates the spatial distribution of grazing pressure, based on André Leroy's estimation of the contribution of each behavioral phase to the flock's diet on summer pasture in 1991. The current objective involves first validating the indicator used, and then developing a diagnostic approach to the spatial distribution of food intake, given the situation and goals. To contribute to this process, researchers from INERM and the Parc National des

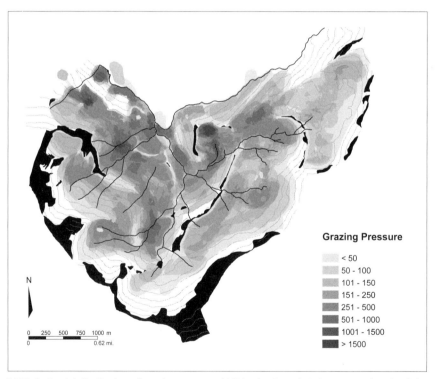

MAP 9: Spatial distribution of grazing pressure (GP) in the Saut-du-Laire pasture (result of the herder's twice-daily assessments for the 1991 season). The GP variable expresses the total number of individual half-day diets ingested in each part of the pasture in the summer. It is calculated, using GIS, as the local sum of the basic grazing pressures (bGP) as assessed for each half-day, for the polygons corresponding to each behavioral phase: bGP = feeding contribution grade (%) x number of sheep / 100 x surface area (ha).

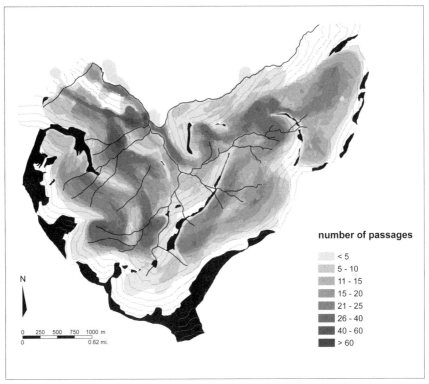

MAP 10: Spatial distribution of the total number of times the flock travels through a section of the Saut-du-Laire pasture (for the 1991 season). It should be noted that, just as the previous map, this one displays the division of sectors as established with André Leroy at the beginning of 1991 (see Map 3 in the color insert).

Écrins drew up the "grazing values" map for the Saut-du-Laire pasture. The inclusion of this map in the GIS database should enable effective methodological comparison of data.

Map 10 is a GIS "report" of the total number of times the flock has passed through each part of the Saut-du-Laire pasture over the course of the same season in 1991. It provides information of interest to several research partners regarding land management, in particular for assessing animal travel on the pasture or to detect areas at risk of deterioration due to the repeated passage of animals.

CONCLUSION

Unlike most prior research, the modeling approach we have adopted focuses not simply on the flock's diet, but on the overall management of high mountain pasture, of which diet is but one aspect. We hope to develop a tool that can supply answers to various questions regarding the future of local agriculture and the multiple uses of high mountain pastoral areas.

As regards the potential impact of this research on other extensive livestock production systems, we will consider three different aspects:

- Results: The development of management entities and rules appears contingent on a number of specific conditions, including a specific environment (a highly partitioned dry mountain area), animal species (sheep), production type (lamb's meat), and management method (constant herding).

- Method: We believe that an approach that addresses the "pastoral land organization" in the way it is used in this context, based on the study of grazing practices, is valid in many areas. The structural layout of pastoral areas is dictated everywhere by the way in which they are used by animals and humans. Our modeling principles are also, in our opinion, widely applicable.

- And last but not least, our scientific method falls under the general interests of INRA's Agrarian Systems and Development Department, its applications (decision-making support), its premises (the stakeholders are involved in the research), and its methods (systemic modeling and action research).

NOTES

[1] Landais et al., 1989.

[2] Landais and Deffontaines, 1988.

[3] Landais, 1991.

[4] Deffontaines et al., 1989.

[5] Legay, 1986; Robinson, 2008.

[6] Favre, 1979; Leclerc and Lécrivain, 1979; Balent, 1987.

[7] Senft et al., 1987; Balent, op. cit.

[8] Guet, 1991.

[9] Particularly, Balent and Barrué-Pastor, 1986.

[10] Favre op. cit.; Leclerc et Lécrivain, op. cit.

[11] Claude et al., 1991.

[12] Savini et Landais, 1991.

CHAPTER 5

Origins and Diversity of Flock Patterns in Summer Range Shepherding

Élisabeth Lécrivain, André Leroy, Isabelle Savini & Jean-Pierre Deffontaines

A flock of sheep stands out in a pastoral landscape particularly because it is mobile, unlike the land relief and plant cover around it. Flock patterns shift and transform according to land features, changes in vegetation, and weather conditions. Patterns are indicative of sheep behavior and the herder's actions, which collectively reflect the cycle of a flock's activities.

The patterns generated by a flock grazing on summer range therefore hold meaning and can be interpreted by herders, depending on their experience, which was clear to us from our earliest conversations with herder André Leroy.[1] Since then, many interviews with other herders have led us to the conclusion that most shepherds interpret and use these patterns, more or less consciously, whether they are positioned near to or far from the flock (e.g., using binoculars). Patterns are considered simple visual indicators that provide a snapshot account of the relationship between the land and the flock under the influence of herding practices.[2] In light of this, it appeared crucial to understand the origins, diversity, evolution, and succession of such patterns in order to assess the advantages of this indicator in managing extensive livestock systems and to specify the rules and conditions for its use. The exploratory study presented here may at first glance appear unnecessary. However, it is the first phase of applied research to document how shepherds interpret and use patterns to work with the flock.

Adapted from: Lécrivain E., Leroy A., Savini I., Deffontaines J-P., 1993. "Les formes de troupeau au pâturage : genèse et diversité." *In*: Landais E. (coord.) *Pratiques d'Élevage Extensif: identifier, modéliser, évaluer. Études et Recherches sur les Systèmes Agraires et le Développement*, 27: 237–63.

Many factors influencing the general pattern of a flock, as well as its cohesion and dispersion, have been studied, but the patterns themselves have received little attention. Both Squires and Bouy reported the importance of the flock's principal activity for the pattern produced.[3] Squires mentions an "arc-like" pattern when the flock is grazing and a "triangular" pattern when it is traveling. However, he does not attempt to draw specific conclusions from these observations. Scattering of sheep depends on the size of the flock,[4] its structure according to age group, and its social composition,[5] as well as the physical condition of the sheep themselves. With regard to land relief, Squires observes that uneven ground contributes to flock scattering,[6] and Arnold notes that topography affects the spatial distribution of sheep.[7] Scattering also depends on plant resources.[8] Overall flock cohesion depends on plant cover and density[9] and on the sheep's background, including the flock management technique they are accustomed to and the number of different farm flocks contributing to the larger flock that is led on summer transhumance.[10]

Given this background, our objective was to interpret flock patterns based on the observation, description, and classification of the most outstanding patterns. The resulting "pattern field guide" has been supplemented with a number of facts relating to the conditions of emergence and evolution of the patterns observed.

UNDERSTANDING FLOCK PATTERNS
Location and Background
We carried out observations in the Hautes-Alpes department in the Saut-du-Laire high mountain pasture (see chapter 4), where André Leroy manages with the help of his dog a flock of sheep of the Commune des Alpes breed. The flock is made up of some twelve hundred ewes from twelve different farms, each of which sends only some of its sheep to graze in high mountain summer pasture.

Data Collection
To identify the characteristic patterns of a given flock and monitor the dynamics of flock movement, we observed and recorded daily grazing circuits over two periods that were as different as could be with respect to grazing sectors, land layout, and obstacles. We made our observations on two standard circuits (see definition in chapter 4), one involving part of the July quarter and the other involving part of the August quarter.

Flock patterns were recorded using two different formats:
- Color photographs of the entire flock whenever possible with two focal lengths (30mm and 70mm).

- Simultaneous recording, on a 1:10,000 base map, of the outline and general direction of the flock, the proportion of sheep engaged in grazing, traveling, or resting, and their orientation. The position of the herder and his actions were also recorded. The time was noted for each flock pattern thus recorded. The flock outline was represented by a smooth curve that includes the outside sheep, and the individual orientation of the sheep is indicated with arrows.

We collected data during one week in July 1991 and one week in August 1992. Observations were made frequently during daily circuits (seventy-two recordings per day on average, at varying intervals), as it was important to record the maximum number of different patterns.

Analysis

The combined photo and map data on the flock outlines were categorized visually based on patterns that were then described according to area and duration as well as sheep activity, orientation, and distance between individuals. The variability in surface area and the duration of each outstanding pattern made it impossible to distinguish patterns based on these criteria. Therefore, the descriptors chosen concern the internal structural characteristics of the flock: the amount of time devoted by the sheep to each activity and the animals' orientation (defined by the axis of their bodies), as these factors resulted in a given pattern and one or more directions of the flock as a whole.

In looking for major links between pattern and activity, we were able to identify "basic patterns" from our observations. To identify major distinctions between the basic patterns we identified, we chose a time threshold of around ten minutes. We supplemented the description of basic patterns with their principal variants. Finally, to illustrate our results, we included drawings made earlier by André Leroy.[11] At a later stage we made an inventory of the circumstances associated with the emergence of each of these basic patterns.

FIELD GUIDE TO BASIC PATTERNS

We have distinguished what we called "stable" from "transitory" patterns. Durable patterns can stabilize and remain unchanged for over ten minutes before slowly transforming. Transitory patterns, on the other hand, are ever-changing and therefore fleeting in existence, not usually exceeding ten minutes. Among those patterns known as stable, we identified travel patterns, grazing patterns (some are mobile and others are stationary), and resting patterns.

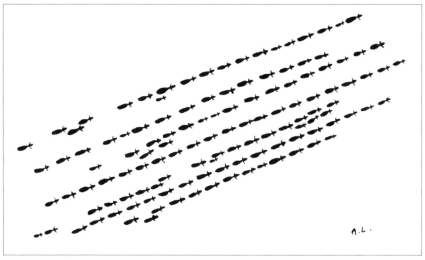

FIGURE 1: Traveling flock: the sheep move in single file without lowering their heads to graze (drawing by André Leroy, In: Landais and Deffontaines, 1988).

Basic Stable Patterns

Travel Patterns

Long Columns Pattern

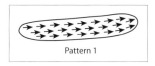

When the majority of the sheep are traveling without grazing, the flock produces a unidirectional, elongated pattern with the formation of parallel columns (Figure 1). There is usually little distance between individuals in these columns, but this distance grows as speed increases (Pattern 1).

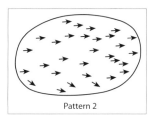

Oval Pattern without Columns

When sheep alternate between traveling and grazing but the majority of sheep are traveling, the flock produces a unidirectional oval pattern without the formation of columns (Pattern 2).

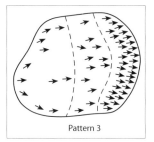

Grazing Patterns

Mobile Pattern with a "Grazing Front"

When the majority of the flock is grazing as it travels, and when the sheep located at the front of the flock are grazing vigorously and the general pattern of the flock remains unchanged despite its spatial displacement, the pattern may be referred to as mobile with a "front." This pattern's main

FIGURE 2: Sheep grazing as they travel, forming an even grazing front (drawing by André Leroy, In: Landais and Deffontaines, 1988).

feature is structural heterogeneity because the sheep at the front and the back (known as the *traîne,* or tail end) of the flock are engaged in different activities and facing different directions (Pattern 3).

The sheep at the front of the flock form a grazing front and travel side-by-side in the same direction (Figure 2). They graze the vegetation before them without much preference, carrying out rapid selection. Grazing is relatively rectilinear (Figure 3, "linear grazing") and results in "lawnmower"-type grazing.[12] The sheep in the middle and at the back of the flock travel more slowly and are scattered in more or less divergent directions. They alternate between grazing and traveling, moving to the right or the left every now and again, generally searching for a specific type of vegetation. These sheep are much more selective in their grazing, which may be referred to here as "searching" behavior.[13] The flock as a whole nonetheless continues to advance in one general direction, despite the shifting of the sheep in the middle or at the back.

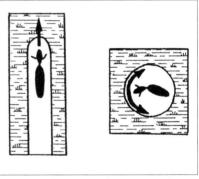

FIGURE 3: Illustration of two types of grazing. Linear (left): the sheep grazes as it moves. Stationary (right): the sheep grazes in place.

Stationary and Circular Pattern

When no notable travel is observed and the majority of the sheep are rotating to graze just the area around themselves (Figure 3,

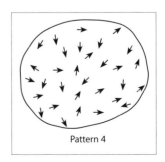

Pattern 4

"stationary surface grazing"), without wandering from the group, the flock's pattern is described as circular and multidirectional, in the sense that the sheep are facing different directions (Figure 4). This pattern lends itself to intense, stationary grazing (Figure 5, Pattern 4).

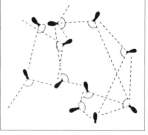

FIGURE 4: Diagram of sheep distribution for one part of the flock. All angles shown are approximately 110°, and correspond to sheep's line of sight while grazing (Source: Crofton, 1958, In: Lynch and Alexander, 1973).

Pattern 5

Day Resting Patterns
Aggregate Pattern
At midday, when at least three-fourths of the animals in the flock cease grazing in order to rest, the flock splits into one or more aggregates that may gradually merge together (Pattern 5).

Basic Transitory Patterns

Basic transitory patterns are dynamic, lasting only a short time (generally less than ten minutes) and resulting in a change in activity. We have distinguished three major patterns: two that result from pronounced group movement (funnel and fan patterns) and a third that exhibits no group movement.

FIGURE 5: In an area with good quality grass, the flock wanders and the sheep, facing all different directions, are evenly distributed over the available surface area (drawing by André Leroy, In: Landais and Deffontaines, 1988).

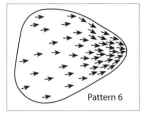

Pattern 6

Funnel Pattern

When the number of sheep engaged in grazing decreases and there is an increase in general movement towards a point of convergence (e.g., daytime or nighttime resting place, salt licks) or a narrow passage, the flock takes on a funnel shape (Pattern 6).

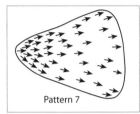

Pattern 7

Fan Pattern

Conversely, when travel decreases and the sheep take up grazing again as they spread out gradually over a larger area, the flock produces a fan pattern (Pattern 7).

Amoeba-like Pattern with Extensions

This pattern can result from either divergent or convergent movement of the sheep. Divergent movement is observed in two situations: either at the end of a resting period when the flock is beginning a new grazing phase, or when grazing or stationary grazing fail. In either case, the sheep move in different directions. Conversely, at the end of a grazing period when the flock is beginning a resting period, the sheep come together from several different directions and the area occupied by the flock shrinks. Whether flock movement is divergent or convergent, the flock pattern may be described as amoeba-like with extensions, with the sheep facing multiple directions and spreading out in one case or converging in the other (Patterns 8 and 9).

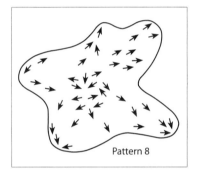

Pattern 8

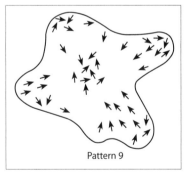

Pattern 9

André Leroy's illustration in Figure 6 demonstrates that a flock does not always follow a single pattern. This is particularly true for large flocks, which form subgroups with different activities from time to time and in certain areas. In this case, the flock is described as producing a combination of several basic patterns that will be elaborated upon later.

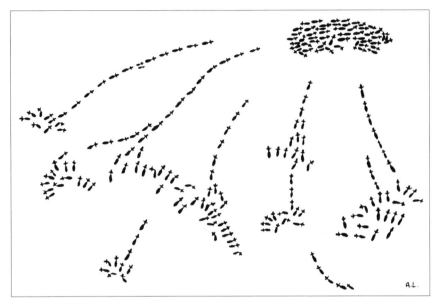

FIGURE 6: End of the grazing period: this drawing represents a typical combination of several "basic patterns." The sheep arrive at the daytime rest area from several different directions while several subgroups finish a circular grazing period (drawing by André Leroy, In: Landais and Deffontaines, 1988).

We have noted the major factors associated with each basic pattern identified (see Table 1). These factors are related to terrain, vegetation, sheep motivation to graze, travel or rest (linked to the circadian cycle), and herder interventions.

CONDITIONS FOR THE GENERATION AND TRANSFORMATION OF FLOCK PATTERNS

The pattern produced by a flock depends on the individual and group behavior of sheep. Their behavior is influenced by several factors, including the endogenous rhythms of sheep, previous activity, weather conditions, and the actions of the herder, who regulates the edible vegetation "offer" and controls the direction and speed of the flock.

The influence of topography has not been studied as extensively, but it is significant in animal behavior and therefore flock patterns. High mountain pastures are particularly suitable for determining the influence of structural constraints on behavioral processes involving the flock-land relationship and therefore on the generation of flock patterns. Marked geomorphologic contrasts in mountainous terrain exacerbate these effects, making it possible to distinguish them from the nature and condition of the vegetation.

From the herder's point of view, the objective is to encourage uniform group behavior in order to achieve "peaceful grazing" periods that enable high rates of intake* and management of summer range resources. The gregarious nature of sheep means that a change in activity led by a small group of individuals is rapidly imitated by the entire flock. Any significant movement therefore requires the herder's full attention. The most frequent response to a visual or auditory disturbance is that a few sheep become alert generally followed by flock movement or sometimes accelerated movement. This is the case with loss of visibility: ewes strive to maintain visual contact between each other, even if this means interrupting their meal to follow the ewes ahead of them. Understanding this behavior as linked to the terrain allows herders to anticipate the consequences of changes in terrain and better control the movement of grazing flocks.

We will discuss, at several levels, the effects of different types of physical discontinuity on flock behavior beginning with the impact of "natural obstacles" that physically block the sheep's way, and then considering obstructions to the flock's line of sight, which also exert comparable influences on sheep behavior. These two types of physical discontinuity, identified at a scale of 1:15,000, split the grazing area into subdivisions, or compartments, which we analyze later. Finally, within these compartments, we will discuss the effects of landforms, slope, and, at an even smaller scale, terrain.

Effects of Obstacles on Animal Behavior and Flock Patterns
Obstacles
Natural obstacles include rocky ridges, ravines, fast-flowing mountain streams, rockslides (which sheep cross with difficulty), thickets, and dense coppice. Whatever their nature, expanse, or appearance, obstacles represent linear barriers that block sheep's passage. Although they make it difficult for the flock to move from one place to another, they can help the herder manage the flock by facilitating his job of guiding, stopping, or penning sheep. The impact of an obstacle on the flock's behavior depends on how the flock approaches the obstacle.

If the flock is moving perpendicular to the obstacle, it can be easier to turn around or stop the flock thus encour-

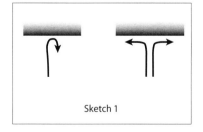

Sketch 1

---

* See chapter 7 for the discussion on this subject between shepherd André Leroy and goatherder Francis Surnon.

121

PATTERNS — Primary directions and activities	REASONS FOR EMERGENCE OF PATTERNS				PATTERN VARIANTS
	Land	Vegetation	Flock	Herder	
STABLE PATTERNS					
Travel patterns — 1. Long column(s) pattern — *Unidirectional* Grazing (G): 0-10% Travel (T): 90-100%	1. Sheep paths (*drailles*) on a steep slope, rockslide, ravine zone, close to particular points of attraction, in a zone with no visibility; 2. Narrow passage (path, crossing ravines, rocky ridges); 3. In a zone interspersed with rocky ridges		4. Reaching a particular point of attraction (catch pen, nighttime resting place (*couchade*), daytime resting place (*chôme*), salt licks); 5. Joining the rest of the flock		**1.1. One column** **1.2. Many columns** (spread-out start, sufficient space)
2. Oval pattern without columns — *Unidirectional* - G: 10-30% T: 70-90%		1. Sparse vegetation; 2. Wet grass	3. No desire to graze: beginning of the grazing circuit, end of a grazing sequence; 4. No desire to graze in that particular area (searching for a better place)	5. Moving the flock towards the catch pen or towards a grazing zone; 6. Channeling the flock	**2.1. Beginning of grazing**
Grazing patterns — 3. Mobile pattern with a "grazing front" — *Directional* - G: 30-100% T: rapid	1. Sufficient, fairly open space with some natural obstacles	2. At the very least, grass is palatable	3. Desire to graze	4. Slowing down an oval pattern without columns	**3.1. Network** ("grazing front" break up: division, merging) Loose front — Tight front — Uneven front

TABLE 1: Basic patterns of a sheep flock grazing summer range: conditions for emergence are linked to land morphology and forage resources, and rely on action by the flock or intervention by the herder.

4. Stationnary and circular pattern *Multidirectional - G: 70-100%*	1. Concave area, sufficient space (no loss of visibility)	2. Palatable grass (relatively abundant of fresh new grass)	3. Desire to graze and to stay put	4. Turning around the flock as a "front"	**4.1. Tight** **4.2. Spread out** **4.3. Small groups**
Daytime resting pattern **5. Aggregate pattern** *Multidirectional and stationary G: 0-20%; nibbling*			1. End or beginning of daytime resting phase *(chôme)* 2. Hot and little desire to graze	3. Bringing together the various groups	**5.1. Flocculent clusters**

TRANSITORY PATTERNS

6. Funnel pattern	1. Arrival in a narrower zone		2. Convergence towards nighttime rest area *(couche)*
7. Fan pattern	1. Exiting a narrow passage		
8. Amiba-like pattern with "extensions" *Multidirectional Spreading out or converging*		1. Vegetation not very palatable & no common direction *(biais)* agreement 2. Gradual departure from a resting place or after a stop at salt licks 3. Sufficient time in this area & no common direction *(biais)*	4. Divergence between the conditions in which the herder attemps to establish circular grazing (#4) and the common direction taken by the flock (it lacks one among the three conditions to established circular grazing)

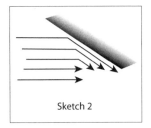

Sketch 2

aging a transition to stationary grazing, where the vegetation and circumstances allow. In other instances, the sheep travel alongside the obstacle as if they wished to bypass it (Sketch 1).

If the flock's movement is diagonal to the obstacle, the obstacle causes the sheep closest to the obstacle to group together, stop grazing, and rapidly move alongside the obstacle; the rest of the flock eventually follow suit (Sketch 2).

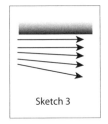

Sketch 3

If the flock is moving nearly parallel to the obstacle, the obstacle serves to channel the flock and prevent it from scattering laterally on the side nearest to it (Sketch 3).

The effect observed also depends on the obstacle's permeability. The herder may decide to allow the flock to clear the obstacle by using one or more narrow passages. The result in this case is a major slowdown and then a "traffic jam" as the ewes wait their turn, unable to graze. At the obstacle itself, the crossing takes place in unidirectional columns, the number of which depends on the width and number of passages. Once the obstacle is behind the flock, the sheep travel more quickly, especially because the herder has to oversee the passage of the last ewes and cannot slow the flock (Figure 7). Permeability poses a risk if it is not feasible for the entire flock to clear the obstacle or if the herder does not want the flock to attempt it. Small groups of sheep can start down a passage and become isolated from the rest of the flock. It is not always simple to assess the permeability of obstacles on a map, or even in the field without the flock. The most reliable information, when it exists, is the identification of small natural paths (*drailles*) on both sides of an obstacle as evidence of past routes taken by ewes when they had to cross.

Obstruction of Line of Sight

Whether horizontal (e.g., ridge or breaking point of a slope) or vertical (e.g., rocky outcrop or arête), the obstruction of a flock's line of sight plays a comparable role to obstacles, even though it does not physically block the flock's passage. Because ewes seek to maintain visual contact, the flock does not end up straddling such obstructions. Instead, the lines influence the flock's behavior in one of the following ways:

- They act as a barrier, and the sheep do not cross them (Figure 8).
- Some of the ewes get past the obstruction, which causes the entire flock to begin moving and rapidly clear it.

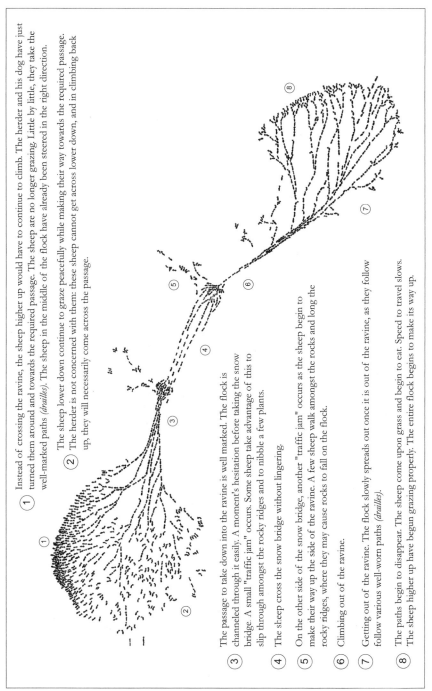

1. Instead of crossing the ravine, the sheep higher up would have to continue to climb. The herder and his dog have just turned them around and towards the required passage. The sheep are no longer grazing. Little by little, they take the well-marked paths (*drailles*). The sheep in the middle of the flock have already been steered in the right direction.

2. The sheep lower down continue to graze peacefully while making their way towards the required passage. The herder is not concerned with them: these sheep cannot get across lower down, and in climbing back up, they will necessarily come across the passage.

3. The passage to take down into the ravine is well marked. The flock is channeled through it easily. A moment's hesitation before taking the snow bridge. A small "traffic jam" occurs. Some sheep take advantage of this to slip through amongst the rocky ridges and to nibble a few plants.

4. The sheep cross the snow bridge without lingering.

5. On the other side of the snow bridge, another "traffic jam" occurs as the sheep begin to make their way up the side of the ravine. A few sheep walk amongst the rocks and long the rocky ridges, where they may cause rocks to fall on the flock.

6. Climbing out of the ravine.

7. Getting out of the ravine. The flock slowly spreads out once it is out of the ravine, as they follow various well-worn paths (*drailles*).

8. The paths begin to disappear. The sheep come upon grass and begin to eat. Speed to travel slows. The sheep higher up have begun grazing properly. The entire flock begins to make its way up.

FIGURE 7: A flock of one thousand ewes crossing a ravine via a "compulsory passage" (drawing by André Leroy, In: Landais and Deffontaines, 1988).

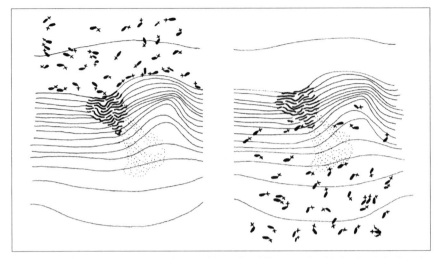

FIGURE 8: Effect of the break in a slope and loss of visibility on animal behavior. Whether the flock approaches this obstacle from above (left) or below (right), this discontinuity represents a barrier (drawings by André Leroy, In: Landais and Deffontaines, 1988).

- A group of sheep sufficiently large to be independent clears the obstruction and becomes isolated, thus leading to flock division.

The division of alpine pastures into "sectors" (*secteurs*), as has been proposed from a flock management perspective (see chapters 3 and 4), is heavily dependent on the network of obstacles and obstructions that block visibility.*

Effects of Landforms, Slope, and Terrain
Landforms
The landforms of the various compartments of the pasture play an important role in flock behavior. A basic concave landform (e.g., basin, small valley) maximizes the flock's eye contact. This encourages stationary grazing (Sketch 4).

Conversely, vertically or horizontally convex landforms (e.g., steep hills, uneven terrain) reduce visibility and make it virtually impossible for grazing to become stable (Sketch 5).

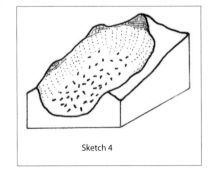

Sketch 4

* See the color insert for the obstacles map (Map 2) drawn for the Saut-du-Laire high mountain pasture.

Slope

Slope also influences animal behavior. Grazing sheep tend to face into the slope. This partly determines the direction the flock moves as it grazes: "Sheep graze on the way up," as herders say. By the same token, when climbing up a hill, sheep do not form columns and nearly always begin "searching"-type grazing.

On the other hand, when the majority of sheep are traveling their natural orientation is perpendicular to the steepest slope. In this case, the flock forms parallel columns at various heights on a mountainside and follows its contours when traveling. At the same time, it is difficult to stabilize a flock moving on a mountainside, especially on a steep slope. This usual direction of the flock (*biais*) eventually becomes etched into the mountain as microrelief consisting of the many *drailles* made by flocks' frequent passage.

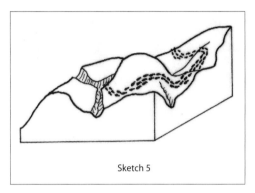

Sketch 5

Terrain

Terrain is the combination of slopes, obstacles, and various minor relief features (e.g., boulders, ravines, rockslides) over a given area. Different combinations of these elements cause loss of visibility and restrict animal movement.

In a sloping area interspersed with parallel rocky ridges that limit lateral visibility, sheep graze as they travel fairly quickly between the ridges. The risk in terms of flock management is that the flock will gradually scatter, with some groups becoming isolated and others lingering in cul-de-sacs.

When rocky ridges are not parallel but irregular, causing sheep to zig-zag between them, only uphill travel is possible, as ewes allow themselves to be guided by the slope. Descending the same slope, which is contrary to the sheep's natural tendency, should not be imposed by the herder due to the number of different crossing points (Sketch 6).

Areas scattered with different elevations reduce visibility, and the uneven terrain created by these landforms affects water flow and soil characteristics. In hollows vegetation is denser, less mature, greener, and sometimes different from the surrounding vegetation; this is more palatable to sheep. Sheep move about and scatter within the reticulate area between elevations (Figure 9). Within this labyrinth, it is much more difficult for

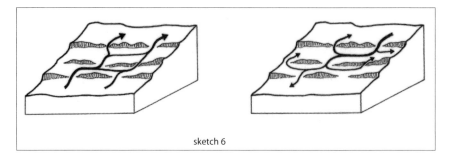

sketch 6

the herder to control the flock. One option is to take the flock through this type of area late in the evening; the appeal of the sheep's nighttime resting place should in this case drive them through quickly.

Scree sometimes covers a significant part of the mountain. In such areas, the slope and low density of vegetation cause sheep to travel in columns along the slope's contour lines. This is often evidenced by well-trodden paths made by flocks' frequent passage. However, the columns thus formed dissolve if sheep find palatable species growing sparsely or in patches along the way. In this case, they stop to graze before continuing to follow the flock's general direction (Figure 10). Here as in many other situations, animal behavior reflects the heterogeneity of their environment (Figures 11 and 12).

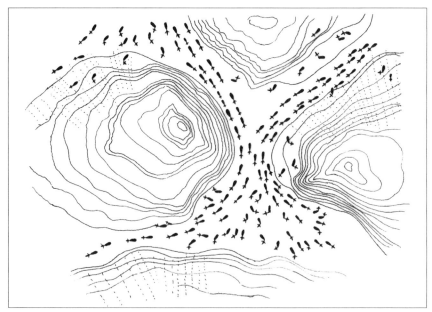

FIGURE 9: Sheep exploring a zone with small elevations: "network travel" between the elevations (drawing by André Leroy, In: Landais and Deffontaines, 1988).

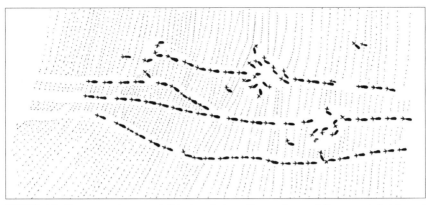

FIGURE 10: Sheep crossing a rockslide travel along the contours of the mountainside and break into columns upon reaching patches of grass (drawing by André Leroy, In: Landais and Deffontaines, 1988).

In high mountain pastures, heterogeneous terrain plays a major role in the complex nature of basic flock patterns and their variants, as we will demonstrate with a grazing circuit.

BASIC PATTERN COMBINATIONS: ANALYSIS OF A CIRCUIT

This example covers a grazing circuit on a July morning: The flock left its night paddock at around 7:30 a.m. (GMT+2) and traveled through sectors

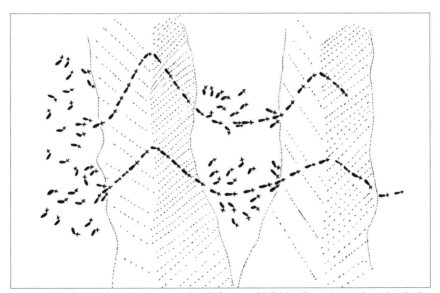

FIGURE 11: Sheep advancing across a deeply furrowed hillside: dispersion and grazing in the interfluve areas; crossing the ravines in columns (drawing by André Leroy, In: Landais and Deffontaines, 1988).

129

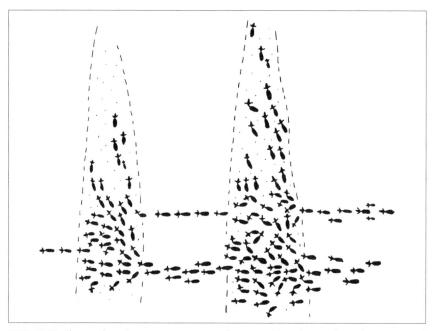

FIGURE 12: Sheep advancing across an uneven slope travel in columns along the contours of the mountainside in zones where they reject coarser vegetation. In the smaller, more humid hollows, where the land has undergone changes and the vegetation is more palatable, the sheep begin to climb up the mountainside while grazing (drawing by André Leroy, In: Landais and Deffontaines, 1988).

1, 8, 9, 10, and 7 before reaching the Petites Sagnes rest area at 11:30 a.m. (Figure 13a). We selected fifteen particularly illustrative general flock patterns from our observations (Figure 13b). Drawing the position of the sheep within these patterns makes it easier to identify basic patterns and their variants. The following descriptions demonstrate how the patterns produced by the flock are influenced by land relief and herder intervention.

Pattern 1 (7:35–7:45 a.m.)
As the flock is led out of the night paddock, it splits into two groups on this slope, with some sheep beginning to make their way up and others heading toward the salt licks. Positioned above the flock, the herder acts as a barrier as he sends a dog to counter the sheep's attempts to climb up the hillside. The sheep travel in columns in two different directions. The flock's general pattern is amoeba-like with extensions.

Pattern 2 (7:45–7:50 a.m.)
The entire flock heads down towards the salt licks. Half the sheep begin to nibble here and there. They graze a few bites, then move on, following

130

each other; some sheep are bleating. The herder watches over the flock's descent and lets them do as they please. This transitory pattern lasts only a few minutes. The flock faces three different directions. Its pattern is amoeba-like with extensions.

Pattern 3 (7:50–7:55 a.m.)
The flock surrounds the salt licks. One portion of the flock takes turns licking at the salt, while the other sheep move about or begin to graze. Here again, the herder controls the flock's direction; he has just shrunk the extension to the southwest and now moves to break up the northern extension. These actions increase the flock's traveling activity and steer it onto the circuit the herder has decided on this particular day (the herder sets the flock's direction). This transitory pattern is amoeba-like with extensions.

Pattern 4 (8:00–8:10 a.m.)
The flock heads in one direction and as the herders say: "The flock has taken up its common *biais*." The majority of the sheep continue to travel, while others begin to graze steadily. The herder makes sure that the last ewes at the salt licks catch up with the main flock and then makes his way to the bank of the mountain stream to keep the sheep from attempting to cross it. This general pattern is a combination of three basic patterns:

1. On the eastern side of the flock, the sheep walk alongside the stream. Because the terrain is flat and has sparse grasses, they travel side by side. This group of sheep displays unidirectional travel without columns.
2. On the western side, the sheep walk alongside a small catch pen, forming a long column. This group displays unidirectional travel in columns.
3. In the middle, the majority of the sheep form a long mobile pattern with a grazing front, a center, and a tail end.

Pattern 5 (8:30–8:50 a.m.)
Half the sheep are grazing while the others alternate between grazing and traveling or are traveling in columns. The herder, positioned beneath the rocky ridge that overlooks the mountain stream, can observe the entire flock and oversee their arrival onto a relatively narrow grassy zone (beginning of sector 8). Again, this general pattern is a combination of three basic patterns:

1. A large number of sheep graze in a scattered manner on the vast projecting ledge formed by the alluvial deposits of the Drac Noir stream and on the lower part of the adjacent slope. The sheep face different directions and display a stationary and circular pattern.
2. The group of sheep nearing the entrance of the narrow passage comes closer together, reduces grazing activity, and increases movement. Because of this bottleneck, the group's outline appears fairly elongated, but its structure reflects a mobile pattern with a tight grazing front, a center in which sheep are grazing in slightly different directions, and a tail end with the most scattering.
3. The sheep moving under the rocky ridge form long lines and produce a unidirectional long columns pattern.

Pattern 6 (9:00–9:25 a.m.)
The flock has entered the narrow passage and grazes while traveling quickly. The herder is in front and relies on his dog to slow the grazing front's progress and encourage the flock to spread out, as it is currently more interested in finding a way out of the passage than in grazing. Just like the two previous patterns, this one is a combination of three basic patterns:

1. At the front, a large group of sheep displays a mobile pattern with a grazing front.
2. On the side facing the slope, a smaller group scatters; the sheep climb in search of palatable grasses and rotate as they graze the area. The pattern is best described as stationary and circular.
3. At the back, a group of latecomers catches up with the rest of the flock in a unidirectional columns pattern.

Pattern 7 (9:35–9:55 a.m.)
The flock leaves a relatively narrow sector and tackles a tight, sloping curve. It climbs up the slope and takes up an increasingly vast surface area. Virtually all the sheep are grazing and traveling rapidly. To slow their speed, increase ingestive bite rate frequency, and limit their scattering, the herder stays ahead of the flock. He walks diagonally to the slope and, with the help of his dog, forces the sheep at the head of the flock to stay within this artificial border. The sheep in the middle of the flock lose sight of each other due to a small elevation. This induces them to increase their speed in order to catch up with the others, and to walk side-by-side. The edge of the ravine forces those sheep on the outside of the turn to advance single file. This general pattern is once again a combination of three basic patterns:

1. At the front, the sheep take up increasingly more space and produce a fan pattern.
2. The middle of the flock may be described as unidirectional without columns pattern.
3. On the southeastern side, the flock forms a unidirectional columns pattern.

Pattern 8 (10:05–10:15 a.m.)
The entire flock is grazing: the animals at the front and in the middle graze actively and move rapidly uphill while the last ewes take their time to graze and allow the space to grow between them and the ewes further up. From a higher position, the herder stops and turns the flock around by requiring it to make a U-turn. As he controls the general direction, he also keeps an eye on the progress of the tail end of the flock. Even though the overall pattern of the flock is oval due to the terrain and the herder's actions, it is also possible to distinguish a mobile pattern with a grazing front within which several small groups of sheep carry out concentrated circular grazing. The general flock pattern is the result of the flock's U-turn as managed by the herder.

Pattern 9 (10:20–10:30 a.m.)
The flock reaches a slightly sloping zone. It forms a tight group and faces northwest. On the northeastern side, most of the flock follows the slope's contours as it travels. However, the ewes on the southwestern side are seeking to climb up the hill. The herder, positioned slightly higher up on the hillside, intervenes to curb these ewes' initiative. From his location, he can see the entire flock, with the exception of three small subgroups that have fallen behind and remained under the rocky ridge. In this case, the flock pattern is mobile with a grazing front and a few small groups of stationary grazing.

Pattern 10 (10:40–10:50 a.m.)
The flock is grazing in a relatively flat zone, and the area it takes up has increased. All the sheep are traveling in a single direction while continuing to graze. The herder brings back the ewes that have fallen behind in order to maintain the flock's cohesion. The flock's pattern is oval and mobile with a front. The grazing front is typical in appearance; however, columns are beginning to form in the middle and at the back of the flock. These columns are a result of a series of small elevations that channel the flow of the sheep.

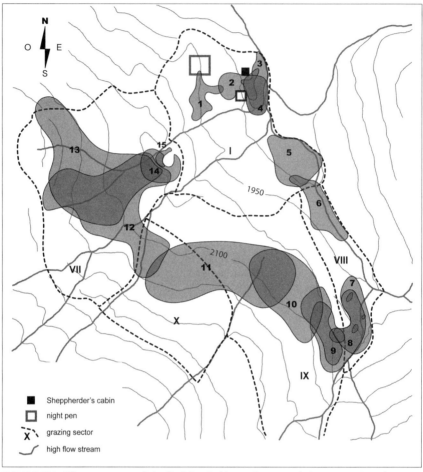

FIGURE 13A: Fifteen patterns of the flock herded by André Leroy during a morning of grazing in July 1991, on the Saut-du-Laire high mountain pasture: location of patterns on a 1:10,000 base map and the boundaries of sectors 1, 8, 9, 10 and 7.

Pattern 11 (10:55–11:10 a.m.)
This pattern is somewhat an enlarged form of the previous one. On the same slightly sloping zone, the sheep are scattered. The entire flock is still grazing and traveling. The ewes at the front, like those on the southern side, have a tendency to climb and pull the entire flock onto the hillside. The herder, who has returned to his overhang position, sends his dog out on the hillside to bring back the sheep that have climbed too high. This general pattern is mobile with a grazing front, along with the presence of several small groups of circular grazing that result from more marked elevations and hollows compared to that previously observed. These groups form in grassy hollows that appeal to the sheep.

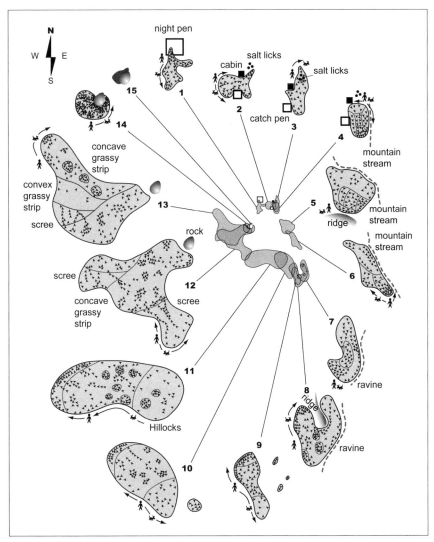

FIGURE 13B: Fifteen patterns of the flock herded by André Leroy during a morning of grazing in July 1991, on the Saut-du-Laire high mountain pasture: drawing of successive patterns, with the position of the sheep, the herder, and his dog.

Pattern 12 (11:15–11:25 a.m.)

The flock is scattered extensively over a zone with many grassy strips and rockslides. The heterogeneous relief and irregular plant cover causes the sheep to disperse and form groups with different activities. This renders the herder's job difficult, as he has to both bring back lagging animals and keep back those that are getting away. The general pattern of the flock is typically a combination of patterns. Some animals are traveling while others are grazing:

1. In zones with fallen rocks, the sheep travel along the slope's contours unidirectionally and in columns.
2. On grassy strips, some sheep begin to graze, but the convex relief isolates them and they quickly cease grazing to follow the rest of the flock.
3. On concave or flat grassy strips at the bottom of the slope (toward the rock to the northeast), the majority of sheep graze steadily for a while. They produce a pattern of circular stationary grazing that nonetheless remains incomplete due to insufficient space given the size of the flock.

Pattern 13 (11:25–11:35 a.m.)
This general pattern has the same characteristics as the previous one. In addition, there are several small groups grazing in flocculent clusters.

Pattern 14 (11:40–11:50 a.m.)
The morning comes to an end and the weather turns hot. The sheep have been out for about four hours and no longer wish to graze. They reach their usual daytime resting place near a rock. The herder, with the help of his dog, gathers the remaining sheep that are still nibbling while climbing alone or in small groups. The general pattern is aggregate with a few flocculent clusters.

Pattern 15 (11:55)
Morning grazing winds down. The sheep are no longer moving; they have come together and are resting (*chôme*). A few of them are sheltered from the sun by the rock, while others protect their heads in the shade of their neighbors by standing close together, heads to tails, or lying down next to each other. The herder is also resting. The flock can be described as an aggregate-type mass.

CONCLUSION

Earlier research on the dispersion of grazing sheep set out to link flock dispersion with the state of the surrounding vegetation with a view to improving grazing management. The primary objectives were to prevent local concentrations of sheep, which deteriorate pasture, and to distribute grazing pressure.[14] We share these priorities with many researchers and grazing land managers. However, it was not with this in mind that we studied the patterns of grazing flocks.

Rather, we based our work on the broader subject of managing pastoral systems in which flocks are herded in daily grazing circuits. Herders know that any grazing land where a flock has become established have points of attraction/repulsion. Herders' work depends on a twofold understanding of 1) the animals' behavior and their "pace, natural direction, habits and little obsessions," in André Leroy's words,[15] and 2) the grazing land. Knowledge of the land is not limited to vegetation, as shown in a study by Chiche et al. on the practices of herders in northern Morocco.[16] Their flocks "do not wander in search of green edible plants and water independent of all other constraints," meaning that not all the criteria herders use to evaluate rangeland are related to vegetation. They also take into account the quality of water and rest areas, topographical structures, and weather conditions. Even more specifically, Meuret demonstrates that the grazing activity of a herd of dairy goats is sequenced by the goatherder.[17] He attributes different roles to the various sectors of the land in a half-day's grazing circuit (appetite stimulator, first course, booster; see also chapters 7 and 8).

How do herders maintain control over flock movement, necessary for following the planned grazing circuit? They do so by tracking a number of indicators, including animal activity, scattering, orientation, the direction and speed of travel, the flock outline, and its transformations. These visual indicators are observed and analyzed comprehensively, which is what we have tried to convey through the composite concept we designate as "flock pattern."

Herders keep a more or less detailed mental guide of these patterns, their meaning, and the rules governing their generation, change, and transformation. This enables them to analyze flock behavior in real time and to anticipate the flock's reactions to the physical environment and different events likely to influence behavior. Flock control depends directly on the herder's ability to anticipate and his ways of countering (*contrer*), orienting, or encouraging the development of foreseeable behavior where it is not possible to apply a laissez-faire policy.

This study, conducted on a partitioned, mountainous environment with rugged relief, illustrates the importance of landforms and terrain on the patterns and activities of a flock of sheep. For instance, intense grazing activity requires certain conditions related to the "spatial well-being" of the flock, defined primarily by visual contact between individual sheep, as stressed by Crofton. Therefore, the actual use of an area with vegetation that is theoretically attractive to sheep depends on the surface area, the terrain, the landforms of the compartment in which it is located, and its location in the summer mountain pasture, among other variables. The patterns produced by the flock reflect the complex relationships that can be considered synthetic indicators of the flock's functioning. Our findings provide formal confirmation of some of the experiential knowledge accumulated by herders.

In conclusion, this work has produced promising results for improving quality assessment and management of rangeland pastures. First, as demonstrated by the "field guide to basic patterns" (Table 1), it appears possible to characterize the diversity of complex patterns of movement and behavior. Second, observing the conditions necessary for generating and transforming flock patterns suggests possibilities for determining the rules that govern the dynamics of these patterns. Taking into account these rules, particularly the effect of the physical environment's structure on flock behavior, should make it possible to better evaluate grazing quality of high mountain pastures and their management. This type of improvement might be extended to other environments. Even in areas with only minor relief, grazing land is made up of points of attraction and repulsion, grazed surfaces are far from homogeneous, and terrain is not without effect on flock behavior.[18] This might pertain to other management systems also; many rules that we are in the process of formalizing seem to apply to both free-ranging flocks and herded flocks, and our research approach should make it possible to identify any differences.

ACKNOWLEDGMENTS

This research owes as much to the twelve hundred sheep in the illustrations as to the two thousand suggestions and corrections made by Étienne Landais in respect to this paper.

NOTES

[1] Landais and Deffontaines, 1988.
[2] Deffontaines and Lardon, 1989.
[3] Squires, 1978b; Bouy, 1988.
[4] Leclerc et al., 1989.
[5] Squires, 1975b; Arnold, 1977 and 1981; Favre, 1979.
[6] Squires, 1975a.
[7] Arnold, 1981b.
[8] Squires, 1975a; Dudzinsky and Schuh, 1978.
[9] Leclerc and Lécrivain, 1979.
[10] Favre, 1979.
[11] Landais and Deffontaines, 1988.
[12] Leclerc and Lécrivain, op. cit.
[13] Leclerc and Lécrivain, op. cit.
[14] Kilgour et al., 1975; Dudzinski and Schuh, 1978; Squires, 1978a.
[15] Landais and Deffontaines, 1988.
[16] Chiche et al., 1991.
[17] Meuret, 1993.
[18] Plana, 1989; Leclerc and Lécrivain, 1994.

CHAPTER 6

Herding Sheep on the Windy Steppe of Crau

Rémi Dureau and Olivier Bonnefond

THE Crau plain lies to the north of Marseilles, in the center of the Bouches-du-Rhône department in Provence. It is a unique territory, the 150,000 original acres being made up of fossil delta from the Durance River flowing down from the Alps. At first glance, the Crau is uniformly flat and monotonous, covered in smooth stones left by the Durance that have become cemented underground, thus forming an impermeable layer of puddingstone. Due to the harsh weather of southern Provence—cold winters, hot and dry summers, and a frequent northern wind called the mistral*—the vegetation of the Crau plain is representative of an arid steppe. This creates excellent habitat for a unique collection of avifauna,[1] including the only surviving French population of the pin-tailed sandgrouse *(Pterocles alchata)*, as well as the little bustard *(Tetrax tetrax)*, stone curlew *(Burhinus oedicnemus)*, lesser kestrel *(Falco naumanni)*, and calandra lark *(Melanocorypha calandra)*.

This area, made up of extensive grazing land properties known locally as *coussouls* (see Photo 1), has long served as rangeland for flocks of sheep, with some shed foundations dating back to Gallo-Roman times. The plant cover has been sustained and regenerated over the centuries thanks to grazing managed by shepherds.[2] It remains the region in France with the

---

* In Provence the mistral blows as often as one hundred days of the year, gusting at sixty to seventy miles per hour.

Adapted from: Dureau R., Bonnefond O., 1997. *Étude des pratiques de gestion pastorale des Coussouls. In: Patrimoine naturel et pratiques pastorales en Crau* (coordinated by CEN Provence & Chambre d'Agriculture des Bouches-du-Rhône). LIFE-ACE Report for the Dry Crau: 61–89. *Updated by R. Dureau & M. Meuret.*

MICHEL MEURET / INRA

PHOTO 1 — A herder in action on a *coussoul* during spring 2008.

highest density of sheep flocks in the winter, spring, and fall—145 sheep farmers for more than 100,000 sheep grazed on 74,000 acres.[3] Each summer, the flocks—primarily the Mérinos d'Arles (see Photo 2), bred for production of lamb meat—are led into the Alps for the transhumance.[4] Since 1939, the Crau has been the home of one of France's herding schools, Le Merle (see chapter 12).

The Crau steppe has endured an age-old process of encroachment, which has accelerated in recent years.[5] The encroachment began in the sixteenth century when people began irrigating grasslands in the northern area known as the *Crau humide*, or "Wet Crau." These grasslands continue to be a precious resource due to the production of top-quality hay, which has received the *appellation d'origine contrôlée* label (AOC).[*] The land was further encroached upon when plots on the steppe were sold for intensive arboriculture, in which tree planting required ground ripping. Other intrusions include a stretch of highway, aeronautic and military activities, and gas and oil pipelines for nearby industries along the Mediterranean coast. The Crau steppe is thus a unique but endangered land.

In 1987 scientists and conservationists drafted a project to convert the remaining 35,000 acres of the Crau steppe into a "strictly protected nature area." This authoritarian move was rejected locally, as it placed too

---

[*] The French certification of highest quality granted to certain French geographical regions for outstanding agricultural products like wines and cheeses.

PHOTO 2 — Most flocks are made up of Mérinos d'Arles sheep, a breed that originated in the Crau.

many constraints on already-established economic activities. France instead decided to create a European Union Special Protected Area (28,500 acres) and to use a more incentive-based approach vis-à-vis local stakeholders. This approach was based on a national scheme under Article 19 of EEC Council Regulation 797/85 as soon as it was applicable in France (1989–1990). The scheme provided aid to sheep farmers if they would continue to graze their flocks on the steppe. Another European Union (EU) environmental procedure provided aid for the purchase of land by people who would commit to protecting the steppe, a measure that greatly benefited conservationists. In 2001, part of the EU Special Protected Area became a nature reserve (18,286 acres), but sheep farmers and herders were not obliged to change their grazing practices.[6]

A strong partnership has formed between conservationists and rangeland technicians from the Chamber of Agriculture of the Bouches-du-Rhône, who together have become coadministrators of the Crau nature reserve. They propose that the ecological diversity of the steppe as suitable habitat for remarkable species is the consequence of continuing the ancient pastoral practice of herding and the diversity in herders' individual practices. According to conservationists, who identify and monitor the interannual population dynamics of wildlife species, it is important to preserve this diversity of practices. To sustain a range of acceptable practices, and prevent radical changes that would negatively impact species' habitats, it is crucial to better document these practices, especially herding, to legitimize as explicitly as possible European funding (around €50/acre/year), which requires the development or maintenance of "environmentally friendly agricultural practices."

OVERVIEW OF SHEEP FARMING SYSTEMS IN THE CRAU

Sheep farming systems in the Crau may be described as follows:[7] Flocks are large, ranging from three hundred to several thousand ewes. The average size is five hundred ewes per workforce unit at the farm, which implies high productivity. The flock production cycle has changed little since the nineteenth century, based on successive grazing of three types of pasture (*in italics*: the surface area utilized by a flock of eight hundred ewes on average):

1. In fall and winter, ewes graze irrigated hay meadow (*200 acres*) aftermath (locally known as *regain*) in the Wet Crau, with lambs being born between September and December.
2. In the spring, the steppe of the Dry Crau (*750 acres*), along with several adjacent areas lying fallow, is used to graze ewes whose lambs have been weaned between January and February, as well as rams and ewe lambs.
3. In the summer, the entire flock is taken for a long-range transhumance in the Alps (*2,500 acres*) when the steppe has dried out and meadows are set aside for hay production.

Ewes lamb once a year, primarily in the fall after enjoying excellent quality feed while in gestation during the transhumance in the Alps. For those ewes not having lambed upon their return from the Alps (known as *tardonnières* or "tardy ewes"), a "catch-up" lambing session is planned for March or April. In the meantime, they graze in the spring on pasture where crops such as alfalfa and cereal are grown for them. Ewes produce an average of one lamb per year, with a productivity of around 0.8 lamb per ewe. Ewe lambs are mated at eighteen months of age. As a general rule, all replacement ewes are produced by the flock.

Most flocks are made up of Mérinos d'Arles sheep, a breed that originated in the Crau. The Mérinos d'Arles is a hardy breed, small and wooly, that tolerates significant climate changes and easily mobilizes its reserves of body fat for lactation in the winter. Its gregarious nature is appreciated for herding, as flocks are tended by herders on the Crau steppe and in the Alps for about seven months of the year.

UNDERSTANDING HERDING IN THE CRAU

Our studies were carried out in two stages over three years (1994–1996). The first stage consisted of semi-structured interviews with approximately thirty sheep farmers and their hired herders who occupy a *coussoul* in the Crau steppe. This enabled us to collect data on the ways the steppe is used for grazing (wintering season 1993–1994). With a vast amount of information thus collected, we then sought to validate and, more importantly, to quantify the results of certain practices in the second stage of our approach; this was conducted over two years and included eight different *coussouls* (spring 1995 and 1996). To do this, we monitored herding practices, combining direct observation and each herder's individual mapping of his or her grazing routes, which were provided at our request. Our choice of study sites reflects both our desire to respect the diversity of herders' practices and the plant cover of the steppe as well as herders' interest in taking part in the study and providing the fullest account of their knowledge. We monitored herding practices in the most prevalent herding conditions during the spring with non-lactating ewes (locally known as *vassieu*).

COUSSOULS AS A PASTORAL RESOURCE

The Crau owes its characteristic steppe features to a combination of climate and soils that constrain the growth of vegetation: marked dryness for three to four months in the summer, which increases along the north-south gradient; rare and violent precipitation with low annual rainfall (five hundred to six hundred millimeters in wet years with only three hundred millimeters in dry years) that varies considerably from one year to the next; a fierce northern wind (mistral) that encounters no obstacles; and puddingstone, a rocky soil horizon featuring hardened limestone cement, which prevents any contact between the surface layers of the soil and groundwater. These harsh conditions are partially offset by the presence of smooth stones on the surface and within the soil that limit evaporation and thus reduce temperature variation during the day and between seasons.

The herbaceous vegetation presents great diversity. One hundred and thirteen plant species have been identified, dominated by annual species (50 percent) and hemicryptophytes (30 percent).[8] *Brachypodium retusum* (Pers. P. Beauv.) is the dominant herbaceous species but varies in its cover (0–80 percent) depending on the site and grazing conditions. The annual productivity of vegetation is around 0.67 tons dry matter per acre per year.

A Pastoral Resource as Seen by Farmers and Shepherds

Long days herding sheep on the isolated *coussouls* make herders the privileged observers of changes in steppe vegetation. In addition to the direct observation of the dominant species' phenology in a given season, the behavior of the flock can contribute to the herder's overall view of plant resources. Farmers and herders identify and use, on the apparently monotonous landscape of the steppe, the functional diversity of vegetation to graze their flocks.

Farmers and herders distinguish two types of vegetation: 1) *le grossier*, or "coarse" vegetation, primarily the perennial grass *Brachypodium retusum*, and 2) *le fin*, or "fine" vegetation, which consists of forage species of better quality according to farmers and herders, primarily other grasses and rosette plants and dominated by annuals with fairly short cycles. The presence or absence of these two types, their relative proportions, frequent mixing, and the height of coarse vegetation allow farmers and herders to evaluate the grazing quality of a given grazing sector (see chapters 3 and 4). They can qualify an entire *coussoul*, or one of its sectors, as belonging to one of three categories: fine, coarse, or mosaic (*panaché*) if the vegetation types overlap. This visual categorization is influenced not so much by the cover of both types of vegetation but rather by the surface area taken up by *B. retusum*, especially in terms of its biomass and total height from the ground (three to eight inches). Everyone agrees that together the mix of both fine and coarse types of vegetation guarantees the grazing quality of the *coussouls*.

We prepared a diagram of each *coussoul*'s composition based on the information provided by sheep farmers and herders. Collectively, the diagrams show the distribution of the three categories of vegetation, as well as the location of the "shed periphery" (*auréole de bergerie*), which is the area most frequently traversed by flocks. In the very stylized drawing in Figure 1, the clear-cut boundaries do not allow for transition zones, particularly with respect to sectors with mosaic-type vegetation. Nevertheless, it is this type of diagrammatic representation, albeit oversimplified, along with the locations of facilities and structures (i.e., shed, stock watering points, tracks, canals, and bridges) that served as a basis for interviews with farmers and herders, as well as for herders' mappings of their daily grazing routes.

As a pastoral resource, fine vegetation, available early in the season, is very appealing to livestock, but also fragile. This vegetation responds most quickly to the first warm days of spring and provides the best resources over the short period of mid-April to mid-May. But fine vegetation also becomes poorer in quality as annual species reach the reproductive stage, and it dries out quickly as soon as the outside air changes from warm to hot. Its development is therefore dependent on climatic conditions, including not only the moisture in the surface layer of the soil but also frost and high temperatures.

According to sheep farmers, four factors are responsible for the dominance of fine vegetation in a given grazing sector:

1. human intervention in the soil, including former crops, the growing of which required the removal of stones, or fertilizer application, sometimes dating back several decades
2. the combination of a thicker surface layer of soil and the absence of smooth stones on the surface
3. frequent presence of the flock around points of attraction, such as water, where the concentration of trampling and dung results in intensely grazed species becoming both shorter and available at an earlier time
4. in some cases, continuous high stocking rate on a *coussoul* over a long period of time.

Coarse vegetation, on the other hand, is the fundamental grazing resource, according to farmers and herders. *B. retusum* is a safety net because, in the event of weather variations, it remains available, whereas fine grazing is either not yet available or is already dried out. This is the species that ensures "the ewes will always have something to eat" in the Crau, including toward the end of winter when the sheep are led out of the meadows and the end of spring before going up to high mountain pastures.

Others sectors, scattered about and often small in size, are also easily identified by farmers and herders because of a dominant species that poses specific management problems. These areas are known as *baouque* grassland (e.g., *Brachypodium phoenicoides* L.) and are located in fallow land

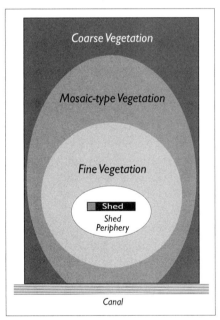

FIGURE 1: Illustrated example of the spatial distribution of vegetation categories on a *coussoul*, as described by sheep farmers.

or wetter zones, as well as zones overgrown with lavender, brambles, or Montpelier cistus (*Cistus monspeliensis* L.). According to farmers, these species are rarely if ever eaten and pose a serious threat to useful vegetation for sheep flocks. The same is true for holm oak (*Quercus ilex* L.) coppice not sufficiently grazed along *coussoul* borders where shrub species begin to colonize the *coussouls*.

HERDING PRACTICES
We analyzed eight *coussouls* of average size (270 to 740 acres; average of 555 acres), each of which constituted the principal or only source of food in the spring for one group of maintenance ewes. When flocks are grazed on the *coussouls*, they do not receive any additional feed besides water and salt and mineral licks.

Structural Constraints of the *Coussouls*
Land encroachment on the Crau steppe, recently curbed by environmental protection measures, has confined the *coussouls* to fragmented areas. This in turn has generated considerable diversity in today's *coussouls* on what used to be a vast, homogeneous steppe plain. Herding opportunities are thus dependent on the *coussouls'* specific shape, their layout, and their facilities, all of which vary considerably.

Location of the *Coussouls*
At the beginning of the twentieth century, all the *coussouls*, as well as the sheds and shepherd's dwelling, were fairly distant from the livestock farms. Today, the only *coussouls* that remain isolated are located in the center of La Grande Crau and La Coustière areas, with 6 to 12.5 miles between the *coussouls* and farms. The *coussouls* located in the northeast of the plain and north of La Grande Crau, on the other hand, provide access from a single shed to many different types of land: irrigated hay meadows, alfalfa and cereal fields, fallow land, and *coussoul*.

The Shapes and Boundaries of the *Coussouls*
The determining factors for the shape of a given *coussoul* are its boundaries with other properties and access to water. There is a wide variety in the shape of the *coussouls*, and some are not suitable for grazing a flock of 1,000 to 1,500 head. Depending on its shape, a *coussoul* may be divided into different sectors, thus allowing for diversification of grazing circuits. The need to utilize the sharp "corners" of some *coussouls* requires herders to use a technical approach to herding, and to obtain the prior agreement of their neighbors to cut across established boundaries (Figure 2).

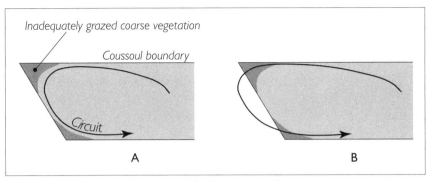

FIGURE 2: "Crossing boundaries" to enable sheep to graze the corners of a *coussoul*.

The external borders of *coussouls* may have hazardous or difficult features, such as a deep canal, a road with fast-moving traffic, conflicts with neighbors over adjoining *coussouls*, or unfenced fields of crops that are very appealing to the flock. On the other hand, some borders can facilitate the herder's job, such as fenced-off areas for growing crops or other activities (e.g., military) and shallow canals that allow for livestock watering. Where there is no other indication of a fixed boundary, small stone cairns (hardly visible to the untrained eye) are set in a line. Only a few isolated trees and scattered metal drums, which also serve as boundaries, can be seen from the sheds.

Location of Sheds within the *Coussouls*

Theoretically, a shed can hold one and a half to two ewes per square meter, but "if you squeeze them in tight," it can hold up to three ewes per square meter temporarily. Sheds often have a sheep pen outside for working the flock and for daytime or nighttime rest when it is excessively hot inside the shed.

Because the land has been continuously carved up for activities besides herding, some sheds are no longer located in the center of their *coussoul*. This requires herders and their flocks to trek long distances to access remote sectors of a *coussoul* and to focus the pressure of trampling and grazing on one portion of the shed area.

Stock Watering Points

Flocks' water access, essential to effective grazing on the *coussouls*, generally consists of small canals for the inflow and outflow of water for meadow irrigation. Each shed has a well, but these have been abandoned due to the laborious task of drawing water for several hours for a large flock. Because the level of groundwater has recently fallen in the southern

Crau, due to the irrigation of adjoining fields, most of the wells are no longer functional. The canals that have replaced the wells are not always located in the best places, given the need to have access to water along the grazing circuit in a *coussoul*, so other watering sources and water storage methods are used: flooded quarries, tank trucks, and cemented basins.

Tracks

Tracks enable car or truck access to each shed. Without tracks, progress would be slow given the high density of smooth stones in the steppe. Like canals, tracks can constitute internal borders between various grazing sectors. Sometimes they influence the *biais* of a flock (see definition in chapter 4), accelerating movement and facilitating rapid and direct access to a remote sector from the shed.

Designing Grazing Circuits

Grazing circuits, which the shepherds drew on base maps at our request, lie within an area carefully chosen by them. This area constitutes their base for the entire day in early spring or half the day when midday rest interrupts feeding during the hottest hours of the day. The area chosen can be an entire *coussoul*, a *coussoul* from which one sector has been cut off from use at a particular time, or a single and precisely delimited sector. A flock's grazing circuit "bounces off" the borders of this area, with some spillover tolerated amongst herders and considered inevitable if the sheep are to "graze the corners" of a *coussoul* adequately (see Figure 2).

Grazing circuits are laid out between two main points of attraction: the shed, which serves as both the point of departure and arrival, and the stock watering point, even if the flock does not drink from it every day. Secondary points either attract the flock, encouraging it to deviate from its initial direction (e.g., a clover patch, a former paddock with more attractive vegetation), or repulse the flock (e.g., a zone of particularly dense *B. retusum* situated at one end of the *coussoul*). In such cases, the herder must direct the flock as he sees fit, taking into account its natural tendencies. Finally, it is also important to note the flock's tendency to return to the shed at night, or even at noon, especially in high temperatures.

Even before this, the herder must set the schedule for grazing, which varies according to the seasons. During the shorter days of fall and winter, groups of sheep are often smaller, and the herder is sometimes occupied with lambing and with changing movable fencing around the irrigated meadows for ewes and their lambs. There is often a single outing for a length of four to five hours per day. In this case, the herder takes his flock to specific sectors of the *coussoul* for more intensive feeding. In the springtime, before hot weather sets in, the flock grows in size as the sheep farmer gradually adds ewes no longer nursing to the flocks. In this case the flock has one outing per day, but the herder chooses a longer circuit of eight or nine hours. Starting in May, many herders change the pace of their daily outings without waiting for the ewes to spontaneously begin resting around noon. The day is thus organized into two outings with the flock returning to the shed halfway through the day: in the morning from 7:00 to 11:00 a.m. (and, later in the season, from 6:00 to 10:00 a.m.) and in the afternoon from 4:00 to 8:30 p.m. (and, later in the season, from 5:00 to 9:30 p.m.). According to the herders, it is imperative that the schedule be kept as rigorously as possible to avoid "taking the flock by surprise"; it is important for the schedule to be predictable for the sheep, except on rainy days and shearing days. While adjusting outings in different seasons is a common practice, schedules vary substantially. The distance covered by the flock is six miles a day on average, but this can vary depending on the spatial layout of the *coussoul*, the herder, weather conditions, the season, and external events.

On the *coussouls*, the flocks' primary grazing activity follows a traveling-while-grazing pattern. Sometimes traveling is predominant—in this case, the flock takes on an elongated shape (flock pattern type 1.2, see chapter 5)—whereas at other times, grazing is predominant, with a "grazing front" that varies in width and marked appearance ("the flock scatters," as the herders say—pattern type 3). The phases of almost exclusive moving or traveling (pattern type 1) are rare and limited to situations where the flock has to reach a remote sector from the shed by way of the track. The same is true for phases of almost exclusive grazing with no visible group movement (pattern type 4). This is observed when the flock arrives in a sector that has not been grazed in several days, known as a "fresh fodder sector" to herders.

A Well-Managed *Coussoul* through Years of Consistent Herding Practices

Two grazing sectors are easily distinguished on the Opéra *coussoul* (see Figure 3), which is used only in the spring. The larger southern sector (known as Crau de l'Opéra), covering 495 acres, displays the characteristic concentric distribution of the three categories of vegetation previously discussed and shown in Figure 1, with a predominance of mosaic vegetation, including two subcategories (Mosaic 1 and Mosaic 2, depending on the relative height of *B. retusum*). The northeastern sector, known as Crau de l'Armée, is primarily composed of fine vegetation. It covers 170 acres and is linked to the southern sector of the *coussoul* by a narrow strip of

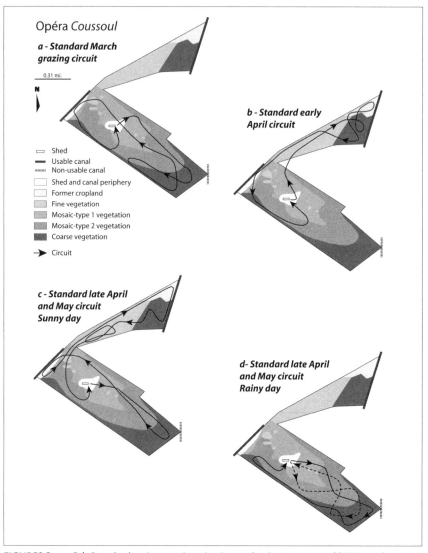

FIGURES 3a to 3d: Standard spring grazing circuits on the Opéra *coussoul* (655 acres).

land. The elongated form of these two sectors determines natural directions taken by the flock. Of the three available canals, the Centre Crau canal, located southeast of this *coussoul*, is not usable because the ewes refuse to drink the water.

The planning of grazing on this *coussoul* appears simple, having been developed by one herder over the past thirty years. He continues to obtain satisfactory results with his flock, which is well-accustomed to this particular *coussoul*. The vegetation dynamics also appear well under control:

in the southern sector, vegetation is coarser, and *B. retusum* is dense, but its blades are short from repeated grazing close to the ground.

Four phases and organizational methods are used successively by this herder in the spring. They may be illustrated by the following "standard circuits" (see definition in chapter 4):

- **March circuit** (Figure 3a): The flock of nine hundred ewes is grazed on the southern sector of the *coussoul*, where "fine" vegetation is not yet available. Coarse vegetation constitutes the sheep's primary resource, as this stock of perennial grass has not been grazed either in the fall or winter. Keeping the flock to the edges of the *coussoul*, where resources are concentrated at this time of year, without spilling over onto the neighbors' land, is made easier by the state of vegetation on bordering *coussouls*. Around this time of year, *B. retusum* is dense, high, and quite dry, and it therefore holds little attraction for the sheep. In addition, the herder must prevent the flock from moving too quickly towards the canal to the northwest. This is facilitated by the fact that watering is necessary only every other day at this time of year.

- **Early April circuit** (Figure 3b): As soon as "fine" vegetation becomes available, grazing is oriented towards the northeastern sector of the *coussoul*, which the herder has left untouched during March. The flock's "morning run" (*biais de départ*) extends into the corner of the adjoining *coussoul*. The herder must try, often unsuccessfully, to keep the flock for a period of time in the rougher outlying northeastern sector. The circuit finishes with a watering stop at the northwestern canal, which renews the sheep's appetite for one last feed along the coarser western edge of the southern sector, before heading back to the shed.

- **Late April and May circuit** (Figures 3c and 3d): Spring has arrived, and all types of vegetation are vigorously growing. Grazing circuits become longer, as a number of ewes—those that participated in the "catch-up" lambing session of the spring—are added to the flock, bringing the total to 1,350 sheep, to allow for mating with rams until the departure for mountain pastures on June 25. With such large flocks, herding techniques are deliberately lax. The entire surface area of the two sectors of the *coussoul* is covered as often as possible to adapt to the short cycle of annual plant species. The generalized growth of "fine" vegetation—very palatable forb species—in "fine" grazing zones and mosaic vegetation zones prompts ewes to seek out as-yet-ungrazed patches of vegetation. "They're looking for fresh stuff," as the herders say.

At this point, the herder merely ensures a balance of the grazing pressure on both sectors (northeast and south) of the *coussoul*, which are of unequal surface area, and adjusts watering (frequency and time) according to the flock's needs as influenced by morning dew, strength of the sunlight, northern dry wind, humidity brought by a southerly wind, and gradual drying of vegetation until the beginning of the summer.

Two standard circuits can be described for this period, depending on pleasant or unpleasant weather conditions:

- With sunny weather (Figure 3c): Both the southern and northeastern sectors are used. The herder is fortunate to have the canal to the northwest, located at the junction between the two sectors. It is possible to water the flock twice a day, just before resting and rumination at noon and at night. The herder prefers to graze his flock in the larger southern sector in the morning to make the most of the morning dew, which stimulates the flock's appetite and helps it to better graze the coarser vegetation of this sector.
- When it rains (Figure 3d): The flock is held in the southern sector, which consists of more "coarse" than "fine" vegetation, for two daily meals. The flock returns to the shed in the middle of the day, without needing to water at the canal.

In June, the widespread drying of vegetation results in the near-disappearance of fine grass. A few late-cycle species persist, primarily *B. retusum* in places where it grows, that enable the herder to maintain a proper diet for his flock until it leaves for mountain pastures. Sometimes, if a neighboring flock leaves for the mountains earlier than expected, the flock that remains may be permitted to go beyond the normal boundaries to better graze along the edges of a *coussoul*, where *B. retusum* generally grows more abundantly. According to the herders, their ability to revive their sheep's appetite for increasingly drier "coarse" vegetation depends on frequent watering stops at the various canals. According to sheep farmers, by applying grazing pressure on *B. retusum* during March, and thus leading to vegetative regrowth of short blades in the spring, it is possible to delay its drying out in the early summer and therefore ensure satisfactory grazing in June.

On this *coussoul*, used only in the spring, the herder's job is facilitated by an in-depth understanding of his flock. He monitors the flock carefully, but often from a distance, on quiet days when all herding indicators are favorable — slow movement, spreading the grazing front, and observing the standard circuits (including schedule, direction, and watering) which have become memorized by the flock. The satiation of the sheep is evidenced by a full stomach, which is still visible after a night in the shed. Any deviation from these conditions, such as the passing of hikers or a sudden change in weather, requires the herder to intervene, with the help of dogs, more frequently and vigorously.

Similar Herding Rules

Herding on the *coussouls* consists of continually correcting the sheep's tendency to move about seeking more palatable young grass—"to rush around trying to find the best food," as the herders say. If carried out successfully, restraining this impulse results in 1) serenity of the sheep once the flock is under control by the herder and his dog; 2) less flock movement, which otherwise causes the sheep to expend unnecessary energy; and 3) less variation in the quality and quantity of daily intake in the spring. The latter two consequences, in particular, enable the flock to recover a satisfactory physical condition, especially ewes arriving on the *coussoul* just after lactation.

Effective management of plant cover is also a major concern for herders, who strive to 1) preserve "fine" vegetation through periods of non-grazing, which allow for this type of vegetation to build up reserves and for annual species to reproduce; and 2) effectively control "coarse" vegetation (mainly controlling the risk of excessive spread of the perennial grass, *B. retusum*) by applying a high grazing pressure on sectors where it is abundant.

While herding management according to season is not always as structured as that on the Opéra *coussoul*, all herders have similar rules that allow them to optimally organize grazing circuits.

Upon Arrival on a *Coussoul*

- Allow the ewes and, more importantly the rams (and the herder), to become accustomed to moving around the pebbly terrain.
- Have the flock graze along the edges of the *coussoul* to mark them with the flock's scent; this ensures that neither that flock nor the neighboring flock will move beyond *coussoul* boundaries.
- Allow sheep to graze zones of attraction that "interrupt the flock's progress" (*cassent le biais*) to avoid further distraction later on.
- Where necessary, keep sheep away from sectors of fresh grass (*parer un secteur de net*) near the shed for later use: for maintaining a small group of ewes after lambing, for shearing or carrying out repairs or construction work, or for times when herders must be away from the flock temporarily.
- Get the flock well under control to show it who's in charge and to ensure obedience to the dog.

A Few Rules for the Rain, Wind, and Sun

- Avoid getting the flock very wet early in the season, or just prior to shearing, by setting aside a sector of *coussoul* near the sheep shed where the flock can be brought in quickly in the event of a rain shower.
- Realize that the sheep walk into a gentle wind, and walk with their back to violent winds. Consequently, on days with strong mistral wind, "Don't get caught too far south of the shed late in the evening."
- Plan a grazing circuit that keeps the sun out of the sheep's faces both at sunrise and sunset.
- Do not hesitate to expose the flock to inclement weather in late spring in order to ease the transition to mountain pastures.

Getting Sheep to Eat Coarse Vegetation

- Take advantage of the winter season, before "fine" vegetation becomes available, to concentrate grazing pressure on sectors with the coarsest vegetation.
- Provide coarse vegetation towards the end of the grazing circuit, especially if the sheep have not yet had time to fill their stomachs adequately.
- Keep the flock on coarse vegetation on short days in winter or rainy days when the sheep "know that the grazing circuit will be shorter."
- "Revive the flock's appetite" by stopping at watering points or in as-yet-ungrazed sectors (*du net*, or "fresh fodder") full of fine grass.
- Encourage grazing on coarse vegetation on the days following shearing, when the sheared ewes are "eager to eat" in order to generate body heat.

Avoiding Excessive Use of the Area Surrounding the Shed

- Have the flock rest far from the shed, preferably high up. There are high points in the Crau, even if the differences in altitude are inches rather than yards, where "the wind gets them back on their feet faster" for afternoon grazing.
- "Send the ewes back out" if they return to the shed too early.
- Manage the flock and bring it directly back from the grazing sector without allowing the sheep to scatter (*s'espandir*) in order to graze around buildings just before going inside.

Keeping Grasses from Reaching the Reproductive Stage

- Extend the length of grazing circuits in the middle of spring, and strive to cover the entire *coussoul*.

Above All

- "Respect the flock's pace" and the fact that it varies over a given season.
- "Stick to a regular schedule" and ensure a minimum of eight to nine hours' grazing per day.
- "Develop a good eye" to appreciate subtle changes in different types of vegetation.

ANIMAL PERFORMANCE IN HERDED FLOCKS

The studies we conducted in 1995 and 1996 included body condition scoring (BCS)[9] in the spring for eight flocks managed on the *coussouls* by herders. The ewes assessed were all of the Mérinos d'Arles breed, with size varying little amongst the flocks. Ewes were condition scored three times: 1) early March, as the flock arrived on the Crau steppe; 2) early May, prior to mating; and 3) mid-June, as the flock left for mountain pastures. In each case, BCS was carried out for the main group of non-suckling ewes.

The year 1995 provided abundantly good weather as reflected in the very regular weight gain of ewes on the *coussouls* in the spring and increasing BCS from 2.0 to 2.75. That year, mating took place as the body condition of the ewes improved. However, in 1996, we observed considerable variation in body condition amongst different flocks. From 1995 to 1996, the ewes' body condition recovery represented anywhere from 0.25 to 0.75 BCS points on average. We confirmed the significant impact of herding techniques (lax herding, some active herding, or tight herding), especially in seasons with poor weather conditions (e.g., high winds and rapid drying of vegetation), on the BSC of the ewes.

We took advantage of the fact that farmers keep a yearly lambing notebook and we recorded the cumulative curve for lamb births during fall lambing. This is an indicator of the success of the principal mating session, which takes place out of season in the Crau and involves the organization of large groups of ewes. We concluded that 90 percent of ewes that lamb in the fall do so in the first thirty days, which bears out the Crau's excellent reputation with farmers for the success of this key phase of livestock management. Even in less favorable spring conditions, farmers are able to maintain a strong prevalence of fall lambing sessions and a good grouping of lamb births, which is very satisfying.

CONCLUSION

Successful herding on the Crau steppe requires a herder to anticipate change and to observe the details of the composition and dynamics of vegetation. Even more importantly, a herder must notice subtle changes in the flock's behavior in order to be able to make appropriate adjustments between seasons, over a particular season, or even in a single day's work. Just as in mountain pastures in the summer, a herder on the steppe must take into account external factors in relation to his flock and pastoral resources, such as the strict observance of boundaries, which are often less explicit and more difficult to memorize on the *coussouls* than in the mountains. That is why the Mérinos d'Arles breed, known for its gregarious nature, is appreciated by herders who need to "get the flock under control" and to clearly convey "who's in charge."

Herding practices in the Crau are diverse due to a variety of factors. The spatial layout of the *coussouls* and the locations of facilities can be more or less constraining than on the mountain, and the diversity and seasonal availability of a particular *coussoul*'s vegetation, the herder's disposition, the sheep farmer's instructions, and the herder's various other tasks also all play a part in modifying herding practices. Some herders practice "lax herding" and simply get the daily "morning run" (*biais de départ*) going, which varies little; make sure boundaries are observed; and ensure necessary watering periods, with most other initiatives left to the flock. Other herders prefer a method that requires "some active herding"; these herders take advantage of a particular *coussoul*'s natural layout that encourages the flock's *biais* (spontaneous movements of the flock—see chapter 4), making them fairly easy to anticipate. Nonetheless, more active herding in certain sectors is necessary for the effective management of a *coussoul*. Finally, some herders practice "tight herding," which requires the constant presence of the herder and her dog to lead the way and set the pace.[10] Such herders base their management on successive grazing of different sectors, when the layout of the *coussoul* lends itself to this type of division. The goal in this case is to boost the herd's appetite during the daily grazing circuit (see chapters 7 and 8) while rectifying excessive growth of "coarse" vegetation and fostering better regrowth of "fine" vegetation.

The managers of the Crau nature reserve traditionally considered the steppe either as a homogeneous stretch of land, in terms of physiognomy, or as comprising diverse patches of vegetation. They have since benefited from the knowledge of the various categories of vegetation described by farmers and herders. Our characterization of grazing sectors categories has also proven useful for research into the distribution of unique avifauna.[11]

We confirmed that the diversity of herding practices on the Crau steppe, together with the resulting diversity of grazing pressure between seasons as well as throughout a single season and between adjoining *cous-*

souls, fosters abundant and diverse avifauna. Analysis of the spatial distribution of unique bird species in mating season has shown differences in habitat selection linked to local grazing pressure. The pin-tailed sandgrouse generally nests near a shed or on other sectors with nitrophilic vegetation and primarily "fine" vegetation. The stone curlew also prefers zones of "fine" vegetation but appears to have greater tolerance for lower grazing pressure, which leads to "coarse" vegetation taking up patches of land. Finally, little bustard males prefer to establish their territory in areas with abundant "coarse" vegetation. Ongoing research on the distribution of bird couples according to species confirms the complexities of habitat selection. Factors that are not directly related to grazing management also appear to have an impact, such as the presence of predators and other potential disturbances of various origins.

Sheep farmers, whose ultimate goal is to sustainably manage steppe pastoral resources through grazing, must reconcile four different objectives: 1) to satisfy the flock's feeding requirements, particularly for ewes' post-weaning body condition recovery and the principal mating season in spring; 2) to reduce feeding costs, as the cost of a ewe-day is inversely proportional to the seasonal stocking rate; 3) to ensure the regrowth or improvement of grazing resources over the years; and 4) to anticipate the risks of inclement weather.[12] The search for a balance between "fine" and "coarse" cover, and the controlled spread of *Brachypodium retusum,* are the result of objectives 3 and 4. Finding a compromise between all four objectives, which can be somewhat contradictory, sometimes proves impossible, especially for less experienced herders.

Just like farmers, herders, and sheep, rare and endangered bird species make the most of the subtle diversity of the steppe. As this area continues to be parceled out and to host a number of sometimes competing activities (including rave parties since 2000), everyone must succeed in using the rich diversity of this environment by constantly negotiating the multiple external constraints, including the accursed chilly gusts of wind from the north.

ACKNOWLEDGMENTS

This collective study could not have been carried out without the contribution of:

Olivier Bardin, project manager at the Établissement Départemental de l'Élevage (departmental bureau of animal husbandry) of the Bouches-du-Rhône.

Sheep farmers Jean Bruna, Jacques Chassy, Albert Garcin, Magali and Louis Lemercier, Max Richard, Michel and Maurice Roux, and Robert Tavan and his son.

Hired shepherds Roger Minard, Gilles Mouzon, Jean Pierre Ricard, and Marius.

Patrick Fabre (Chamber of Agriculture) and Michel Meuret (INRA) for the analysis of grazing circuits.

NOTES

[1] Meyer, 1983.
[2] Cheylan et al., 1983.
[3] Wolff et al., 2008.
[4] Legeard, 2002.
[5] Deverre, 1994.
[6] Boutin, 2002; Buisson and Dutoit, 2006.
[7] The following is based on Fabre, 1997.
[8] Bourrelly et al., 1983.
[9] Russel et al., 1969.
[10] Meuret et al., 2013.
[11] Wolff, 1997.
[12] Dureau and Fabre, 1999.

Amazing Appetite of Herded Animals

CHAPTER 7

How to Stimulate Animals' Appetites:

Shepherd and Goatherder Discussion

Michel Meuret

A NDRÉ Leroy, a shepherd, was hired to tend a collective flock of 1,200 head on 2,500 acres of high mountain pasture in the Hautes-Alpes region. Goatherder Francis Surnon tends his own herd of forty dairy goats on 320 acres of Mediterranean rangeland, including 290 acres of oak coppice, on a low-altitude limestone plateau in southern Ardèche. At first glance, these herders may seem to belong to two different worlds. While their situations might be said to represent opposite extremes for France, Leroy and Surnon are both passionate about their occupation, and their herding practices highlight certain similarities. Based on the discussion of these two experts, recorded in 1991, we have identified several rules governing the art of herding.

Neither speaker was selected randomly, either in the field or statistically, for the purposes of this discussion. Both have been partners in our research for several years.

ANDRÉ LEROY

André is forty-three years old. Born in French Flanders, he moved during his teenage years to Paris, where he went to high school. He then began a university degree, which he quickly dropped to take up vocational training in industrial carpentry. In 1974, after working in a factory for a few

Adapted from: Meuret M., 1993. "Les règles de l'Art : garder des troupeaux au pâturage." *In*: Landais E. (coord.), *Pratiques d'Élevage Extensif: identifier, modéliser, évaluer*. Études et Recherches sur les Systèmes Agraires et le Développement, 27: 199–216.

years, André decided to realize an old dream and became a shepherd. He started as an intern on an Hautes-Alpes sheep farm and the following summer herded a flock on high mountain range for the first time with another herder who was equally inexperienced.

Starting out with little else besides strong environmental convictions, André learned his trade on the job. "I tried to apply what I had learned. But even beyond any rule or specific technique, I tried to maintain a way with the sheep that I had developed with the help of livestock farmers, especially the older ones." Over the years, André experimented and polished his "good shepherd" methods, constantly looking out for the best interests of his animals. In doing so, he acquired the reputation of a first-rate herder in the eyes of local sheep farmers who scrutinized his activities from the valley with binoculars. In addition, he gained recognition intellectually in the 1980s through the close relationship he developed with INRA researchers. André's first contact with INRA was entirely co-incidental, when he met Jean-Pierre Deffontaines (agronomist and geographer for the Science for Action and Development Department of the INRA Versailles Research Centre) on a high mountain pasture while tending his flock.

For the past seven years, the same INRA researchers have sought to understand grazing practices, with André's help, in order to develop a functional interpretation of a given grazing area in mountain pastures (see chapters 4 and 5). Their work has resulted in papers and a documentary film, titled *L'espace d'un berger* (A shepherd's working space). All of this supports ongoing research to assess the management of alpine pastures with the CERPAM (the Pastoral Service Bureau for the Provence-Alpes-Côte d'Azur Region), and serves as educational material for vocational training.

Every summer for nearly twenty years, André has returned to high mountain pastures in the Hautes-Alpes region, where he herds sheep for local producers. In the winter, he runs a flock of about 250 ewes on scrubland and in oak forests for a producer in southern Ardèche; this area is fairly similar to that used by Francis.

FRANCIS SURNON

Francis is twenty-six years old. He was born on a beef and cereal farm in central France. At the age of eight, he moved to Lyons, where he attended school for another ten years. Every summer he went home to work on the family farm. Finally, faced with failing grades, he dropped out of school to work a full year on the farm. Following that, however, he chose to break away from industrialized agriculture, where professional relationships involved "squeezing out one's neighbor."

He left for Ardèche, where he was put in charge of setting up and running building sites for an association of young people seeking to revive a village in ruins. In 1977 the village had set up a dairy goat farm, including production of farmhouse cheeses, which were sold directly at local markets. The aim was to demonstrate that livestock production was possible and profitable using Mediterranean rangeland.

The association's collaboration with INRA began in 1983, when Michel Meuret met the village managers at an ecology conference at the University of Paris VII. The village's goat farm was of interest to INRA for two reasons: 1) its commitment to fairly high milk production (i.e., 185–200 gallons of milk per goat per year) and 2) its use of forestland grazing resources. The relationship with INRA was an interesting opportunity for the young association to demonstrate both for science and society that a technical business could be carried out successfully by "inexperienced but well-organized young people."

In 1988, the herd of forty goats was entrusted to Francis, and he found himself participating in an INRA experiment that had been scheduled prior to his arrival. The research involved a specific supplement designed to stimulate intake of tree leaves and shrubs on range. His training included help provided by a veterinarian, the standard "bibles" published by the Sheep and Goat Technical Institute (ITOVIC), and the technical journal *La chèvre* (The goat). The grazing herd management recommendations Francis received from his predecessors referred solely to the use of the various grazing quarters of the farm according to season. No guidelines on grazing circuit design were passed down to him.

The following year, he decided to curb the increasingly production-focused methods employed on the farm. He opposed the farm's plan to double the size of the herd and to place greater importance on distributed feed. No doubt Francis still had in mind the industrializing tendency of his family's farm (i.e., the large Charolais bull-calves) that he was rejecting.

He restarted herding and, in addition, launched discussions on ways to combine rural discovery and farming activities with the preservation of natural resources. Francis began teaching the empirical craft of herding on the job, in a methodical way, to several interns who had joined the association. The challenge is for interns to be able to take over the herding for half a day from time to time, without adversely impacting milk and cheese production.

THE DISCUSSION

André Leroy and Francis Surnon had never met, though they knew of each other. Francis had seen the INRA documentary film about André, and André had read an INRA student's paper on Francis's herding practices. Nevertheless, André had never tended a herd of goats, in a forest or elsewhere, and had never visited the rangeland used by Francis. Francis was not familiar with high mountain pastures. He had visited sheep farms in Ardèche but never the rangeland used by André. The moderator of the discussion, Michel Meuret, had been familiar with Francis's land for nearly ten years. He had only briefly visited André's high mountain summer range and the rangeland lower down where he herded his flock in winter.

The following discussion, which lasted five hours including a coffee break, took place in a farm located in Ardèche on November 12, 1991. It was recorded and transcribed in its entirety so that researchers could discuss the contents in detail. The presentation herein is not an analysis of the discussion, sociologically speaking; rather, it attempts to put into perspective several large excerpts of the dialogue between André and Francis (the moderator's words have been deleted).

We focus the experts' discussion on the reasons underlying their daily actions aimed at stimulating their flock or herd's appetite while grazing. We selected the passages that most clearly present and explain several "meta rules" regarding grazing herd management. These rules emerge through the two speakers' remarks, which are often in agreement.

SITUATIONAL FACTORS
Animals are Selective When it Comes to Food

A domestic flock is made up of individuals that are constantly making different food choices as they graze. This selection process can be observed at any given time, but it is difficult for the herder to predict the outcome of such a process in unfamiliar situations.

André Leroy: They only eat certain species.

Francis Surnon: Oh, really? They don't eat everything right down to the ground?

AL: No, sheep are just as selective as goats about shrubs, if not more so.

FS: Hmm, I had no idea. . . . But if you had half the same surface area, they'd have to eat the plants they won't eat now, right?

AL: Actually, I don't know what would happen. There's always some left over, always some species they won't eat. You can come back again and again, but they still won't eat them.

Selection is Relative and Variable over Time

Food choices vary according to season, depending on plant abundance and phenology. The sequence of choices animals make with regard to plant communities involve several different strata of forage (grasses, creepers, shrubs, and tree leaves), which vary from one year to the next, depending on weather conditions.

FS: Take the goats here, for instance. In the summertime, they won't touch holly oak [*Quercus ilex* L.]. Even if they're absolutely starving, if you take them into areas with holly oak, they won't touch the stuff. But now [in November], they get into it straightaway. Because there's nothing else around.

AL: Well, there you go.

FS: It's like dogwood [*Cornus sanguinea* L.]. As long as the dogwoods haven't withered dry, and haven't all been eaten up, they're not going to even look at downy oak [*Quercus pubescens* Willd.]. It wasn't so true this year, actually, but last year it was really obvious.

AL: In the springtime?

FS: Toward the end of spring, around July. The dogwoods were all dry at the end of July. And after that, the goats seriously got into the downy oak. But before, they wouldn't eat it. And then, once the downy oak is all gone . . . well, they're maybe going to start looking at holly oak. But it has to be all gone.

The herders' observations focused more on the behavior of grazing animals than the state of the vegetation. Plant phenology and the structure of plant communities are rarely mentioned. When they are, it is usually only to describe differences in palatability. Animals select their food based on a number of plant resources they have learned, the range of which can sometimes cause an animal to hesitate when making its selection ("food selection inertia").

AL: There are some spots they'll pass through in June without looking around much. But in the fall, they do stop there, because they know there's nothing left to eat higher up. So they take what they can get further down. But this is what usually happens between the months of July and September. In July, you know, they'll try to go higher and higher whenever possible—climbing higher to find the grass that has grown just as the snow melts, very green and very tender grass. The tougher grass further down doesn't interest them. Even if you keep them there, they'll never graze it as well. In September, on the other hand, they'll eat the tougher grass. They'll patiently graze, being more selective than usual . . . of course, there are some types of grass they just won't eat. I'm not sure whether it's the species or what.

FS: Well, here's what happened this past year: First, we had the goats eating dogwood [very palatable]. Then, we went on to downy oak [less palatable compared to dogwood]. But there was an area we hadn't yet visited, where there happened to be a lot of dogwood left. So, one day, I herded them into that area with the dogwood. Believe it or not: it took them a whole five days before they got hooked on dogwood again! They were still looking for the oak! And then, when we went back to previously browsed areas, they started to look everywhere for dogwood again, well, actually dogwood and other shrubs, the types that grow toward the end of spring, instead of oak.

Learned Locations

On heterogeneous grazing lands, plant communities form a patchwork of different palatabilities one relative to another. Except when one extremely attractive resource becomes available (e.g., fallen fruit, legume shrubs at a certain stage of development) and disrupts herd behavior, it is possible to predict herd movement. This is all the more true as animals become familiar with certain locations, including those off-limits to them.

Attractive Zones

AL: It's not just the plant species that's important for the sheep. It's also the shape of a place. If the sheep can see each other and if they can spread out, the flock can stop and eat peacefully. On the other hand, if the animals can't keep each other within sight, they'll start to follow each other and the whole flock begins to move. All these things are important, but maybe the same isn't true for your forty goats.

FS: Yes, I think the main thing is the number of animals in the herd.

AL: Yes, it's the number. With a large flock, you see, "cohesiveness" is important, almost as much as the forage resources available.

FS: Although . . . it's not that clear how important the size of the herd is. Because sometimes, when I'm starting out for the day and the herd is really hungry, I try to find areas where I can keep the goats bunched together. Otherwise, phew, they run all over the place. If you have an open area, they'll start running around. Here, too, it's important to group them closer together. The idea is to stabilize the herd so that it eats, no matter what.

AL: It's more about the place than specific plant species. If there's a place the sheep really want to get to, there's no point in trying to keep them from it. You let them eat for a while in that spot, and then they'll be okay with moving to another, less good area . . . but you shouldn't frustrate them.

FS: I had a really interesting experience with scorpion senna [*Coronilla emerus L.*]. Last year, I worked hard to keep the senna for the end of the herd's meals, or to boost the goats' appetites, and that's a nightmare since they can smell it from two hundred yards away. Then this year, I don't know why, but senna was growing everywhere. So I took the herd everywhere there was senna and let them eat it, because I knew I never could have held them back or kept them from getting at it. You can't manage them that way, it's impossible . . . you think they're going one way, but then they get a whiff of the senna and they turn, and all of a sudden you and your dog are all alone.

AL: But when you're up on summer range, it's a whole different scale. It's like . . . I don't know how to explain it, it's like an entire sector can draw them with one attractive resource, and that's where they want to go. It's better to have them eat a stomachful at the beginning so that afterwards they're calmer . . . but it's not necessarily a particular species. Although in the case of acorns in Ardèche, for instance, it is. In that case, the flock itself eventually loses its way and forgets about direction [*biais*]. It starts to go after the acorns of one oak tree, then another, then another, and all of a sudden, they've lost track of their usual route. Generally, they're used to more or less set grazing circuits, which are planned out. Is that the way it is with goats?

FS: It's the same!

AL: Really?

FS: Yeah. If they haven't eaten their fill in acorns, there's no point in trying anything. Plus, it's annoying in tree-felling areas [within the oak coppice]. You can't go there, especially the recent ones. For instance, at this time of year [November], you can go through them, because the goats won't really touch oak, and they mainly nibble around them. But once you get to the edge of tree-felling areas and you have to stop the goats . . . well, you can spend two hours trying to get them to turn around.

AL: And they always want to get in there.

FS: They do, because in there there's . . . well, senna and everything.

AL: It's kind of like areas in Ardèche where there are farm ruins, and you can be sure that manure has been present around the farm. There are these areas of really green grass and it's kind of similar to what you're talking about: when you get near a place like that, you know they're going to run toward it, and it's not worth trying to stop them. You might as well let them eat for a while before you get moving again.

Places that are Off-Limits

FS: If you fight long enough [with regard to a place that's off-limits], well, at least the goats get it after a while and don't try and go there anymore. They know it's off-limits.

AL: Yup—they know it all right. They learn that there are certain places where—

FS: Yeah, it's specific places.

AL: Yes, places, rather than environments. For example, if the herd is moving along a crop field and they know it's off-limits to them, they won't try and go there. But if one day, at that particular place, you call them over to cross into that land, well, afterward they're going to look for that place.

FS: Behind the large wall over there at Bois La Roche, where I am constantly trying to block the herd's way, right behind there is tons of senna. Well, they don't try and go there anymore. They know that there's no point.

AL: Dogs also learn which areas are off-limits. It's true; they go into those areas before you tell them. But it also depends on how you approach the place; that can make a difference. If you approach it head on, or along the side, you have to think about that, too, you know? It can be harder or easier, depending on whether the flock is coming from this direction or that direction. So, if you've got a place you're saving up, it's a good idea to always go past it the same way. It's easier to go past it on the way out rather than on the way back in. . . . I don't really know why that is.

OPERATIONAL FACTORS

The herders' understanding, based on careful, repeated observation of their herd's behavior in relation to their environment, helps them successfully manage their herds, design a feeding schedule, and live in close proximity with the animals. They avoid open conflict with the herd at all times. Good herding management, according to André, is "knowing when to lead the flock and when to leave it be."

Investing in Education

Livestock's past history on farms or ranches is a key factor in how easily a herder is able to manage a herd. Animals form social relationships within and among herds and develop grazing habits that may, or may not, assist in establishing a relationship of trust and understanding with a herder. A well-managed herd is one that is followed closely by the herder, rather than from a distance with binoculars. In any case, this is André and Francis's preferred technique.

Building a Relationship of Trust

FS: You have to work at building a relationship with the herd. Your herd is almost surely going to test you . . . it's a well-known fact. I think it might be worse with goats.

AL: Yeah.

FS: Right from the first day, the herd is going to challenge you! I see it all the time here with interns. When I'm in charge of the goat herd, everything's fine. Then, if an intern takes over, well, they're going to see what they can get away with—right away!

AL: Well, that's maybe the difference between a herd of forty goats and a large flock up in the mountains. A large herd or flock will challenge you less. The herd itself has its own way of doing things, you know? It depends less on you. We're not talking about animals you milk every day—these, you can hardly come within a foot of. This year, I remember going to get some animals when they were in their fenced pasture in the spring. I even went the day before taking them up into the mountains, but . . . well, they were eating. When they notice you, they prick up their ears and then . . . the entire flock gathers together and takes off in the opposite direction. The larger the flock, the harder it is to establish a relationship with the animals. But, if the flock is well-managed, it's a lot easier. You can tell the animals have been herded and managed well. When you take over, there's no problem.

FS: Yeah, it's the difference between animals that are herded and not herded. Because if the herd has been managed well, it doesn't matter who the herder is; as long as he works more or less the same way, the animals, well, then they understand the herder, you know?

AL: The main thing with sheep is how they were herded the previous spring or in previous years. This year, there were a bunch of sheep in the flock that . . . well, there were groups of sheep that just weren't following. You know, I work with twelve different farmers, so. . . .

FS: Geez. That's tough!

AL: There were groups [originated from certain farms] that just weren't following the rest of the flock. It makes things difficult! They're all over the place. They didn't even stick together—instead, they were in these small groups, here and there . . . they didn't follow each other. It wasn't a real flock.

Fostering Flock Cohesiveness

FS: Doe kids are like that, too.

AL: It's like a group of "strangers."

FS: Right now [November, eight months after the kids were born], you see, things are changing, they're getting used to the herd. Plus, it changes over time: first, we put them in rather small fenced areas where they're all together; it's kind of like "school" for the goats. There, you spend a little bit of time herding them, and bit by bit they learn how to form a group.

When you're really herding is when you can talk about a herd [behavior]. Well, then again, there's always one weird goat in the herd.

AL: That's like the grazing quarters we use in July up in the mountains, where you keep the sheep closer together because often the grass is more abundant. Plus, I took them to the night pen the first couple of times, where they sleep close together.

FS: It's true that the first couple of times we go out with the herd . . . it's along the banks [of the Ardèche River]. There, you have a lot of animals moving around close to each other. Then we spend some time in clearings. That does the trick.

AL: Exactly—places where the herd won't spread out. For example, the first few days, it's not a bad idea to avoid spots where you know the flock's going to disperse. If you start out there, whoa. . . .

FS: Yeah, good luck to you!

AL: It's better to contain them a little, keep them together. Now I don't know if it actually works or not. . . . That's what one says, anyway.

Planning Meals

Every day, animals select a ration from among the resources provided. The day is made up of several continuous feeding phases, or "meals." In between these meals, animals spend time resting and ruminating. Each day, the herder is responsible for planning the animals' food choices in space and time. He looks to create positive food interactions between the different areas to be grazed and make the most of each.

To do this, the herder has to think about the land in a way that preserves areas of different palatability. More importantly, he has to decide on the pace of the flock or herd over a given day and over a series of days, thus making it possible for the animals to learn the various sequences of choices available to them. This forms the basis of the flock's trust in the herder, who takes care to ration new forage resources, especially those the animals prefer. At the time of their discussion, André and Francis could not rely on scientific and technical information about the benefits of diet variety for the nutrition and health of their herds. Rather, as they discuss knowledge gained from personal experience, they try to confirm that the choices they make are valid and the art of herding becomes central to the discussion.

AL: There are herders I see who, when they start out on an August grazing quarter in the mountains, say, "Well, I'm not even going to try and hold them back . . . just let them run all over." So for four or five days, they let them run all over the place and they think that the sheep will calm down afterwards. So the sheep eat up everything they like. . . . And these herders say, "Afterward, they know there's nothing left," nothing much attracts them, since it's all been eaten up, and so they calm down and settle down to eat the less good stuff. But in my case, I prefer to have the sheep eat the good and the less good gradually, a little each day, going a little farther every day so that they always find some fresh forage. I don't want to necessarily give them all the good stuff in one go.

FS: That sounds a little strange to me too. Basically, their animals are going to eat well for ten days and then they're going to spend the next twenty days. . . . But they need the same quality food every day, especially dairy goats. So, you work with all types of areas — less good, the best, and everything in between. You can't give them all the best stuff in just ten days, even if you're dealing with large surface areas, and then have nothing left.

AL: But sometimes I think, for a flock of sheep, that it's their condition that counts. Fat isn't the same thing as milk . . . but maybe it doesn't matter? Sometimes, I wonder: maybe the sheep will get into the good stuff for ten days, and then they'll maintain better. But, overall, meaning over a month or five weeks, maybe it's all the same, huh? Managing the flock one way or another?

FS: Well, I think . . . I suspect it won't be the same result.

AL: I'm more for managing the flock each day.

FS: It makes sense. Because even if giving sheep the best grass puts the weight on them, they're going to waste it. I mean, not everything they eat is going to turn itself into body fat, you know? I don't know how to put it. Plus, they're probably going to lose the fat they gained in the next few days . . . 'cause they won't want to start eating again, see? Anyway, I think animals' intake should be consistent.

AL: It should be consistent, rather than in "peaks." Even if it's more work.

FS: It's more work, but I mean, if you're going to do a job, do it well. And even as far as your relationship with the herd goes, I'm not sure how to put it. . . . If you manage the herd, well, you take the herd into a good area, you split up your half-day herding circuit to give them a bit of a treat and everything, they'll be calmer, or else that will boost their appetite. And then you can give them a little bit of the less-good stuff, after which you'll use a booster again . . . in the process, you're forging a relationship with the herd.

AL: Yeah.

FS: You see, there is something, I mean . . . but if you give them only the good stuff for ten days, and then afterward it's all bad for twenty days, you're acting like an "electric fence." I think there's less of a [good] relationship created.

AL: Yes, I agree. I mean, the herders who do that sort of thing say that it helps the animals calm down. But it's not necessarily true. Because they're going to keep on looking, and often it happens that they just can't find any more good-quality forage anywhere, so they're never satisfied and won't settle down. So they go back and forth fifty times around the quarter, but they never settle anywhere. But if you reserve a little bit of the good stuff and just give them some from time to time, then they settle down fine, and then they're happier to graze the coarser vegetation. It doesn't necessarily mean more work, either, because if you let them do as they please . . . then it's all gone, there's nothing left. If you have an area that they know is good, and you allow them to graze it gradually, they'll tend to go back to it every time. So you know you'll always find them there. Even if they make a huge detour, they'll always go back there. So your management of the flock also becomes easier. You give them another taste of the good stuff, and then you send them elsewhere. But you know that the entire flock will come back to that place, even if some of the flock scatters much farther on. So, it makes herding easier.

Using the Structure of the Land to One's Benefit

FS: I can [also] start them off in a particular direction, but I can't set their course for a whole circuit [which corresponds to a meal, taking about three hours to complete]. Maybe a half-grazing circuit, but it's impossible over an entire circuit.

AL: But I don't work on that basis, either!

FS: I thought you said that you could leave them in the morning and be sure of finding them in such-and-such a place the same evening.

AL: Not at all!

FS: Oh, really? . . . I had that picture in my head for herding sheep in the mountains.

AL: No, no. You see, there are some places that are enclosed because they're surrounded by rocky ridges. You can leave them there but otherwise . . . if you leave them alone other places, they're likely to go to another quarter entirely! Or, actually, you can leave them on their own on the first couple of days when you start out in a place that's got really good foraging. But they're quickly going to look elsewhere. They'll go over to the neighbors' land. Really, you can only leave them for less than half a day maximum. You see, it's only for a little while, for example, two or three times in the morning, or in the afternoon.

FS: I see.

AL: Or at the end of the day, when you know they're going to bed down there. So you can leave them at seven o'clock at night. And you know they're going to sleep there.

FS: Well, that's also true for a herd of forty goats in coppice. Sometimes last year, we would find a spot, you know, where there was no senna. You let the goats go and you know that thirty to forty-five minutes later, they'll come back. You go sixty feet further and then, well, you do it again. That way, you go around in loops. It's great when it works out that way.

AL: Oh yeah?

FS: Loops only work depending on the herd's relationship with the herder. If you take the herd to another spot, they know it's going to be for eating; they don't tire themselves out trying to find food on the way, they trust you.

AL: Shade is a factor, too. At the beginning of the afternoon, if there's a shady spot, we'll take them there right away. Otherwise, you start out two hours later. If there's a shady spot in the afternoon, you've got to keep it for then . . . or toward the end of the morning, sometimes it's a good idea to find shade so that they continue to eat for another hour, instead of resting right away. . . . For example, if you have the flock rest on a slope right in the sun, they're not going to get going again until 6 or 7 p.m. But if you choose a hillside that you know will be in the shade in the afternoon, that loses the warmth of the sun quickly, well, as soon as five o'clock comes around, they're up and moving. So you can get in more grazing time. Of course, if you decide to let them have a little more freedom, they'll maybe make up for it by bedding down later at night. But you still start out later in the day.

FS: I use that technique, too. I even use sunny areas to keep the herd away from certain places.

AL: Yeah, me, too, in the early afternoon, when they're getting back up from resting. You see the whole flock staying in the shade. And you know you have a nice, quiet time ahead because they're not going to leave the shade. And then, once the temperature has gone down or if the sky becomes overcast, then they'll get up. But there's a little time there where it's kind of as if they were in a pen. . . . Herders can use that, too, to prolong grazing time. It's kind of known as "weather well-being." Everybody laughs, but it's sort of true, you know: the herder has to try to always place the sheep where they're happiest, in terms of temperature, wind, exposure to the sun, etc. So when you're starting out in the morning, you're going to take them to a sunny hillside, because the grass there dries fast and then, as the sun gets higher in the sky, you can get to a shady spot. You can use that.

FS: That's exactly it. In the morning at La Tour, you send them to somewhat overgrown areas and rock slabs in the sun. And then you take them into the woods around 9:00 or 9:30 a.m. They browse in the woods, and you can be sure they won't go back out into the sun. And even if across the way there's an area they're not supposed to go, you don't need to try to keep them from it . . . they won't even try. It's only when it's windy or something that they might think of going there.

AL: I use that a lot here in Ardèche, especially starting in May, when it gets warmer. All the hillsides that have shade toward the end of the morning—I make sure to keep those for the month of May. Because then I know they'll be able to eat a little longer.

DESIGNING A GRAZING CIRCUIT AND ADEQUATE MEALS

A grazing circuit is the route a herder plans for the flock or herd on a given day or half-day. Although an uninformed observer may describe the herder as "doing almost nothing" while the flock follows the intended circuit, he is in fact witnessing the concrete result of the herder's plan to relate the flock's needs to an area of rangeland, based on the previously mentioned rules of flock behavior and management. When a herder decides to herd closely, meaning that he does not merely mark the boundaries of the space allowed or let the animals roam free according to their daily rhythms, he has to plan different sequences. This allows him to achieve consistency in both ration and grazing impact.

Thus, a grazing circuit divides access to forage resources in an order designed to stimulate the animals' appetite during meals in line with the schedule of use for these resources according to season and the grazing land. A circuit enables the herder to compose a meal that is sufficient in quantity and quality. That way, the animals may perform as expected based on the diversity of plant communities, even though the feeding value of any single community may be relatively poor. The process links the use of various land types, and different "courses" of the meal, each of which play a role in the constitution of a meal. Grazing circuits give meaning to the diversity of vegetation by providing complementary combinations and thus producing food synergies between the various resources available.

The following dialogue addresses key components of a conceptual model called "MENU" (see Figure 1 and chapter 8 for details). This model was first developed in 1991, based on preliminary surveys and measures of a herd's intake behavior under the herder's guidance, including Francis and his interns. It helps a herder to conceive grazing circuits that ensure rapid and massive intake in a grazing sector, referred to as the "target sector," that contains vegetation of medium quality (dense, fibrous bushes in forests, or more mature grassy areas) that must be used to best manage animals and rangelands.

Starters

FS: When I take my goat herd out, it all depends on what happened over the previous circuit. I can either start with an "appetite stimulator," or an "appetite moderator."

AL: What's the difference?

FS: An "appetite stimulator" is for when you know the herd has eaten well over the previous circuit, so they're hardly hungry now.

AL: Oh yeah?

FS: If the goats have eaten well during the previous circuit, you're going to try and stimulate their appetite a little, you know? That's what an "appetite stimulator" is for. Otherwise, when the goats are really hungry, either because they didn't eat well before or they've digested well or something . . . then I give them a "moderator" course to calm them down.

AL: Okay, I see. That's what I call "getting them going." The beginning of the day.

FS: And I choose the different areas according to —

AL: I think that for me, there's also that "starting up" phase. But with sheep up in the mountains, it's nearly always the same thing.

FS: That's because they're sheep. The difference is that when you're herding [dry] sheep, it's the time factor; you don't have any time constraints.

AL: Yes, that's true, too.

FS: The sheep start out when they want to, and stop when they want to. So usually, when they stop, it means they're full. It's not the same thing for dairy goats.

AL: Yes, but there's more to it than that. Because actually, the conditions I work in change all the time. I have all the time in the world, but C [the sheep farmer for whom André works in the winter in Ardèche] is kind of like you, when he's on his own. He has a lot of other things to do besides herding, like making hay. . . . So, he's always got a limited amount of time, too. Whereas in my case, when I'm there [in high mountain pastures], I only have herding. When I get back from herding, I know I'm nearly done, that I have nothing else to do. So I don't have that constraint. And it's true that that makes my situation really different.

FS: Especially if you have them grazing tender young grass in the spring, they'll eat faster than if it were a woody species. So you don't have time to give them an "appetite moderator," instead you need a place where —

AL: Where they'll stop to fill their stomachs.

FS: Exactly!

AL: Whereas you save the "appetite stimulator" for when they've settled down. Then, you can give them some of the good stuff.

FS: Exactly. I give them the fresh stuff . . . you have to choose the right spots. What's good, for instance, is when I can put the herd in with some of the less palatable stuff, for an appetite moderator. If the place is well-enclosed, where they won't run all over, like areas with boulders or practically inedible brush. . . . Whereas to stimulate the animals' appetite, you'd better have some of the good stuff for them because if you give medium quality stuff, it will not work. . . . And there're areas that can serve as an "appetite stimulator," an "appetite moderator," a "main course," a "dessert," everything, you know?

AL: You don't move them around?

FS: No, but actually you feel it with the herd when a change occurs. You don't observe the same patterns. For an appetite moderator or appetite stimulator, they quickly take a nibble here and there . . . and then later, for the "main course," you notice that they're eating better, without rushing or anything.

AL: It's the same spot, but they don't eat the same way.

FS: Not at the same pace, yeah.

Boosting the Herd's Appetite between Courses

FS: But, up there on your summer range, you can afford to cover more distance since you have more time.

AL: But I also can't keep the sheep moving indefinitely. If I'm there at nightfall [points to a spot on the table], and there's somewhere for them to bed down, I'm going to have them bed down for the night, rather than come back here [points to another spot]. So if I have a really long way to go, I'll have them do it in two days. I'll have them sleep elsewhere.

FS: What distance can you cover in a day?

AL: I don't know . . . I don't know how to calculate distances. But it's a lot, that I can tell you.

FS: Okay, well, this drawing [showing the MENU diagram] represents a half-day, made up of five phases. Yes, five . . . when I get in five phases, it means one didn't work out well.

AL: What, five phases in four hours?

FS: You have to count one hour for travel, so that makes for three hours of grazing. It's a lot, but still. . . . But it's five [phases] when it doesn't work out well.

AL: Here in Ardèche, we tend to have several "minor courses." That's how it works in the winter: they eat for a little while, and then you change areas, and they eat a little more somewhere else before changing again, and it's kind of like this [he makes notes in pencil on the MENU diagram—see Figure 1].

FS: Okay, but how long do you herd?

AL: Seven or eight hours, tops.

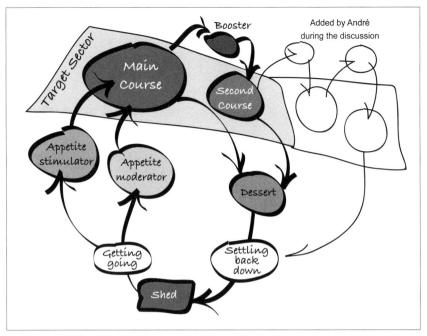

FIGURE 1: Prototype diagram of a Menu for a herd grazing a rangeland area during a half-day period. This conceptual model was first developed in 1991 based on preliminary surveys and measures of a herd's ingestive behavior conducted by herders, including Francis and his interns.

FS: Several minor courses . . . but is there a main course at some point?

AL: No, there isn't a main one. Between courses is when we spend some time in the woods. It gives them a change of scene. They move about a little, they eat a little. They're happy to be in a different place, a new spot, and so they start eating again for a while.

FS: So it gets them going again?

AL: Yes, it boosts their appetite.

FS: So it's a course, then a booster, a course, then a booster. How many of those sequences do you get in a day?

AL: A lot. Where I herd [winter pasture in Ardèche], we never have enough space for 250 sheep to settle for an hour. The grazing areas are never very big. [Up on summer range], sometimes just a main course, or two half-courses . . . or an appetite stimulator and a main course, and then they're done, they've eaten enough. That's why this diagram (Figure 1) looks good to me. . . . In Ardèche, when the sheep's appetite starts to flag and you call them over to move to another spot, the flock follows straightaway. They know that you're not calling them over just to annoy them, it's obvious. You can see it—some of the sheep are starting to look around, and then you call them and right away, the whole flock comes running. But if they're some place where they're still eating well, you can call them all you want; not one of them will budge, they'll keep eating without even looking up! To boost their appetite, all you have to do sometimes is move to another spot.

FS: Sometimes, that's all you need.

AL: Sometimes, yeah. It's a change of scene. That's what's different with a flock that's not herded.

FS: It can be more palatable species, or something else, or just moving about.

AL: It depends on what you've got.

FS: But it also depends on where you've been and where you're going! And where you want to go later. If you have a "booster" area nearby with better stuff, well, you're going to use it.

AL: Yes, and actually, that's when the animals would lie down if they were in a fenced pasture. Let's say they've made their way around the pasture, they've eaten some, they haven't really finished their meal, but they're bored. They've been around two or three times and then they lie down, and they wait at the gate for someone to move them somewhere else. That's where the herder has an advantage. Just the other day, we went to pick them up in the pasture at around 5 p.m. They were all lying down, waiting. Well, with the time it took for us to take them down the track a little to get back to the shed, they had all started eating again. Whereas, in the pasture . . . but I'm sure they would have easily eaten another hour where they were!

FS: In theory, if a booster works, a "minor" course can be given in exactly the same spot as the main course. In theory. But if you have animals that have eaten for a while in one place, there's something to do with the smell of the place that means that, well, they don't feel like coming back to graze in the same place. You can come back the next day, but not as part of the same grazing circuit.

AL: It's really the boosters that are crucial. That's how you get them to graze the areas with poor quality forage. You have to take them out for a while, then put them back in, then take them back out, then put them back in. . . .

Dessert

FS: I think the goats' favorite "dessert" is when I take them down along the banks of the Ardèche River so they can graze the tender grass that grows there.

AL: Senna is like a dessert, too, right?

FS: Yes, but in the small valleys [20 to 50 meters wide] where senna grows, you only have enough for three desserts, no more than that . . . there's not much of it. We could create more of it, maybe grow it, but it'd have to be here, down below [near the goat shed, on farmland]. Do you also use the concept of "dessert," or a similar concept for areas toward the end of a grazing circuit?

AL: Around the shed [in Ardèche], there's some land that was cultivated and fertilized by manures in the old times. When I have some, when it's not all eaten, I try to get there half an hour before nightfall, and I take them to better spots than those found in the hills. And there, they'll eat as much as you like of what you call dessert. But up in the mountains, it tends to be . . . I mean, after the minor course, the sheep move to an area where they'll rest at noontime. And in the evening, they move to a place where they're going to bed down for the night. And before actually bedding down there, they'll graze for a while practically without moving. Then, little by little, the flock will bed down. It's a really peaceful time. Even if it's coarse vegetation, they'll eat it. They're patient, you know? They'll sort through anything. It's a good idea to try and use that behavior to have them graze in poorer quality areas. At night, they'll accept much coarser vegetation. Well, they're selective in their grazing. They patiently graze in areas that they wouldn't even go to in the morning.

FS: Here [with dairy goats], if I tried to finish a grazing circuit with coarser stuff, there's no way they'd eat it!

AL: Here, there's a final moment of peaceful grazing, where the sheep will eat nearly anything. It doesn't have to be very good, even if it's an area where they're not all within sight of each other, you see—dangerous spots and everything—they'll spread out and they're calm, because they know that they're all going to gather together in that spot.

Getting Going . . . and Settling Back Down

FS: What do you do to get them up and going?

AL: That's only necessary in the morning. It's the time it takes for them to stretch their legs. It doesn't have to be top-quality grass. Even if it is, they're not going to stop in the morning, they're going to walk right through it. They don't feel like eating when they get up and start out. Here in Ardèche, it's a little bit different because they have to travel a bit, they have to go through some woods. That gets their appetite going. And in the mountains, we're usually up in higher zones, which we have to come down from slowly. It's a stony area, without much grass, only a little here and there. I think the main thing is to get them going, because my sheep are always hungry. [Laughs] In the afternoon, they start eating right away. But that doesn't mean you should give them the best stuff, either. Because they'll often waste it that way, if they're just moving through and trampling it. In the mountains in the afternoon, it's better to choose an area with a little shade, to let them move around as they wish, but without really getting down to business.

FS: Oh yeah . . . you actually pick up your sheep just as they're waking up!

AL: Yes, it's the same thing in the afternoon, when half of the flock is still resting, especially a large flock. Sometimes, only half the flock has begun eating a little. The others are resting or moving slowly, and then they lie back down to rest. You have to wait until they're all fully awake before taking them to a "main course" grazing zone, otherwise you waste resources.

FS: That's not accounted for in the drawing. My goats, for example, are awake when I go out. I mean, they've already had their supplementary feed, they've been milked, and then we have half an hour to travel afterwards.

AL: And at night, when the sheep are nice and full, there's one last period in which you can get them to eat a little more.

FS: For us, that's when you put them in a fenced area at night. When we bring them back at night, they eat a little bit more. They start to bed down, and then just before night falls, they start eating again.

AL: I think it's a specific behavior pattern of flocks and herds at night. Often, you just get there and put them straight into the shed. But if you take your time and leave them for a while . . . well, maybe for goats it's different, I don't know, there's the milking effect and everything that can have an influence.

FS: Yeah, but I milk them before taking them out in the evening.

AL: Oh?

FS: But it's true that they tend to nibble at high speed just before nightfall. I let them. It's not so much about a certain quantity of food, it's more for the herd . . . the herd's behavior. To calm the herd down. It's little things like that. If you take your time coming back, you finish your day peacefully, instead of rushing back and pushing the herd with the dog at its heels.

AL: I think that's really important.

FS: What happens is that you help the herd settle down. It doesn't necessarily [have an] impact on the next morning's herding, but it will on the herd's night, and of course on the herd's general behavior. Less stressed out and everything.

AL: The general feeling of the herd.

FS: You can tell that the herd is better off.

AL: Yes, sometimes, you can sense that things are going well. It feels right, you know!

Using the Leftovers

AL: I thought that for something like this to work [pointing to the MENU diagram, see Figure 1], either you had to have grazing circuits that included a main course and the animals ate well, or you had to have grazing circuits where you had to work at it, including four or five courses spread out. For example, at the beginning, when you get to a new quarter, there's the appetite stimulator. Then, the main course, after which the animals will go and rest. And at the end, there's an appetite stimulator, then a smaller minor course, then a booster course and again a minor course and then a booster course, like that, three or four times [draws on a bit of paper]. I think it fits well with what . . . right away, I understood exactly where this was coming from, with different roles assigned to different grazing zones. There's just the difference between "appetite stimulator" and "moderator" course that I didn't understand at first. And I think, if we want, to classify things [referring to his ongoing research with INRA—see chapter 4]. . . . So we have two years of documentation, which represents about two hundred days of grazing circuits. With the morning and evening herding, that makes four hundred. So, if you want to try and classify them somehow, this is a great method to use. Actually, it's funny because as the grazing gets more meager, you have to work harder to get them to eat. You know you have a small area there that will last them half an hour, that'll make them happy for half an hour, so you give them a little bit there and then you go back to coarser foraging, and then you go back again to different stuff.

FS: This diagram [Figure 1] helps us think about how we can try to put together parts of the landscape to fashion meals for the herd.

CONCLUSION

The herd or flock is highly mobile, selective, and capable of learning. Rather than imposing the herder's preferences, it is necessary to use clever tricks to assemble adequate sequences of meals, or to use one's "cunning," as André puts it. Building "a relationship of trust" with the herd (the mere expression is proof that herders see this relationship from an emotional perspective) provides the flexibility needed to mitigate the effects of sudden changes in the herd's situation or feeding pattern. Once a bond has formed based on authority and trust, and a system of references has been established for the herd or flock, the herder is able to direct the animals' grazing in different ways: stimulating intake of high-quality plants; encouraging the consumption of coarse, less palatable plants; regulating the impact of grazing on a given area; etc.

The importance of designing a grazing circuit, based on the herders' dialogue, reinforces the fact that it is necessary to rethink approaches that rely only on plant biomass and nutritional value to evaluate grazing lands in hills and mountains. The nutritional value of a plant community in a given area depends on its place in the grazing circuit sequence. The role of a given grazing area in a meal, and the manner in which its diverse plant species are consumed, depends on the characteristics of the grazing circuit, and more generally on herd management.

Just as a sentence and context give words meaning, so do circuits and a grazing context give grazing "resources" their meaning.

ACKNOWLEDGMENTS

1993 – In addition to the two herders recorded, André Leroy and Francis Surnon, I would like to extend warm thanks to Jean-Pierre Deffontaines, Etienne Landais, Elisabeth Lécrivain, Gilbert Molénat, and Isabelle Savini, without whom this dialogue would never have taken place, and who also helped me put together the text. Etienne Landais deserves special gratitude for his contribution to the formatting of the final text.

2013 – If André and Francis had ever imagined that photocopies of their discussion would be folded and carried around by herders and farmers alike and, further, that ten years later it would be made available on the internet, then twenty years later published in the United States, they might have tried to speak in loftier terms. Thankfully, they did not. That's why their passion comes across so powerfully. Thank you, dear friends.

CHAPTER 8

MENU Model:
The Herder as a Restaurant Chef

Michel Meuret

FIFTEEN years ago, ten or so motivated and experienced sheep- and goat-herders helped us build a model called MENU as part of a research partnership. MENU deals with the way a herder can manage feeding motivation of his herd over the course of a half-day's grazing circuit.

The objectives are threefold: Firstly, the model aims to demonstrate, in an accessible format, that herders often originate clever techniques to stimulate herd appetite, thereby improving the feeding value of grazing areas. Secondly, the model is designed to encourage animal scientists to further explore the concept of relative palatability of foods in a situation involving diverse food options and sequenced grazing over a day. Finally, the model aims to provide key concepts to novice herders (who sometimes become discouraged with their herds) to help them observe and act more effectively. This is especially important where herders must have their herds consume resources of apparently mediocre palatability, such as coarse shrubs and very mature grasses.

HERDED FLOCK BEHAVIOR SURPRISES RESEARCHERS
Animal Nutritionists at a Loss

In the early 1980s, I attempted to estimate the energy balance of dairy goats herded on rangeland in southeastern France (the Alps and Massif Central). My goal was to determine whether nutritional requirements were satisfied by the food supply provided by supplements and grazing on rangelands. As recommended in animal science, I used tables of food nutritional values, based on data recorded under controlled conditions with animals fed individually in laboratory crates. When interactions between the different foods were also taken into account, this approach proved relevant for a number of farming systems, such as high-yield dairy cows raised in confinement.

I concluded that, in theory, the feeding value of the natural forages consumed by herded goats, as estimated by chemical analyses, could satisfy only 50 percent of their total energy requirements. It was imperative, according to the recommendations in feeding manuals,[1] to make up the difference by supplying considerable amounts of hay and concentrated feed. However, I observed that many goatherders did not provide much supplement. In addition to grazing on rangeland, their animals received only a little grain (400–500 grams per day) in addition to salt and water. The goats should therefore have wasted away. Nevertheless, halfway through the summer and at mid-lactation they were in good body condition, each producing 0.5–0.8 gallons of milk every day. This is close to the French national average, regardless of the type of farming system, which suggested that current scientific and technical references were not relevant for goats herded on rangeland.

With colleagues, we therefore developed a noninvasive method to record the individual intake of livestock on farms with small ruminants being herded on rangeland.[2] The method enabled us to record the total daily intake of several dozen plant species, from herbs to trees and shrubs, as well as instantaneous intake rates of forages (grams of ingested material per minute) during each grazing meal. I used direct visual recordings of the ingestive bites taken by focal animals grazing within their herd.

When we published our findings (see black triangles on Figure 1), renowned nutritionists were surprised and suspected erroneous measurements. To determine if this was the case, we worked with dairy goats fed mixtures of fresh oak foliage (*Quercus ilex* L. or *Q. pubescens* Willd.) offered in specially designed digestibility crates.[3] We obtained similar results (see grey triangles on Figure 1). More recently, we redid the experiments with a much better documented animal species and practice: sheep grazing in fenced pastures (see grey squares on Figure 1).[4] In every case, we found similar results.

The nutritionists' surprise was understandable. For each type of rangeland and grazing condition, we recorded daily intakes that were much higher than the reference data obtained from animals fed in laboratory crates with forages of similar nutritive value. The goats ate more on the rangeland than in lab crates because the herders were successful at stim-

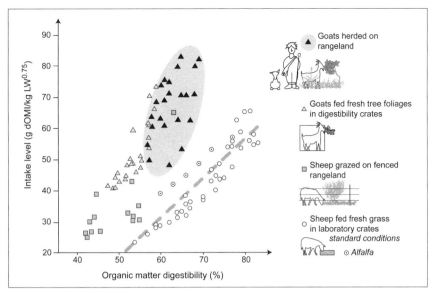

FIGURE 1: Intake by goats and sheep eating mixed diets on rangeland (black triangles and grey squares) or fed with fresh oak foliage in specially designed digestibility crates (grey triangles). Each data point corresponds to the average daily response of an individual during five to twelve consecutive days. With equivalent digestibility of organic matter, we recorded double the intake reported in the literature for sheep fed in laboratory crates with cultivated fresh grass (white circles) or fresh alfalfa (spotted white circles). Intake level is expressed here as digestible organic material ingested (DOMI) per kilogram of metabolic weight ($LW^{0.75}$) of the animal (after Agreil and Meuret, 2004; Baumont et al., 1999; Jarrige 1988; Meuret, 1989). The reference linear model on the right (thick gray dotted line) is based on those of Morley (1981) and Van Soest (1994).

ulating appetite. This was especially the case with herded dairy goats. Assuming equal nutritive value of the diet, the animals were consuming twice as much as expected by the reference model in science (see thick gray dotted line in Figure 1). Given diets of medium nutritive value (50 percent to 70 percent digestibility of organic matter), the intake of digestible organic matter is often higher for sheep on rangeland compared with sheep fed under standard conditions in laboratory crates, even when fed excellent forage such as fresh alfalfa (lucerne, *Medicago sativa* L.). Goats can thus satisfy their maintenance requirements for energy while living on the range, including travel, and also up to half their requirements for lactation.[5]

Providing goats with a small amount of grain to supplement range forages was appropriate on the herders' part. However, it was still unclear why the animals, especially the herded dairy goats, ate so much forage on rangeland. To gain some insight, we examined cumulative intake within a meal, which reflects foraging motivation. Our calculations demonstrat-

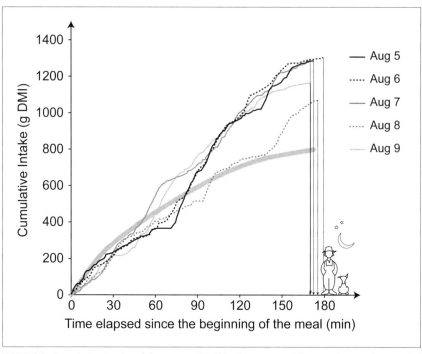

FIGURE 2: Cumulative intake of dry matter (DMI) in the course of five evening meals recorded in summer for a dairy goat being herded on woody rangeland (after Meuret, 1989). The slope and regularity of the curves reflect the animal's motivation to eat the forage. For comparison's sake, there is also a curve for the intake of fresh grass eaten out of a trough by a non-lactating sheep (gray curve in the background, after Baumont, 1989).

ed excellent grazing motivation when the goats were closely herded on rangeland (Figure 2). Intake rates (grams of dry matter ingested per minute) at the beginning of a meal were often as high as recorded with sheep provided with a first-rate grass forage in troughs,[6] and the "constants of deceleration" for the curves, as a function of the satiation process, were low.[7] Thus, in the example of the five summer evening meals in Figure 2, the herder was successful in getting his goats to consume between 1.1 and 1.3 kilograms of dry matter per meal, which is significant, especially given a time span of only about three hours for feeding just before nightfall.

These meal curves, or meal kinetics, have a quite different shape from those of animals fed in troughs, where simple exponential models accurately fit cumulative intake during meals (see gray curve in Figure 2). With herded animals on rangeland, the meal consists of an irregular succession of phases characterized by higher or lower intake rates. For nutritionists, this means that after a phase of partial satiation, an animal quickly regains a hearty appetite during the next phase of the meal. How does herding prompt the frequent renewal of appetite within a meal? To answer this question, we began to work directly with experienced herders.*

Herders' Rules for Managing Meals

As conventionally trained animal scientists, we were confused by the information we initially obtained from interviews. Indeed, the terminology and guidelines used by herders hardly resembled the usual references in our field.[8] The herders stressed the need to design a good quality "herding circuit," based on criteria that had little to do with, and were sometimes in contradiction to, ours. For instance, they emphasized the "usefulness of the novelty of a specific plant or grazing sector" as a way to stimulate appetite, whereas animal feeding studies claimed that a lack of any experience with a particular food or habitat could suppress appetite.[9] The herders also pointed out how "the layout of the land as compared to the size and gregariousness of the herd" can influence grazing motivation, whereas "stocking rates" (the number of animals per unit of surface area and of time) are generally determined with little regard for the uniformity of the land. Herders also emphasized the "role of plant diversity in stimulating appetite," whereas animal nutritionists and agronomists typically attempt to optimize intake of diets — total mixed rations and monocultures — that are extremely simplified in their components. Finally, herders stressed the value of "the effective management of phases that boost the herd's appetite throughout the grazing circuit." This empirical rule especially piqued our curiosity. We showed them our graphs and the irregular rates of intake observed (Figure 2). The results did not surprise the herders, with one offering the following explanation: "Since we often can't herd all day, we move the animals around from time to time to stimulate them. It gives them a change of scene and revives their appetite." They then unanimously stated that "The main thing is to plan a grazing circuit that allows animals to encounter a diversity of forage in an order that boosts their appetite!"

Such empirical rules as 1) designing a meal based on the order of the forage resources available, 2) leveraging diversity, and 3) boosting appetites are not easily translated into the language of animal nutritionists, though there are ongoing attempts to do so.[10] Animal nutrition assesses the value of foods offered individually on consecutive days, and in the case of studies that deal with interactions, typically only two or three food sources are offered. Therefore, a herder's organization of herd intake, ap-

---

* In this chapter, the term "herder" will be used to refer to people who tend either sheep or goats, whether they own the livestock or are hired for the purpose of herding. Where specific situations pertaining to goats arise, the term "goatherder" will be used.

parently founded on making several dozen to hundreds of different foods available to the herd, is difficult to study from an animal nutritionist's perspective, given the multiple interactions at play.

The herders interviewed thus gave us the opportunity to begin original research on topics that were not much considered then or now. To carry out our research, we had to change scientific perspectives. Using herding practices as the basis for our work, we attempted to understand herder's influence on intake behavior in animals faced with the great diversity of forages on offer at pasture. We focused primarily on the herders, highlighting their empirical experience and practical principles.[11]

RESEARCH APPROACH AND SURVEY METHODS

Our goal was to understand and assess feeding practices in herding situations, which required simultaneously recording several types of information at different organization levels — herder, herd, individual animal — using an array of methods from different scientific disciplines. In-person interviews of herders were combined with animal performance recordings, maps of vegetation grazed, and data on behavior and intake levels during meals.

Iterative Approach Including Discussions between Herders

From 1991 to 1994, we conducted surveys of goatherders and shepherds. We chose cheese-producing goatherders where possible because they had a reliable and easy-to-record indicator of foraging success: the twice-a-day variation in milk and cheese production, which reflected the quality of the corresponding meals. We observed herding practices in situ and interviewed individual herders over several months and years. Our first participants were the herders with whom we had worked through INRA: a goatherder herding on wooded rangeland[12] and a shepherd herding in high mountain pasture (see chapters 4 and 7).[13] Based on our research interests, these herders referred us to others likely to be interested in our work, and they, in turn, referred us to yet others, and so on. We then circulated the various perceptions and statements obtained from the twenty-four herders we had interviewed, without citing individual sources. We thus avoided any conflict between herders with regard to their skills. We also prepared a few organized discussions (see previous chapter for a conversation between a shepherd and a goatherder), which resulted in clarification of some statements. Some participants, quite attached to their personal experiences, were critical of the way their individual expressions and thoughts were impoverished. However, our objective was always to

MICHEL MEURET / INRA

PHOTO 1 — A goatherder, while out with his herd, sketches the route of his circuit in real time, at the same time noting down the reasons for every action he has taken.

start with personal experiences in order to develop a broader understanding that would hopefully be representative of all participants.

When we asked the herders why they had agreed to participate in our study (none had received compensation), they replied that they "enjoyed debating with others, and how that resulted in their seeing things differently and further improving their know-how." It is important to note that, at the time, herders, sheep and goat farmers, and livestock advisers did not exchange much information on herding techniques. Rather, the prevailing idea was that "everyone does their own thing."

Mountain Shoes, a Tape Recorder, a Stopwatch, and a Laboratory Balance

Dialogue was our first means of survey. We used a method described in the social sciences as "semi-structured interviews."[14] These were informal interviews wherein we accepted any type of response to our questions. The initial questions focused on the herders' personal herding practices, but the herders also discussed related topics. The interviews were recorded and transcribed in their entirety.

A second means of survey was the notes herders took during their grazing circuits. This included exact timing, the sequence in which the

MICHEL MEURET / INRA

PHOTO 2 — Recording from direct observation of the intake behavior of control animals in a flock under a herder's management. The observer is conducting focal sampling, entering successive bites on a coding grid of bite categories based on the nature and structure of plant portions clipped.

various areas were grazed, and the reasons behind these choices, as well as the surface area used by the flock or herd. All this information was noted on a blank base map (1:1,500 or 1:3,000, depending on grazing land extent) as the herder led his herd along a grazing circuit. Finally, the herders were asked to jot down any other useful comments (see Photo 1).

The third means was research that involved making simultaneous measurements in situ during a time of year when the entire intake at pasture was under a herder's management (see Photo 2). Measures were carried out by direct observation of: 1) the type and condition of grazed areas; 2) the pattern of activity of the herder and the herd in grazing circuits, and 3) the intake of a focal animal. Cataloging this information, and recording it on a 1:1,500 base map, required rigorous preparation, observation and sampling: ten to twenty days of mapping based on aerial photos and field notes; several days for the herd or flock and the observers to become accustomed with one another; five to ten consecutive days observing forage intake; and several days for collecting and conditioning plant samples representative of all the categories of ingestive bites. These activities were done in ways that did not interfere with the herder's actions.

TWO ESSENTIAL RULES FOR HERDERS
Develop a Predictable Herd

A herd is a man-made biological construct. Herders often say, "The herd has understood," "The herd is not yet accustomed," referring to the herd as its own being with a collective behavior unto itself (see also chapter 5). Herders know that group behavior often prevails over individual behavior and that they have to account for this when modulating their own behavior toward the herd. At the same time, the stability and cohesion of the herd are reinforced by rearing practices. Training the youngest members of the herd is very important, but so is the careful selection and retention of adult animals that are not only productive (milk, lambs) but also serve as models for foraging behaviors, as the herder or farmer keeps or attempts to retrain individual animals depending on whether they have a positive or negative influence on the group. In any case, categories of individuals, and even of strong personalities, are easily observable.

The Herd, Groups, and Individuals

Herders see their job as managing three target entities: 1) the herd, 2) groups or categories of individuals, and 3) individuals. At the individual level, the herder is able to identify health problems, body condition, a drop in milk production, and sometimes preferences for atypical foods. Skilled herders are able to identify problem individuals in herds of over two thousand sheep. Some of the herder's means of managing the herd (e.g., selecting animals to retrain, placing of bells) involve individual animals. At the group or category level ("those that . . ." as the herders say), the herder is able to identify behavioral qualities or problems likely to impact the herd. Herds grazing in high mountain pastures are usually composed of animals from several different farms. In this case, effects of breed, size, agility, and feeding habits help herders distinguish among different group behaviors. As one herder says, "While the Métis [small Mérinos d'Arles sheep] climb up scree, the Iles [large Ile-de-France sheep] stay put down below." For each group, or category of individuals, herders use "control" animals (*mes repères*, or "my markers," as herders say). Some individuals are chosen to play the role of a permanent control to monitor the behavior of the group, while others are controls for a specific activity. A control animal is recognized as specialized following the repeated observation of a certain behavior (e.g., "the big eaters," "the speedy ones," "the stragglers," "the adventurers," and "the ornery ones"). The typical control animal may be described as a default control: "If those two have eaten well, it means all of them have." Finally, the herder seeks to develop a relationship of trust with the herd, and he trains his herding dogs and/or guard dogs with the herd in mind. Feeding practices often take into account the herd as a whole, as the total number of lambs ready for sale on a given date or the total number of cheeses produced is the most important information recorded at the farm.

Many shepherds, and all goatherders, focus their attention on two groups: the "experienced guides" and the inexperienced animals, the latter being mostly the youngest. An experienced guide is said to "understand quickly," to realize "what is expected of her," and to "induce others to follow." They are kept in the herd even if their performance is only average. They are fitted with a sheep bell, which reinforces the herd's cohesion, especially in the event of fog or in shrubby or wooded areas. With these two management groups the herder is assured of a minimum amount of trouble from the rest of the herd, all the other individuals often referred to as "nameless ones."[15]

Training Inexperienced Animals

The inexperienced animals are mostly the youngest, but they can be adults. Nowadays, many salaried herders are faced with a growing number of naïve flocks of sheep entrusted to them for rangeland grazing during summer and winter transhumance. The sheep farmers want to limit their feeding costs at the farm, but herders say farmers are quite unaware about the fact that their sheep ignore the variety of rangeland forages, not recognizing most of the plants as edible material because the fenced grassy pasture within which they have been confined do not contain these plants. Naïve sheep also ignore herding dogs. Such animal inexperience comes from the intensification of sheep farming conditions. Sheep and lambs are grazed only on high-quality cultivated meadows. Groups of animals are moved from one pasture to another with quads and trucks rather than herding dogs. When released from the transhumance truck, these sheep are confused, and a herder can quickly lose control of them. They spend most of the time searching for young grasses that resemble foods they already know. Without constant and heavy pushing by the herder, they are reluctant to become part of the herd that comprises the already experienced animals. We observe this behavior in all breeds, including the highly gregarious such as Merino sheep.

Training of the Youngest

Young replacement animals (ewe lambs or doe kids) must be "prepared" for herding. Learning varies depending on whether the herd is composed of suckling or milking animals. However, from the herder's perspective, three successive types of learning are necessary for all young:

1. Food plant recognition: Young animals select foods by imitating their mothers.[16] In order for this to work effectively on range, however, mothers and their young must be led to places that allow the young to recognize the entire range of plants eaten by adults. This must be done from the first few months of age. For young animals no longer with their mother, it is important to learn to associate the area outside the shed with foraging rather than play. When the young are between two and six months of age, depending on the farm, fresh forage (grasses or shrubs) can be distributed in troughs on top of average-quality hay. The animals understand that "whatever's in the trough is supposed to be edible." After one or two days, these plants are preferred over hay.

2. Recognition of the herder's authority: When young animals are not following their mothers around and where fresh grass is already recognized as food, the group of young is turned out onto pastures, either on its own or under the watchful eye of the herder and his dog. The group should become easy to manage after three or four of these short outings. If the young do not already recognize fresh grass as a food, it may take ten or more outings for them to become manageable, which is quite burdensome for the herder.

3. Going out for grazing as a part of the herd: The herder designs a few mini–grazing circuits for the herd to train the young, whether or not they have maintained contact with their mothers. These mini–grazing circuits, or "training sectors," must include miniature versions of the types of places the herd will encounter later on, with the exception of rocky ridges and scree. The rate of success is higher when non-food related travel is limited, and when hungry adults are placed in front of palatable vegetation.

Adult Training

From herders' experience, training adult sheep involves three successive steps:

1. Upon the arrival of transhumant sheep, the herder places them for two or three consecutive days within a rather small fenced pasture (about one hectare) with already known and palatable grasses. This is helpful to make distant observations about how the sheep behave

in the new environment and also to let them meet with the dogs. As the herders say, "This is to check their initial state of mind."

2. The herder mixes naïve and experienced sheep, then herds the whole group within a specific grazing sector, mostly made of grass but surrounded by mixed vegetation patches with still unknown edible forages for the naïve sheep. Once they are partly satiated with grass, the naïve sheep see the already experienced ones grazing and browsing the other forages, and they grow curious to smell and taste them. As the herders say, "We put them in a kind of schooling place, to learn them that the young grass is not the only valuable fodder."

3. Progressively, the herder leads the sheep on larger daily grazing circuits with longer phases on familiar forages, sequenced with shorter ones on patches with novel forages. The learning is better if the naïve sheep have reached a state of partial satiation with known grass and if they can be directly inspired by, and going to imitate, the feeding diversification made by the experienced sheep. This step takes place at the temporal scale of weeks, but it has to be partly redone every year. With lambs, kids, or sub-adult females, the procedure is about the same. It is highly accelerated in suckling animals, due to the imitation behavior favored by the youngest for its mother and/or some other inspiring adults.

This diet-training management aims at minimizing unknowns: "We can anticipate the herd's behavior," as the herders say. At the same time, it helps improve the herd's ability to predict and interpret the herder's actions, assuming, of course, that the herder and his dog adopt unambiguous behaviors that are easily interpreted. The herders explain that "Through the process, the herd gets to know us really well."

Adjust the Herd's Feeding Expectations
To Help It Memorize Designated Areas

In France, as elsewhere, one of the major concerns of livestock farmers and herders is keeping the herd from overstepping its boundaries, including neighboring parcels of land, the mountain pasture allotted to another herder, and protected forestland. Herders on high mountain range often complain about colleagues whose herds "don't know their limits" and graze other herds' areas of fresh grass, or even mix with other herds, which can be a serious health concern.

Newly established farmers or freshly recruited herders therefore benefit greatly when informed by their predecessors or neighbors of the boundaries that must be observed to avoid conflict. Nowadays, it is possible to use not only stones and trees to mark boundaries but also aerial photographs available on the internet. However, these are useless in wooded areas covered in tall shrubs, where even hunters tend to lose their way.

Herders whose designated areas are not strictly delimited by impassable obstacles, such as cliffs, rivers, and fences, do not enjoy acting as a "movable fence" for the herd. As they say, "I don't want to play the sheriff." They much prefer to be a "guide" who relies on positive rather than negative reinforcement to enforce boundaries. That is why they use herding dogs to explicitly mark the boundaries. They also condition the herd to observe the boundaries automatically based on its excellent spatial memory. This is part of specific training carried out the first time an area of land is used, and also at the beginning of each season, "in order to refresh the herd's memory." This is essential for animals "who are not yet familiar with grazing areas," and even more so for those who are young and inexperienced.

"Enforcing boundaries" consists of allowing the herd to move spontaneously toward a given boundary and then firmly preventing them from crossing it. For the first few days, the herder places himself alongside the herd, not far from the boundary, where he remains visible and audible. When the leading animals approach the boundary, the herder shouts a specific command (e.g., "Hooo!" — the animals have learned already that cry means that the herder disagrees) and uses his dog to clearly mark the boundary based on where the dog runs and the dog's attitude. All of this serves to turn the herd around. In the days following, the herder simply has the dog sit calmly and quietly along the boundary. If the herd attempts to cross the boundary again, the herder may cry out as on the first day, but this time, he remains behind the herd. Afterwards, and throughout the season, the herd "turns itself around" once the leading group of sheep reaches the boundary. When herding goats, or when the resources lying on the other side of the boundary are considerably more palatable than within the boundary, the herder and dog must pay close attention to the herd.

This teaching takes full advantage of the herbivores' excellent spatial memory. By experience with different origins of herds and grazing places, herders state they can rely on the persistence of that memory for about two or three consecutive years. That's why they ask breeders to entrust them each year with a majority of already experienced animals:

"It's much easier for me to work, as most of the herd already respects the boundaries of the grazing place!"

To Adjust Animals' "Temporary Palatability Scoring"

"They're so selective," "They're always looking for something that's no longer there," "There are times when they won't touch it, but now they get into it straightaway." Most herders are extremely curious by nature and attentive to their herd's food choices. Some have even created their own herbarium. All herders agree that grazing areas, rather than individual plants, increase or decrease a herd's appetite. Thus, herders must distinguish different areas, which are more or less appreciated "depending on the range of choices available to the animals at a given period of the season." These areas are also more or less attractive to the herd depending on what the animals have eaten just before and what they "expect to find afterwards." This notion of "expectation" is related to the herders' interpretation of "contrary behavior," observed following visibly unproductive foraging. This kind of behavior can include a "questioning attitude," such as when animals prick up their ears, stare wide-eyed in the herder's direction, or bleat. Another form of this behavior is "sulking," when animals eat plants they normally ignore.

According to herders, animals develop a "temporary palatability scoring" as they judge, in a comparative way, whether the food supply in a certain area is satisfactory or not. Herders state that they can successfully modulate this palatability scoring by organizing sequenced access over several days to distinct series of grazing sectors that allow for minor foraging transitions. It is important, for instance, to prevent the herd from having a much better experience eating particular foods one day as they will spend most of the other days searching for those foods and fail to use all of the other forage resources that must be grazed. As one herder says, "It'll take several days to make them understand that there aren't any more [highly appreciated] acorns, which will be a huge waste of time for both the herd and me!"

There are two situations a herder tries to avoid, because they lower daily intake: 1) allowing the herd to consider a range of palatability scoring that is much too wide for what is actually available at that time and in that place, which results in a constantly frustrated herd, and 2) restricting the herd to a very narrow and overly predictable range of palatability scoring that can lead to "grazing weariness." Between these two extremes, the herder seeks to adjust the herd's temporary palatability scoring in three different ways:

1. Make schedules and daily foraging patterns predictable for the herd. For example, always begin a morning grazing circuit, or end the evening grazing circuit, with the most palatable foods to prevent the herd from looking for them the rest of the day. That way, the herder creates different types of temporary palatability scoring based on time of day.
2. Make the different types of areas grazed over a day or a half-day predictable for the herd. This helps the animals quickly understand the range of available resources and limits attempts to travel in search of more palatable food.
3. Carefully ration access to the "best spots" during each grazing circuit to reinforce the herd's reliance on and trust of the herder. Thus, as a herder says, "The herd is rapidly satisfied with the forages, as it knows that it is usually satisfied with my offer."

MENU: SEQUENCING FOODS TO STIMULATE INTAKE

For herders, a grazing circuit is a nearly uninterrupted time of foraging over several hours. It corresponds to a "meal" in animal nutrition science. It is designed to influence food choices and create synergetic effects on intake within time limits allowed. Herders are convinced of the effectiveness of identifying the right combinations of grazing sectors to be offered within a circuit. They focus on the advantages gained by diversifying sectors and fodder resources.

Designing and Leading a Grazing Circuit

The practice of herding may be seen as a system with three hierarchical levels[17] (Figure 3, see three boxes on the right):

1. The circuit plan is drawn based on information (see dotted arrow "i," top of Figure 3) the herder collects throughout the season (weeks and days prior to grazing) on the state of the various sectors to be grazed, depending on the abundance of resources and their relative palatabilities for the herd at that time.
2. Having chosen the grazing sectors for the day, the herder decides on (see "j") the route he will take from one sector to the next during a half-day circuit (evening or morning). This route follows an order he thinks will allow a meal to be eaten quite rapidly, even forages the herder predicts will be "the most difficult to make them eat," over several hours without many interruptions.
3. The herder guides the movements of the flock from time to time (see thick "k" arrow), either authoritatively with the help of his dog or by relying on the herd's trust in following the herder to prefer-

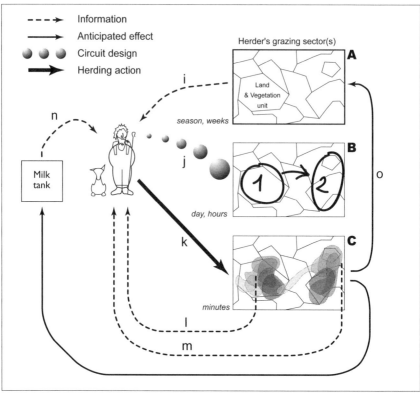

FIGURE 3: The practice of herding can be represented as a three-tier system (after Meuret, 1993). It is summarized here for the herder's responsibility to ensure proper feeding of the herd over a half-day meal and grazing circuit.

able sectors. The herder therefore manages the various phases of the meal according to the order established over time spans of minutes. To adjust the circuit, the herder uses two types of information. The first relates to the herd's reactions during the circuit (see dotted arrow "l"), which reveal its attitude and pattern of activity. The second is based on the herder's analysis at the end of the circuit (see dotted arrow "m"), when he assesses the degree to which the flock is satiated by looking for visibly full stomachs or observing when the flock begins to ruminate. With dairy animals, the herder can obtain the required information at a later point (see dotted arrow "n") by assessing the quantity of milk produced during the next milking session. The repeated use of the same sectors has a direct impact on the nature and local abundance of resources (see "o" arrow), which in turn prompts the herder to revise, or maintain, the grazing circuits he has planned for the next few days (see dotted arrow "i").

Locally Abundant Forage Does Not Imply Higher Intake

One can imagine that a clever herder simply identifies the best sectors within the grazing place, that is, the ones with abundant forage resources and uniform quality and palatability. This would allow the herd to graze without the herder moving it too frequently during the meal. This is not the case, however.

The main reason is obvious to herders: no herding territory has enough excellent foraging sectors for an entire season. Each territory has some, but as our maps of relative abundance of forages show, these often represent only 5–10 percent of total surface area. Herders refer to these rare sectors as "intern sectors" or "weekend breather sectors." Another reason is that herders must optimize management of the herd's motivation given the resources available over the entire herding territory. The preferred use of "top-quality" foraging sectors is sometimes risky, as it can adversely affect the herd's temporary palatability scoring (see previous explanation). Herders are convinced it is more effective to identify the right combinations of grazing sectors within a circuit. From the beginning, they focus on the advantages gained by diversifying grazing sectors and mixing forage resources.

We attempted to test this rule by monitoring intake spatially with forty dairy goats herded in the summer on 270 acres of woodland range. We mapped 605 uniform and contiguous vegetation patches and classified them according to five qualitative variables meaningful to the goatherder. These were then organized into various classes (n), based on type and structure of vegetation (7), penetrability for the herd (4), extent to which the area was scrub growth (4), abundance of edible and accessible forage (4), and rate of previous consumption (4).[18]

After mapping and assessing ten successive grazing circuits for a total of nearly thirty hours of intake, we attempted to identify relationships between grams of dry matter intake per minute and each of the characteristics of the vegetation patch grazed during the minute of the circuit being considered. We concluded that, when considered individually, the variables had no statistically significant effect on intake rate, including the local abundance variable.[19] The goats did not eat more when there was more forage available. We then assessed phases of rapidly increasing intake rates during a meal.[20] In so doing, we were able to demonstrate that these acceleration phases occur mainly when the herd moves from one vegetation patch to another, whether such a change is led by the goatherder (42 percent of the occurrences), spontaneously by individual goats (17 percent), or the herd as a whole (10 percent). These findings backed the herders' empirical rule, according to which overall feeding value is

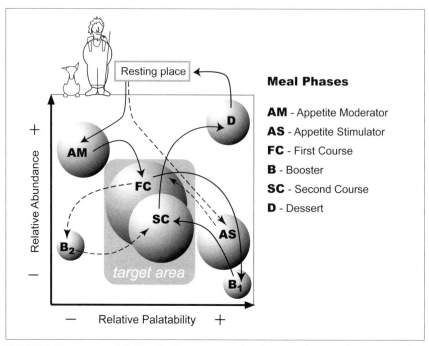

Meal Phases

AM - Appetite Moderator
AS - Appetite Stimulator
FC - First Course
B - Booster
SC - Second Course
D - Dessert

FIGURE 4: The MENU model offers herders a way to plan their schedule in order to successfully stimulate the herd's appetite in a "target area" (center) that would be insufficiently palatable for the herd without the herder's intervention. The herder draws on the grazing place's diversity by designing half-day grazing circuits with effective sequencing of very different grazing sectors (meal phases) for the herd, in terms of palatability and relative abundance of resources (after Meuret, 1993).

not produced so much from good local feeding values as from the right sequencing of various grazing sectors in a grazing circuit.

MENU Model
Challenges Addressed by the Model

Developed as a joint effort with ten experienced herders, MENU (Figure 4) aims to assist herders in designing half-day grazing circuits. Each circuit cover a series of grazing sectors with varying forage resources and which are assessed according to their relative abundance and palatability. Relative abundance (y-axis) is easy to evaluate even for an inexperienced herder. It consists of vegetation that is edible at that season (the same herd has eaten it, here or elsewhere) and accessible (growing less than five feet from the ground). Areas of undergrowth may not include any such vegetation after several seasons of repeated grazing. Relative palatability (x-axis) is a bit more difficult to assess. It requires prior observation of the herd, in similar grazing areas, during the same season. Inexperienced but curious herders nevertheless manage this type of assessment effectively. They simply need to distinguish: 1) toward the right of the x-axis, the sectors the herd would rush towards (e.g., leguminous shrubs in flower or fruit), and 2) toward the left of the x-axis, the sectors the herd would, if left on its own, ignore completely (e.g., strips of very mature, coarse grass).

The challenge is to motivate intake in one or two "target sector(s)" chosen based on an annual grazing schedule, with some forages needing to be eaten during a given season. It can also be part of a commitment to better control vegetation dynamics through grazing, for instance a scrub clearing or mature grass to limit the risk of avalanche in high mountain areas. The space located in the middle of the model diagram is only moderately attractive to a foraging herd. If the herd were restricted to such a sector for an entire meal, using a small fenced pasture, for instance, it would eat insufficiently and might attempt to escape in search of better food elsewhere.

Principles for Creating Synergies between Meal Phases

Grazing sectors can play six standard roles in a circuit (see the six meal phases on the right legend block of Figure 4). At the beginning of a circuit, the herder focuses on two types of sectors; the choice depends on the herd's initial appetite, as estimated by the herder, when leaving the shed or a resting area. If the herd lacks appetite, which may occur for instance due to ineffective rumination of the previous meal or a sudden change in the weather, the herder may take the animals to an "appetite stimulator" sector (see bottom right of MENU model). This sector must contain highly palatable forages, although not necessarily in abundance. "You have to provide a variety of food choices," say herders. This variety is found either by taking the herd to a specific sector or by allowing it to wander around a large area: "You have to make them want to look around." Conversely, if the herd shows signs of excitement or other behavior that leads the herder to believe it is very hungry, he can take the flock to a sector referred to as an "appetite moderator," which helps to "stabilize the herd." There must be an abundance of forages in this case, but palatability has to be very low (see top left of MENU model).

When the herder considers that the rate of foraging has stabilized, he takes the herd to its "first course" on the target area (center of model). Palatability and abundance in the target area serve as a reference for the entire model—all of the other sectors are evaluated relative to this one.

The first course can also be the first stop in a grazing circuit, if the herd's appetite does not need to be either stimulated or moderated from the outset. Ideally, the herd should eat most of its meal without significantly reducing its foraging activity; this makes the herder's job simpler. In reality, the herd's foraging activity often slows rapidly after about an hour of eating the first course. The animals have "been there, done that," say herders, and get bored with the average quality of resources available.

Herders then use the main trick modeled in MENU: a "booster" sector to renew the herd's appetite. There are five types of booster techniques: 1) allow the herd a few dozen minutes in a highly palatable sector (B_1, see bottom right of MENU model) that is often considered the herd's favorite local grazing spot. Examples of this are diversified hedges or small valleys where plant phenology is delayed and fine grasses grow between the rocks; 2) lead the herd to a much less palatable sector (B_2, see bottom left of MENU model). Here "you have to make the herd understand that the resources from the target area are not that bad, comparatively speaking." Examples are strips of dry grass, stretches of thorny shrubs, and undergrowth with just a bit of inedible moss or ferns; 3) regroup the herd authoritatively and travel along a track to "give the animals a change of scenery"; 4) water the herd, if a watering point exists; and 5) distribute salt. With regard to techniques 4 and 5, which are not included in the model, herders have observed that "it changes the taste of grass for them afterwards." The booster sector is strictly rationed, all the more if it is small, as it is critical for making abundant sectors more valuable via synergetic interactions. The booster phase is limited time-wise and must not be predictable because the herd will eat less of the first course.

After a successful booster phase, the herder can return the herd to the target sector to continue the meal with a "second course." This sector can be located next to that of the first course (see center of MENU model) and can therefore be similar in nature. Nonetheless, as the herd is reaching the end of the meal, it is important to offer it something slightly more palatable (see right side of model).

At this point the herder estimates the time the herd has spent eating and assesses satiety. If the herder considers that the herd is not yet satiated and that the remaining time will not allow him to carry out a new "course-booster-course" sequence, he can decide to use a "dessert" sector. The main thing here is to ensure rapid intake over a short time; that's why dessert sectors offer resources that are both highly palatable and highly abundant (see upper right of MENU model). It is of utmost importance that the herd not be able to anticipate the introduction of a dessert phase. This could generate disastrous effects by triggering a slowdown in activity during the prior meal phases in anticipation of dessert. The herder ensures the unpredictability of the dessert phase by making use of dessert sectors sporadically. In addition, when the herd is clearly expecting a des-

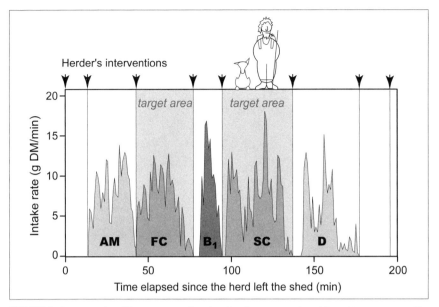

FIGURE 5: An example of how one goatherder structures a meal and its consequence on the intake rate of a control animal in a herd of dairy goats herded in an oak coppice in the summer. Using an effective sequence of sectors that assigned roles based on the MENU model, the goatherder can successfully stimulate intake, as demonstrated by significant accelerations of the instantaneous intake rate (after Meuret, 1993).

sert phase (foraging activity suddenly drops and most of the animals start regrouping, with some looking toward the herder and/or beginning to bleat), the herder stays put for the first few minutes, then begins to move as if he is heading toward another sector, and finally stops the herd while still within the second course sector. Some herders say, "It takes two weeks for them to understand that waiting for dessert is a waste of time."

What Impact on Intake?

Figure 5 illustrates an example of a circuit based on MENU, together with its impact on intake rate. The circuit was designed for a herd of forty dairy goats grazing in a downy oak coppice (*Quercus pubescens* Willd.) in summer. The intake rate was particularly high, increasing by more than 10 grams of dry matter per minute. The accelerations were frequently the result of the goatherder's actions (see arrow at the top of the graph), which prompted the herd to travel short distances in order to sequence, in this case, five meal phases: appetite moderator, first course in the target area, booster, second course in the target area, and dessert.

We also compared the daily intake dynamics of dairy goats in the summer, when herded in undergrowth or grazed on fenced natural meadow

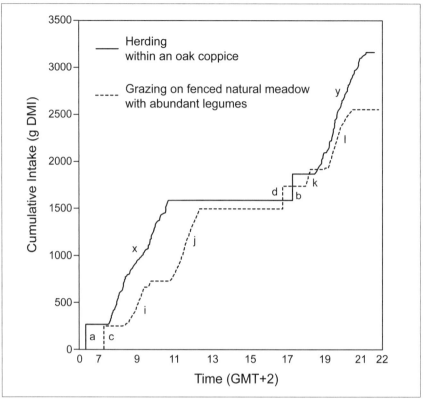

FIGURE 6: Comparative kinetics of total daily cumulative intake (expressed as grams of dry material ingested) for two goats grazing in the summer within their herds. One herd was tended in oak coppice while the other grazed in a fenced natural meadow with abundant legumes. The herding day includes four meals: two foraging meals (x and y) and two meals of supplementary feed (250 grams of barley: a and b). A day on fenced meadow includes six meals: 4 spontaneous foraging meals (i, j, k, and l) and two meals of supplementary feed (250 grams of barley: c, d) (after Meuret, 1993).

with abundant legumes. The example in Figure 6 shows the intake of two goats of the same Alpine chamoisée breed and of the same size. Both goats produced the same amount of milk (0.65 gallons/day) and received 500 grams of barley twice a day as supplementary feed. The first goat (solid line) belonged to a herd in downy oak coppice, while the other (dotted line) belonged to a herd on fenced natural meadow. The resources within the fenced pasture were "new" as it was the first day the pasture had been used that season.[21] Expressed as the cumulative intake of dry matter (DMI) over a day, intake was very high in both cases; however, it was still lower for the goat on fenced meadow than for the goat herded in coppice: 110 against 135 g DMI per kilogram of metabolic live weight ($LW^{0.75}$). When we corrected for digestibility of the dry organic matter ingested (DOMI), which is less in coppice, intake is nearly equivalent: 80 and 83 g DOMI/kg LW$^{0.75}$. The goatherder, who takes advantage of the full fourteen hours of daylight, organizes two meals at eleven-hour intervals around a long period of rest and rumination at midday. In doing so, he makes it possible for his goats to eat more to compensate for the lesser nutritional value of the coppice resources.[22]

Assigning Roles to the Various Parts of a Herder's Territory

MENU allows a herder to categorize all the herding sectors on the land allotted to him/her according to their potential roles in grazing circuits.[23] A given section of land is considered to be of good feeding value if the sectors included are effectively laid out relative to one other. For instance, the sectors likely to play the role of an Appetite Moderator or an Appetite Stimulator must be situated close to the herd's resting areas. Otherwise they are useless, and the value of the target-area courses is diminished. Likewise, booster sectors must be located close to first course and second course sectors, but with a layout that allows the herder to keep the herd from rushing unchecked to the booster sectors. Herders can use MENU to mentally visualize their territory and assign roles to each grazing sector. Figure 7 is an example of a goatherder's use of a summer grazing area covering some twenty-five acres, illustrated by him on a 1:1,500 base map at our request.

Importantly, MENU sectors may change roles during the season, depending on plant growth and phenology, as well as the herder's use of these sectors (see Figure 3, arrow "o"). For instance, if a first course or second course sector has been used heavily in the current season, and the herd's favorite foods have been grazed repeatedly, which in turn makes the sector much less palatable, the sector may play the role of an appetite moderator, as long as it maintains sufficiently abundant forage. Later, after repeated grazing, the sector may play a booster$_2$ role, as it is no longer sufficiently abundant or palatable. Similarly, an appetite stimulator sector may remain partly useful in a booster$_1$ role if it maintains some area rich in highly palatable forage. An area that played the role of a first or second course sector in the summer may, if it has not been overgrazed, be an appetite stimulator in early fall, once the fall regrowth and recently fallen fruit such as acorns and acacia seed pods have significantly improved palatability. Finally, an area generally used as a first course or second course sector may be used as a dessert sector if, after being left ungrazed for a few weeks, the phenology and particular dynamics of its vegetation provide the right qualities, for example a river bank.

FIGURE 7: An example of a map inspired by Menu for the location of useful sectors in circuits depending on the roles assigned to them. Here, a goatherder identified their location on a 1:1500 base map for one of his sectors covering about twenty-four acres located in a sparse coppice.

To appropriately assign roles, herders must remain particularly atten-tive in identifying and rationing appetite stimulator, booster$_1$ and dessert sectors. These are "rare" goods on the range, since the sectors with high-est palatability are, by definition, only palatable as compared to all the resources available to the herd. The herd is already familiar with those resources from its experience over the course of the current season as well as previous years, as it has an excellent memory.

MENU AS AN EDUCATIONAL TOOL
A Source of Inspiration for Case-By-Case Application

MENU is presented here in its most basic form. In the field, it must be adjusted for species and herd size, herding season and, of course, the state of mind and individual "herding style" of each herder. The model is therefore mainly a source of inspiration that should be adapted and developed on a case-by-case basis. For example, herders working on summer range at altitudes of more than 6,500 feet, or on the plains in the winter, have told us that it is crucial to include a preliminary "getting going" or "warm-up" phase when nights are cold and damp. In this case, the herder should look for a sector that receives the first rays of sunlight in the morning. That way, the herd will have greater initial appetite for the morning grazing circuit. Likewise, herders who work with large flocks of sheep know that "you can often get the herd to eat any old thing at the very end of the evening circuit." The sheep or goats, who are still hungry but "have forgotten all their references" because they are hurrying homeward, more or less accept "whatever they find at hand." Finally, herders reminded us of an ancient practice: boosting the herd's appetite during the circuit by cutting and distributing tree foliage. This sparks the anger of many forest managers around the world. However, in the south of France, where old oak coppices abound and are often left abandoned, "The herd comes running as soon as it hears the chainsaw."

A Training Tool for Interns or for Multiple Herders

MENU can be used to help inexperienced herders learn how to establish a relationship of mutual trust with a herd. The model is also useful for sheep farmers who tend their herds but who sometimes have another person take over the herding because they have many other activities. In this case, it is beneficial, as the herders say, to "pass the herd on to someone else with somewhat the same style of herding, so it doesn't get confused." MENU then becomes the basis for rules of conduct, which is especially useful for internships.

In addition to our activities with herding schools, we contributed to a real-life test carried out at the initiative of a dairy goatherder in charge of training two young interns. The objective was to test MENU's usefulness in teaching inexperienced interns to take over a herd from an experienced goatherder for half a day, without affecting the herd's milk production. The test period was three months in the summer, a season during which the stakes are high in terms of animal performance. The herder had to stabilize the production of a herd of forty goats at between twenty-one and twenty-three gallons of milk per day until August 20, when the first

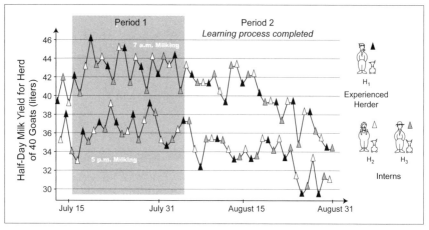

FIGURE 8: Milk production by a herd of forty dairy goats at the morning (7 a.m.) and evening milkings (5 p.m.), recorded during a test of the Menu model used as a training tool for two beginner herders. For forty-eight consecutive days in the summer, the herd was tended on a rotational basis by the regular, experienced goatherder (H_1), and his two interns (H_2 and H_3). After the milking, the one responsible for the herd for the previous half-day noted the quantity of milk obtained on this graph, initialed it, and posted it in the milking room.

goats came into heat. The test began with a presentation by the goatherder on the theory behind Menu. The inexperienced interns were then able to ask questions and tour the grazing land, covering about 198 acres. The herd did not accompany the herder and interns on this tour, nor did the herder specify the location of Menu sectors he normally used. After three days of familiarization between the interns and the herd, the interns were given forty-five consecutive days to herd the goats, rotating every half-day between the goatherder (H_1) and the two interns (H_2 and H_3). The herd's milk yield was recorded twice daily, at 7 a.m. and 5 p.m., and the resulting graph (see Figure 8) was posted in the milking area. In summer, body reserves of the goats are low and milk yield is then strongly correlated with the amount and quality of feeding during the previous twelve hours. This means that the skills of a herder during a grazing circuit can be assessed from the amount of milk produced at the next milking.

We analyzed milk production over forty-five days (for the statistical method, see Meuret and Dumont, 2000). During the initial twenty-one-day period (Period 1, Figure 8), the skill level of H_3 was significantly lower ($p<0.05$) than that of H_1, who herded the previous half-day, and of H_2, who herded on the following half-day. In contrast, over the same period, no significant differences ($p>0.05$) were observed between the skills of H_1 and H_2, who herded on the previous half-day. When we looked at the three herders' sketches on a 1:2,000 map, it appeared that during Period 1

H_2 managed to use the full sequence of MENU sectors, while H_3 failed to use either an appetite moderator or booster sector. During the last twenty-four days (Period 2, Figure 8), there were no significant differences ($p > 0.05$) between the skills of the three herders, as H_3 had completed the learning process and now used, if required on that day, the full sequence of MENU sectors.

CONCLUSION

For a herder working with MENU, the various grazing sectors visited in sequence during a circuit constitute the herd's "foods" to be incorporated judiciously twice a day into its diet. The surface area of these sectors depends on the size and gregariousness of the herd. The same land area may be carved into several sectors for a herd of forty goats or used as just one sector for a flock of a thousand sheep. These sectors frequently comprise a number of vegetation communities as well as the border areas between them, especially on landscapes composed of vegetation mosaics. Consequently, a scientist seeking to identify the various sectors and their functions must undertake an overall analysis of the territory allotted to the herder, using a scientific approach that is closer to landscape ecology than to forage crop agronomy.

None of the sectors included in a grazing circuit has any intrinsic value that might be predicted reliably using plant ecology inventories or biomass measures and plant nutritional values. It is therefore not relevant to qualify a sector's value strictly based on the plants within it, even though this continues to be done by pastoral consultants after becoming standard in seeded pastures. Maps of "grazing value" of herding territories produced in France and elsewhere are made up of juxtaposed polygons that have been delimited using aerial photographs or satellite signal analysis. Each polygon is assigned a value, which is generally expressed in units of "optimum stocking density," the recommended number of livestock animals per unit of surface area. In practice, however, the value of the sectors as used by a herder is relative and instantaneous in nature, a function of the sequence of sectors within the circuit and the likely synergetic effect on the herd's motivation to eat. The value of polygon A is determined by the consequent use of polygon B, in accordance with effective sequencing of the meal.

The feeding value of a herder's territory is directly dependent on the herd's motivation to eat more or less abundantly. It should therefore be considered as value created by the herder through on his effective organization. The key to this value is the schedule involved in the feeding process and the proper mixing of forages within the diet.

There are four interlinked temporal processes in a given herder-herd-resources interaction, all of them driven by the herder's practices: 1) teaching the animals to recognize all edible resources (years); 2) modulating the herd's "temporary palatability scoring" to enable it to appropriately anticipate resources likely to be available in a season (months, weeks); 3) planning the herd's order of access to the resources available in a circuit (hours); 4) enhancing overall feeding value by stimulating the herd's appetite based on the synergetic effects between meal phases (minutes).

Given the same territory, the same breed of livestock, and the same size herd, no two herders will achieve identical feeding values or succeed in having the herd eat with the same appetite. Success depends on the herders' ability to design and then adjust their circuits.

The MENU model was designed, with the help of professional goatherders and shepherds, as a means for learning how to observe a herd and how to feed it more effectively through herding. MENU is not a technical prescription, to be applied blindly with a view to standardizing or generalizing individual herding techniques. Its application is most useful for two groups of herders: a) inexperienced herders at the learning stage, and b) more experienced herders who face the challenge of getting their herd to eat coarser material (see "target area" in the middle of the model).

Over several years, we were invited to present MENU to herders involved in providing professional training to adults in herding schools (see chapter 12). The herders were not familiar with our research. The following paragraphs serve as our conclusion by providing reactions of herders after our presentations of the MENU principles. Following those presentations, we observed four types of reactions:

- One herder accused us of "stealing [their] know-how." He immediately received a strongly worded response from his colleagues, who stated that MENU legitimizes herding practices by describing the technical skills involved. It counterbalanced the now somewhat obsolete and folkloric image of the trade (see chapters 2 and 15).
- Some herders told us that "it was exactly how [they] worked," meaning "it was nothing new." They then added, "But you're saying with your own [scientist's] words some of the reasons for what we observe, you measure forage intake, and by doing that you confirm that we're doing things right, even if it's extra work."
- Some herders remained doubtful because MENU "means you have to stay on the herd's ass all day," and they did not want to adopt such a method.
- Many herders showed interest and asked questions, most of which we were unable to answer, given the wide range of local herding

conditions. They nearly always concluded with: "We'll try it!" For us researchers who appreciate hands-on training, that reaction was a success. It showed that MENU renewed interest in and desire to further develop professional skills.

ACKNOWLEDGMENTS

I cannot begin to thank all the herders who contributed to our surveys, observations, and experiments. Many of the same people went on to initiate and assist with the time-consuming development of MENU. Everyone enthusiastically offered their help, as if they had nothing else to do. I would like to extend particular thanks to: Nicole Amsaleg, Catherine Arnaud, Robert Arnaud, Marie-France Bénistant, Michelle Gascoin, Mick Gascoin, Clément Gaubert, Jean-Marie Gautier, Antoine Le Gal, André Leroy, Gérard Loup, Marie-Hélène Marino, Jean-Louis Meurot, Sophie Rosenberger, Francis Surnon, Julien Valade, Marie Vernerey, and Bruno Vidal.

I would also like to thank the interns who agreed to join me in this adventure, equipped with a tape recorder, a stopwatch, good walking shoes, and extraordinary motivation: Philippe Maître, Charles Ouedraogo, Olivier Poty, Caroline Viaux, and Jean-Jacques Waelput.

Finally, I would like to express sincere appreciation to my colleagues, including animal scientists, ecologists, biomathematicians, geographers, agronomists, and educationists, who agreed to support this "daring" research that spanned various disciplines: Claude Béranger, Chantal Blanc-Pamard, Claude Bruchou, Jean-Paul Chabert, Joël Chadoeuf, Jean-Pierre Deffontaines, Bernard Dravet, Philippe Faverdin, Bernard Hubert, Étienne Landais, Hubert Mazurek, Philippe Miellet, Gilbert Molénat, Pierre Morand-Fehr, Pierre-Louis Osty, Jean-Louis Peyraud, Fred Provenza, Daniel Sauvant, Pascal Thinon, and Bertrand Vissac.

NOTES

[1] Morand-Fehr and Sauvant, 1988.

[2] Meuret et al., 1985.

[3] Meuret, 1988.

[4] Agreil and Meuret, 2004; Agreil et al., 2006.

[5] Meuret, 1989; Meuret and Giger-Reverdin, 1990.

[6] Baumont, 1989.

[7] Meuret, 1989.

[8] Meuret and Landais, 1997.

[9] Provenza 2003.

[10] Provenza et al. 2003, Provenza and Villalba 2006.

[11] Maître, 1991; Viaux, 1992; Meuret, 1993.

[12] Meuret et al., 1985.

[13] Landais and Deffontaines, 1988.

[14] Yin, 2003; Kauffman, 1996.

[15] Landais and Deffontaines, 1988.

[16] Provenza, 2003.

[17] Meuret, 1993.

[18] Miellet and Meuret, 1993.

[19] Viaux, op. cit.

[20] Meuret et al., 1994.

[21] Ouedraogo, 1991.

[22] Meuret and Giger-Reverdin, 1990.

[23] Meuret, 1997.

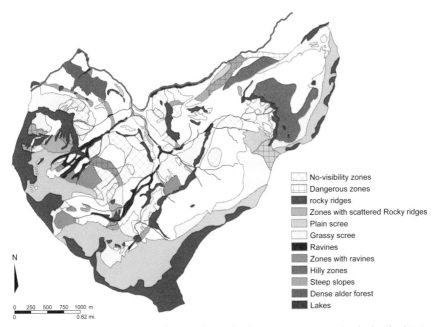

CHAPTER 4 - MAP 2: Obstacles and constraints to flock movement, as seen by the herder (Saut-du-Laire high mountain pasture).

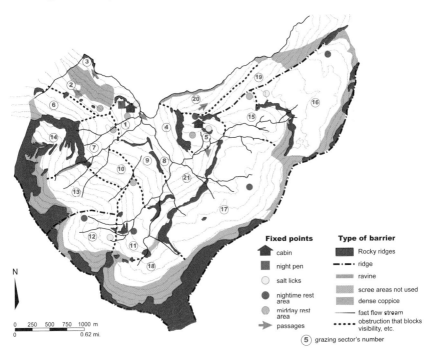

CHAPTER 4 - MAP 3: Division of the Saut-du-Laire pasture into sectors and location of fixed points.

213

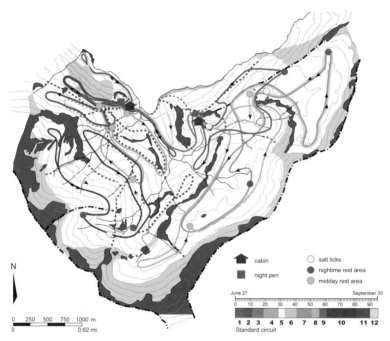

CHAPTER 4 - MAP 4: Outline of standard circuits in 1991 in the Saut-du-Laire pasture.

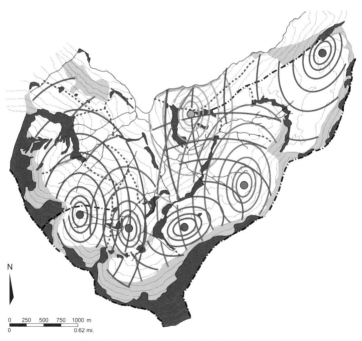

CHAPTER 4 - MAP 5: Night points of attraction in the Saut-du-Laire pasture and their area of influence.

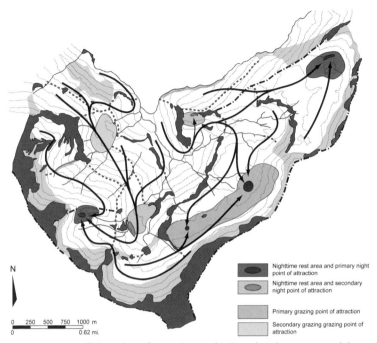

N

0 250 500 750 1000 m
0   0.62 mi.

Nighttime rest area and primary night point of attraction

Nighttime rest area and secondary night point of attraction

Primary grazing point of attraction

Secondary grazing grazing point of attraction

CHAPTER 4 - MAP 6: All the points of attraction on the Saut-du-Laire pasture and the preferred paths that reveal the flock's "direction" (biais).

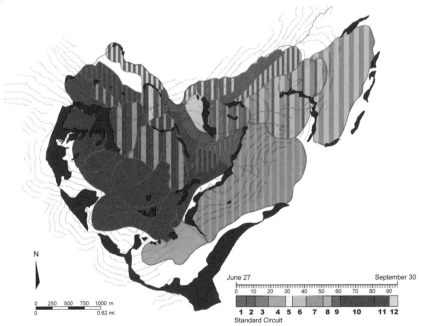

N

0 250 500 750 1000 m
0   0.62 mi.

June 27   September 30
0   10   20   30   40   50   60   70   80   90
1 2 3   4 5 6   7   8 9   10   11 12
Standard Circuit

CHAPTER 4 - MAP 7: Utilization schedule for the Saut-du-Laire pasture in 1991. The colors correspond to the standard circuits (see Map 4).

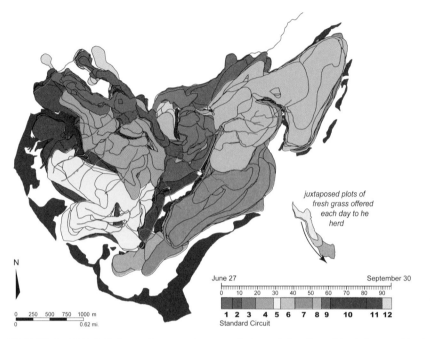

N

0   250   500   750   1000 m
0   0.62 mi.

juxtaposed plots of
fresh grass offered
each day to he
herd

June 27   September 30
0   10   20   30   40   50   60   70   80   90

1 2 3   4 5 6   7 8 9   10   11 12
Standard Circuit

CHAPTER 4 - MAP 8: Daily grazing extension: morphology of the plots of fresh forage visited day after day by the flock (1991 season, Saut-du-Laire pasture). The colors correspond to the standard circuits (see Map 4).

MICHEL MEURET / INRA

MICHEL MEURET / INRA

MICHEL MEURET / INRA

MICHEL MEURET / INRA

PIERRE CONSTANT

PATRICK FABRE

MICHEL MEURET / INRA

GUILLAUME CONSTANT

MARIE LABREVEUX

PIERRE CONSTANT

MICHEL MEURET / INRA

MICHEL MEURET / INRA

MICHEL MEURET / INRA

Shepherds and Nature Conservation

Grazing with Herders on Natural Area Conservancy Lands

Francis Muller & Michel Meuret

NATURAL area conservancies (NACs) are nongovernmental not-for-profit associations established throughout metropolitan France since the 1970s.* Within a region, or sometimes a department, their function is to contribute to the four tasks of making outstanding natural or seminatural areas: better known (e.g., wildlife species inventories, surveys and scientific studies); protected (e.g., multiple-use regulation with public information and nature area's rangers); managed (e.g., conservation and restoration activities), and promoted (e.g., national and international networking). They purchase or rent land or sign agreements with landowners, municipalities, or other parties. They also manage many national or regional nature reserves. Lastly, they often make their services available to municipalities and regional or departmental administrations to help them determine and apply public policies aimed at promoting biodiversity.

As associations, NACs do not have many members, 8,540 in 2013. Belonging to nature protection associations is less widespread in France than in other European countries such as the United Kingdom and Germany. The Bird Protection League, for example, which is the French branch of BirdLife International, has 43,000 members,[1] compared to several million for the United Kingdom's Royal Society for the Protection of Birds. The annual budget for NACs comes primarily from public grants provided

---

* For the sake of convenience, the generic abbreviation NAC will be used here to designate all conservancies that contributed to this study, regardless of the fact that in some cases they have slightly different names, depending on the department or region. The official names are given in the acknowledgments at the end of the chapter.

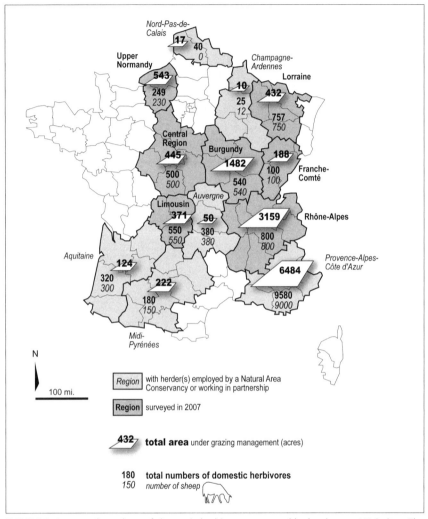

FIGURE 1: Areas and numbers of domestic herbivores managed by herders on NAC sites. The seven regions surveyed in 2007 in preparation for the present summary are identified.

by the European Union, the French government, and local and regional authorities. It currently totals €25 million.

In 1988 NACs formed a national federation mandated to represent them in dealing with governmental bodies such as the Ministry of the Environment, and to conduct nationwide operations. An example of such an operation is the European Union's LIFE* program and projects' funding, "France's relict dry swards" (1998–2001).

---

* The EU's financial instrument supporting environmental and nature conservation projects throughout the EU (see: http://ec.europa.eu/environment/life/index.htm).

As of 2014 there are twenty-nine NACs with a total of 724 employees, including approximately fifteen hired herders. NACs currently manage nearly 332,000 acres distributed over 2,498 sites, including 21,500 acres that they own outright. Most of the sites are open to the public, and over 700 sites feature information boards or signs, marked discovery trails, and the like.

The areas managed by NACs are mainly natural grasslands, seminatural dry swards, and scrublands, but they also manage wetlands (ponds, marshes, and bogs), forests, coastal dune ridge systems, and grottoes. For management decisions NAC teams rely primarily on their own resources and their scientific boards, but it is not unusual for them to establish relations with other bodies, such as national botanical conservancies, as well.

NACs currently manage 482 sites under agreements with 817 farmers and/or livestock producers. Figure 1 shows the thirteen regions where domestic herbivores are grazed on sites under NAC management. The total area of sites on which animals are grazed under the responsibility of one or more herders is currently 13,526 acres, with very wide regional disparities: under 25 acres in the Nord-Pas-de Calais and Champagne-Ardenne regions, compared to over 6,000 acres in the Provence-Alpes-Côte d'Azur region. These sites are grazed by 14,020 herbivores, of which nearly 95 percent are sheep. The remainder (not shown in Figure 1) are mainly goats, although there are some cattle and horses as well. For all thirteen regions, NACs own a fifth of the 13,312 sheep herded on their sites. However, the Provence-Alpes-Côte d'Azur region is exceptional in that the 9,000 sheep that graze NAC-managed sites in that region all belong to farmers, many of them users of rangeland in the Coussouls de Crau Nature Reserve (see chapter 6). If that region is omitted, NACs own nearly 60 percent of the sheep.

REASONS FOR HAVING A SITE GRAZED BY LIVESTOCK

Most NAC-managed sites are "open" and "seminatural" environments, environments that have been molded since their origins, centuries or millennia ago, by agro-pastoral practices (see chapter 1). Today, those practices have been abandoned or greatly reduced for decades, owing partly to the dwindling numbers of farmers and partly to the fact that nearly all the remaining farmers have fallen back on areas that are suitable for intensive agricultural practices such as maize cropping. Environments rated "difficult" or "disadvantaged" from an agricultural standpoint have consequently been subjected to spontaneous and sometimes rapid encroachment by brush and tree species. The mission of NACs is thus to attempt to bring these processes under control as effectively as possible to preserve habitat structures favorable to species that thrive in open or mosaic environments. Sometimes a site is so extensively overgrown when a NAC assumes management that it would be more appropriate to speak of active ecological restoration, as opposed to maintenance, of the environment (see Photo 1).

Mechanical Brush-Clearing Proves Unsatisfactory

The earliest site restoration operations involved mechanical brush-clearing methods rather than grazing. Heavy, power-driven shredders were brought in, or, where the terrain was too rocky or too steep, small portable brush saws were used. There were several reasons for this approach: (1) a machine can be rented by the day or week and stored in a garage when not in use, whereas a flock of sheep must be fed and herded every day; (2) mechanical equipment is readily obtainable, whereas purchasing a flock of sheep or negotiating the use of a flock of sheep with a farmer, are complex operations; (3) NACs had members who knew how to operate machines, but they generally did not have anyone accustomed to working with livestock or any skilled herders; (4) most scientific and technical reference works assert that domestic herbivores eat only herbaceous

MICHEL MEURET / INRA

PHOTO 1: An example of a seminatural dry sward that required restoration because it was overgrown with sloe, juniper, and pine at the time a NAC was about to assume management.

NICOLAS GREFF / RHÔNE-ALPES NATURAL AREA CONSERVANCY

PHOTO 2: A restoration operation featuring mechanical brush-clearing with heavy power-driven equipment is frequently devastating to the ecological quality of sites.

plants; (5) apart from a few goatkeepers, most farmers are not interested in allowing their livestock to be used to graze any pasture of unknown quality.

In a number of regions, then, NACs undertook many restoration operations featuring mechanical brush-clearing (see Photo 2), but it was soon apparent that this approach had three discouraging results. Firstly, heavy machinery works indiscriminately, and mechanical brush-clearing could have disastrous impacts on vegetation, wildlife, and the visual quality of the site. Secondly, the weight of heavy equipment can adversely affect soils and seed banks, even when fitted with low-pressure tires. Finally, brush shredding or cutting operations stimulate regrowth. A number of NACs learned to their chagrin that their site, which at first had appeared to be well cleared, quickly transformed into a sea of young brush species, some of them thorny, and all growing vigorously. The work had to be done over again at frequent intervals, and this led to a search for alternatives that were less costly and would not compact the soil or adversely affect plant and animal habitats—in a word, solutions that were more appropriate.

Whether on seminatural dry swards, scrublands, or wetlands, NACs came to realize that they should reintroduce practices, such as grazing, that had molded the sites in the first place. The next questions were what type of livestock to use and how grazing should be organized. In the early stages, there were two competing paradigms.

The "Free Grazer" Paradigm Encounters Difficulties

What we shall term the "free grazer" paradigm was initially very popular, especially following the publication of Thierry Lecomte's synthesis *Grazing as an Ecological Management Tool: Experience from Nature Reserves Network*, which was based on the thinking of naturalists at the National Museum of Natural History in Paris.[2] That paradigm began by postulating that contemporary domestic animals have practically lost their ability to live outdoors and sustain themselves from natural resources. Accordingly, it would be preferable to use semi-wild grazing animals similar to the breeds that existed before domestication (Highland cattle, Soay sheep, and the like). These animals were known to be "hardy," and thus could be turned loose into large fenced areas and left there all year round, with human intervention kept to a minimum; they would be given no dietary supplements, and they would receive no veterinary care. This initiative, which seemed attractive to anyone from the world of naturalists, was tried in various regions. But on NAC-managed sites, its limitations soon became apparent:

1. These sites are small, with areas of roughly one hundred to one thousand acres, not nearly enough to support groups of herbivores that must resort to seasonal mobility (migration) when local food resources became scarce.

2. The edible plants on the sites are frequently uneven in terms of palatability and accessibility (with areas heavily overgrown with brush, subject to flooding, and so on), and this encourages a flock or herd to remain in the most comfortable places, with the attendant risks of local overgrazing and parasite infestations, especially if the animals are left to graze year round in a single fenced area.

3. The use of these herbivores often fostered a negative perception of a NAC's action at the local level (most of the sites are open to the public). For rural people, it was not reasonable for livestock, even if they were closely akin to their wild cousins, to be left in a state of weakness or near death with no hope of assistance from a farmer responsible for them.

The "Herded Grazer" and the Arguments in Its Favor

In recent years, a number of NACs have preferred the "herded grazer" paradigm. This more pragmatic approach, comparable to the practices of the farmers who pasture their flocks or herds on rangeland in southern

France,[3] is designed to attain site preservation or restoration objectives and to ensure livestock kept on the site are adequately fed and in satisfactory body condition, regardless of whether they are owned by a NAC or by a farmer under an agreement with a NAC.

Drawing on the History of Local Practices

The history of local agricultural practices frequently serves as a guide to the selection of one approach to grazing rather than another. In the Upper Normandy region, for example, itinerant grazing by flocks of sheep was traditional on the dry swards of the hillsides along the Seine river until the early twentieth century. Once that practice was abandoned, the swards became degraded through colonization of native grasses and shrubs with a high capacity to dominate the swards. The decision to reintroduce grazing was reached after careful consideration backed by scientific research and in the light of the experience of NACs in some of the other regions. NACs adopted itinerant grazing by sheep in 1995, but the flock of 220 animals is not managed in the traditional way: there is less emphasis on the use of herding and more on movable electrified fencing. This technique enabled the NAC to apply heavy grazing pressure locally and for short periods at appropriate seasons to keep grasses and shrubs under control.

A willingness to innovate has also been apparent on occasion. In 2001, for example, transhumance drives with flocks of sheep were introduced along the banks of the Loire River, in the Central region, where they had never been known before (see Photo 3). This novel practice unexpectedly enabled effective communication between riparian owners and other users of the land, especially helping people understand the objectives of conservation-oriented management. Transhumance has also been reintroduced in the department of Moselle (northeastern France).

When Experience in Practice is Backed by Scientific Research

Early in the first decade of the twenty-first century, the NAC Federation published a number of reports on conservation-oriented site management.[4] These reports contained some empirical findings: (1) domestic herbivores seemed to be useful in reducing the dominance of brush species, provided the plant dynamics of the site had not previously been disrupted by mechanical brush-clearing; (2) in contrast to power-driven brush shredders, grazing did not produce instant homogenization of the environment, and thanks to the selective feeding behavior of livestock, species and habitats became progressively more diversified year after year, a highly satisfactory outcome. But how were these findings to be supported by evidence when an overwhelming majority of scientific and

PHOTO 3: Transhumance on the banks of the Loire, organized by the NAC. This practice, formerly unknown in the region but now very popular, facilitates the task of informing riparian owners and other users about the reasons why sheep grazing along the banks of the river has been reintroduced.

technical references asserted flatly that domestic herbivores ate nothing but grass?

Consequently, the NAC Federation welcomed new scientific knowledge suggesting ways in which "direct" grazing (i.e., without prior mechanical brush-clearing) could be used to advantage in heavily overgrown environments.[5] A number of INRA research projects conducted in situ on livestock operations had concluded that herds of sheep, goats, or cattle of ordinary breeds could thrive on a mixed diet of grasses and brush species. This outcome, however, was subject to two main provisos (see also chapter 8): the animals must have been accustomed to grazing environments of that kind early in life, and they must have access to a variety of plant communities every day, including edible plants that can be eaten in large bites, thereby enabling the animals to eat more rapidly.[6] Furthermore, most brush species proved to possess nutritive value comparable to or greater than that of grasses.[7] Thus on NAC sites it is advantageous to aim at conserving or reconstituting "dietary biodiversity" consisting of edible grasses and brush species. Mechanical brush-clearing should be used, sparingly, as a means of creating gaps in exceptionally dense or thorny thickets to facilitate access by livestock.

Herding: A "New Occupation" that Should be Encouraged?

Some NACs regard herding activities as a "new occupation" that should be encouraged. Considering that herding is an occupation that belongs to the era of herbivores' domestication, this may seem ironic, but it is understandable in light of the fact that many NACs are located in northern and central France (see Figure 1), where agriculture has become highly artificial and industrialized. Pastoral husbandry with herders has been out of vogue there for the past seventy to a hundred years. The remaining flocks of sheep consist of very prolific breeds and thus are very demanding: they are fed indoors and on cultivated grasslands. All the "herder" has to do is turn them out to graze the top-quality grass; monitor their state of health; provide them with water, salt, and concentrates; and, above all, check the condition of the fences. Consequently, in the Limousin and Burgundy regions, for example, the idea of hiring herders to graze sheep on natural environments appeared eccentric, or at best marginal, as recently as twenty years ago. This made it difficult to find young herders locally, as few were prepared to embark on such an adventure. More recently, however, possibly as a result of recurrent droughts, which have caused concern and financial loss for farmers using cultivated grasslands exclusively, the resources of natural swards, scrublands and underwood have begun to attract more attention. The idea of reverting to grazing natural environments is gaining ground, even in regions where it has been in disuse for decades.

Other Reasons

There are many other reasons for a NAC to turn to grazing for site management, but we shall not list them all here. Sometimes a NAC adopts a grazing initiative originated by local elected officials or farmers, as, for example, along the banks of the Loire River, where the Central Region NAC has provided guidance and support for a project initially designed by the Association pour le Pastoralisme dans le Loiret. In contrast, the initiative may originate from personal awareness on the part of a NAC's board of directors. These individuals may have been persuaded of the relevance of grazing management from thematic visits organized in France or in other countries, or they may have had a favorable personal experience they hope to reproduce in the context of the NAC's activities. Grazing thus ceases to be merely a management method and becomes an objective in its own right, alongside other site conservation goals.

CHARACTERISTICS OF SITES UNDER HERDING MANAGEMENT
Shared Characteristics
Plant Community Mosaics with Varied Growth Dynamics

Most sites managed with the assistance of a herder are former agricultural lands that have not been used for livestock grazing for some time. They consist of seminatural swards and scrublands as well as wet meadows, some of them subject to flooding; alluvial meadows; or in some cases meadows located on the immediate periphery of a bog.

Before the reintroduction of grazing, most of these sites were characterized by plant community mosaics and overgrown with brush to varying degrees: isolated bushes on sward, more or less continuous and contiguous thickets, scrublands in various stages of closure, forest fringes, or groves of trees. Depending on the nature of the soils, the microclimate, and the capacity of certain plant species to dominate, domination by shrubs may be slow (ten to fifteen years to a stage deemed harmful to species habitats on a scrubland with skeletal soil, e.g., boxwood or juniper) or rapid (two to four years on former cultivated land with deep soil, e.g., bramble, broom). As most of the sites also include some plots cultivated for centuries, during which time the soil was cleared of stones by hand and its tilth improved, markedly different growth dynamics are frequently observable over distances of no more than thirty to forty feet.

Small Sites, Fragmented Ownership

Most NAC sites suffer from two major constraints: small size (some of them consist of no more than a few acres), and, even more important, a severely fragmented land ownership pattern. A number of NACs must manage what amount to "strings" of areas, most of them localized, relegated to the fringes of the land currently occupied by field crops, cultivated grasslands, production forests, and urbanization (see Photo 4 for an example). For a livestock farmer to use one of these sites profitably for grazing (i.e., stock it with an adequate number of animals), and a herder to organize his activities to make good use of the site's pasture resources season by season, it must be at least 250 acres, according to the herder employed by the Lorraine NAC. Even when the entire area is available, the herder must sometimes spend more time on roads than anywhere else to enable the animals to graze, in sequence, a number of widely separated stretches of land. In such cases, the use of a herder is not worthwhile; the solution then is for the NAC to manage small numbers of its own animals distributed over the various stretches of land and kept inside fenced areas throughout the year.

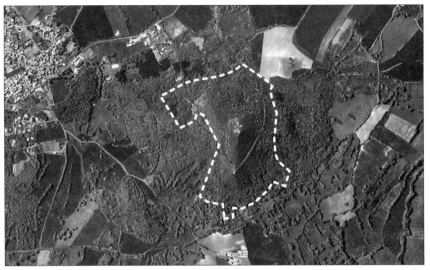

PHOTO 4: Aerial view of the Puy d'Ysson Natura 2000 site in the Auvergne region (perimeter shown by dotted line), a typical example of a small area managed by a NAC, with pasture surrounded by cultivated woodlands, cereal crops and urban development (after Golé S., 2002 - photo: IFN 1999 Puy-de-Dôme Infrared Color coverage).

Selecting the Appropriate Type of Herbivores

In theory, the selection of an appropriate type of herbivore should be made on a case-by-case basis, having regard to the condition of the site and the available information on the comparative abilities of different species and breeds. Goats are desirable for heavily overgrown sites, while cattle, horses or donkeys are best for a site covered with coarse grasses. Lighter animals are preferred for rugged sites with steep slopes, rocks, or fragile soils. It is advisable to graze different species of livestock, simultaneously or in succession, for the sake of complementarity in the animals' dietary choices and grazing impacts.

As a rule, sheep have been more commonly reintroduced (see Figure 1), being sometimes grazed together, or in succession, with goats, horses or cattle. Reasons to favor sheep are: lower initial purchase and maintenance costs of the flock; greater convenience in handling and transport; less concern about the effectiveness of fences than with goats; and ease of finding sheep farmers who are interested, as most cattle farmers are reluctant to try the unconventional grazing offered by NACs.

The use of complementary livestock species is an option fraught with difficulties. Firstly, most French livestock farmers, in contrast to their counterparts in other European countries (Ireland and Scotland in particular), specialize in a single species. There are exceptions, including farmers in France's Basque country, but that is the rule. They are unwilling to see their stock turned out to graze with animals from other operations, primarily for sanitary reasons. Secondly, many a herder who is accustomed to tending a flock of sheep is not eager to be given goats to look after as well. The same applies, to a lesser extent, to heifers or steers. Donkeys or horses are a different matter, as they have traditionally accompanied flocks of sheep, especially in regions where transhumance is practiced.

With regard to breeds, a number of NACs have been guided by efforts to save endangered or rare breeds disappearing in France due to widespread preference for a few "improved" breeds that lend themselves to intensive production. It is a form of biodiversity, domestic animal biodiversity, with genetic, behavioral, and even cultural characteristics worth preserving. In Upper Normandy, for example, the herder chose to replace the NAC's Mergelland sheep, which are native to the Netherlands, with hardier Solognot sheep, a breed originally from a forested wetland south of Paris known as the Sologne. Solognots are good at browsing on heavily overgrown land and can mobilize their body reserves effectively during periods when forage is scarce.

In regard to flock performance, most NACs told us they consider this a secondary issue. Only a few of them, such as the Rhône-Alpes and Limousin NACs, seek to reduce their site management costs by earning income from lamb sales. While of secondary importance, flock reproduction is not left to chance. All NACs want to cull and replace old sheep and ensure that the flock grows larger every year. Thus they have to make sure that lambing takes place at a time of year when site conditions are suitable to support ewes and their young. No NAC is interested in following the costly practice of raising lambs in special barns on purchased feed.

When the flock is owned by the NAC, the main idea is always to give natural reproduction cycles free play. But this is sometimes incompatible with the objective of site restoration by means of grazing. For example, if the adult ewes are bred in September or October, the lambs will be born in February or March, when weather conditions are sometimes still undesirably harsh. Moreover, under those conditions grazing on heavily overgrown sites cannot begin in April, because the lambs are still very young and their dams are busy suckling them. Compromise solutions have to be devised on a case-by-case basis. The expertise of local farmers and experienced herders is invaluable here, as no NAC is interested in using a flock of castrated males as non-reproductive "ecological mowers."

The Search for More Satisfactory Grazing Schedules

Site grazing schedules are rudimentary in many cases. Greatest emphasis is placed on times of year when most of the site's resources are attractive for the flock, including grasses and shrub species that could become exceedingly dominant. NACs have become accustomed to leaving a flock or herd inside a large fenced area for fairly long periods (see the previous "free grazer" paradigm). To this day, for example, the Limousin region NAC keeps its livestock grazing the same fenced area for six or seven months at a stretch, whereas the regional farmers prefer shorter periods of no more than one or two months. This practice of protracted grazing cycles has attracted criticism from a number of herders, including outside hired herders and herders who are NAC members. Long grazing cycles cause the animals to lose interest in forage resources and entail health hazards. A number of proposals for more diversified grazing schedules have been put forward. In Lorraine in particular, the NAC herder has suggested a plan whereby for every site, depending on the time of year and weather conditions, there should be periods when the sheep are managed by herders and other periods when the sheep graze the same areas but are confined by mobile electrified fencing, which could be adjusted depending on the state of the site's forage resources and the sheep's dietary requirements.

Who Will Be the Herder?

When a NAC decides to work with a herder, it must first choose whether to hire and pay one itself (this is known as the "force account" approach) or whether to make use of the services of an established farmer-herder nearby (the "contractual" approach). We shall discuss the administrative and legal advantages and disadvantages of each of these formulas later. The current trend is to look for a farmer-herder who can be engaged under contract. In that case, either the farmer himself serves as the herder, the herder is a person already employed and paid by the farmer, or the farmer hires and pays a herder expressly for purposes of the contract.

In most cases when the NAC owns the site but the herder is not one of its employees, the land is made available free of charge for the farmer-herder. This is also the case when the land is owned by a municipality. If a grazing fee is charged by the NAC to the farmer-herder, it is only small, so the use of grazing for site management remains an attractive proposition. In Burgundy, for example, the NAC is not the landowner, but it must manage a number of dry swards on calcarous hillsides and a number of alluvial prairies located dozens of miles away. Accordingly, it has concluded two contracts, one with the municipalities that own most of the land in question and another with a farmer-herder.

Herders are employed under other arrangements as well. In the Villé-cloye NAC in Lorraine the herder has become a municipal employee who works within the framework of an agreement between the municipality and the NAC. At Champlitte, in the Franche-Comté region, none of the local farmers was interested in working on the site, and the NAC had no wish to have a flock of sheep to look after. NAC decided to help a young person to get started as a sheep farmer-herder by providing him with sufficient amount of NAC's land to be grazed. NAC also helped this person to get a foothold in his chosen occupation by recruiting him for some months as a hired herder. In Burgundy, in contrast, a farmer-herder seeking to launch his own operation in the region was readily located. The NAC was able to help him administratively and economically by placing one thousand acres of natural swards at his disposal.

The Issue of Fences

Although herding flocks is favored over fencing them, fences also represent a potential concern and a substantial financial cost. Temporary fences are used to confine the flock at night. The herder has to move these fences frequently to ensure that dung does not accumulate to the point of degrading the site from organic matter overloading. Permanent fences are not acceptable to private landowners in some cases, nor do hunters like them. On sites managed under agreements, NACs have found that permanent fences, however unobtrusive, are regarded by other users as evidence of creeping privatization. Temporary fences are not viewed quite so unfavorably, and with a herder tending the flock, the issue of land monopolizing by NACs does not arise (see chapter 15).

Distinctive Aspects of Some Sites

Some of the sites grazed at the initiative of a NAC are quite unusual. One example is the site that lies within the La Valbonne military camp in the Ain plain east of the city of Lyons (see chapter 10). This contiguous area of nearly 3,340 acres is managed by the Rhône-Alpes NAC, which purchased a flock of four hundred sheep and then hired a herder. The site is surrounded by fields of corn and wheat, villages, roads, highways, and industrial plants. It consists of seminatural dry swards, including 1,000 acres overgrown with brush, and also contains 250 acres of deciduous forest. The herder must allow for the weekly schedule of military exercises, complete with gunfire. He currently herds the flock in a series of large, temporary fenced areas, each of which is used for fifteen to twenty-five days in succession. All these areas in the aggregate represent no more than a quarter of the total grazable land. The herder reports that the sheep like the brush species, but he is afraid that this resource may become depleted within a few years. One alternative is to diversify the current system of grazing within fenced areas by adding herding circuits combining grasslands, overgrown former fields, and underwood areas. These additions should make better use of the site's resource diversity, something not accessible inside fenced areas, which herders sometimes regard as excessively monotonous, however extensive they may be.

There is an equally distinctive site in the Central region beside the Loire (France's longest river: 630 miles). It consists of three thousand grazable acres stretching for ninety miles along the river, including some sandbanks. The land is extensively overgrown, a situation that calls for heavy but short-lived grazing pressure over the entire area. Despite various constraints, three hired herders undertook the task, each with a flock of two hundred to three hundred sheep. Management of the area is subject to the regulations governing public riparian lands, which prohibit permanent fences. The river often floods unexpectedly, inundating the banks and adjoining areas. These areas are frequented by numerous other users: fishermen, amateur ornithologists, hikers, ATV drivers, and picnickers. The three herders are managing to juggle all these constraints. Thanks to targeted brush-control efforts, they are helping to restore prairies and seminatural swards and to enhance the flow regime of the Loire.

GRAZING SPECIFICATIONS

NAC prepares a document of specifications for each site for herders to use as a reference. These specifications should be clear and accessible, but this is not always the case, as they may be a compromise among divergent and conflicting opinions held by members of the drafting committee or their scientific advisers. Frequently a number of items in the specifications are strictly enforced, such as a prohibition on parasite control measures harmful to soil organisms, or a requirement that such measures may be applied only to a limited extent late in the year. Sometimes the herder is asked to contribute to drafting specifications, especially regarding his views on how the site should be zoned into (a) areas that can be grazed in their current condition, and (b) areas that require preparatory work: facilities, localized brush-clearing, and identification of no-grazing areas to ensure that flocks are kept away from areas of significant biological value. This issue of appropriate zoning, which depends mostly on the herder and his previous experience, can create conflict between the herder and the NAC when the NAC wants all zones to be grazed, even those that are heavily overgrown or not readily accessible to the flock.

Specifications may be discouraging for a herder for two reasons: (1) they provide little information about appropriate grazing management, having been drafted mainly by persons not qualified to judge the matter; and (2) the list of constraints is frequently long and detailed. To illustrate: the herder must use existing sheds, however primitive; permanent fences may not be erected on specified plots of land; the sheep may not graze during the hunting season; and guard dogs are to be used for protection against stray dogs and thieves. The herder may also be asked to keep a "grazing record" stating the number of sheep put out to graze and the dates and areas used. This provides data for a subsequent NAC field survey on the impact of grazing.

The grazing record is not always perceived as a limitation by the herder. It provides him with hard evidence for what can be done with a flock of sheep and his pastoral management decisions when reporting to persons who know little about sheep or herding. In Lorraine, for example, the herder kept notes on various observations concerning the sheep and the vegetation, and he also prepared a map of "grazing pressure" (see chapter 4). This evidence is highly useful for a herder, as NACs, or at any rate their scientific advisers, sometimes desire "tightly focused" grazing impact: preservation of a particular rare plant here or a particular insect there, elimination of one particular shrub species but protection of another, and the like. As a practical matter, highly selective outcomes of this kind cannot be achieved by means of grazing; grazing is not gardening, after all.

THE SHEPHERDS

On a NAC site, a competent shepherd can meet objectives unattainable by grazing sheep in fenced areas. A herder's professional skill and personality are key to the enterprise: the conservation or restoration of the site will depend on his experience and management.

Where is a Qualified Herder to be Found?

It is not always a simple matter for a NAC, especially one in a region of plains, to find a herder with practical experience on rangeland who is prepared to work on small, scattered areas of pasture and knows how to manage a flock with the necessary skill, even on land overgrown with brush. This has sometimes prevented NACs from implementing projects featuring a flock tended by a herder and forced them to fall back on fenced grazing.

As a rule, a NAC offers a herder satisfactory working conditions in a natural setting and a good deal of freedom in managing his flock. The shepherds on the Côte de Delme site in Lorraine, for example, say they are "generally satisfied," even if they are not happy about having so little land on which to work.

The herder's work will be quite different from what it would be if he were working for a farmer. He will have to be just as attentive to the sheep, especially regarding their state of health, but his objective will not be maximum flock performance. With a NAC, there will always be two objectives to reconcile: (a) the sheep must obtain enough to eat from grazing to ensure their physiological condition is good during periods of reproduction and lactation and the remainder of the year, and (b) grazing must be managed in such a way as to attain the objectives of site conservation or restoration. The second objective justifies hiring a herder, but the first objective is also crucial, for NAC flocks are more than a means of "ecological brush control." The NAC's credibility — in the eyes of the entire local community, not merely its agricultural component — is at stake. Above all, the herder's motivation to perform his duties is at stake as well. Every herder must be "proud of his flock."

Sharing Two Professional Cultures

In many instances, herders and NACs have professional cultures very different in origin. A herder is primarily concerned with the flock, whereas NAC members focus mainly on the site, with its biological and heritage resources. Even their respective languages can be difficult to translate. Everyone involved speaks French, to be sure, but NAC people, when referring to species or habitats on the site, sprinkle their statements with scientific names of Latin origin, while the herder uses the specialized vocabulary of his occupation. It is necessary to take the time to explain, for example, the herder's word *empoussées* (approximately, "bulging") refers to ewes whose udders are in a condition indicating that they are going to lamb within approximately a month, or that a NAC person's "*Brachypodium pinnatum* fringe areas" are forest outskirts covered with tufts of coarse grass.

The current trend is to develop a culture shared by both parties, which will happen when they can spend extended periods of time together. Personnel turnover is thus undesirable. But time is not always enough; each party must also be willing to listen and try to understand what the other is saying. The herder must learn to internalize the nature-related concerns of his employers, while the NAC must do the same with concerns relating to the herder's work of caring for a flock of sheep. Among NAC members, scientific advisers and administrative officers are less attentive to a herder's activities than their colleagues who are frequently in contact with him or her. It is thus advantageous to appoint a "grazing liaison," even on a part-time basis, who is mandated to acquire a better understanding of the herder's concerns (see chapter 10).

Most NACs we surveyed emphasized the independent character of their herders, whether they were hired by the NAC itself or working under contract. A desire for independence appeared to be inherent in the herder's choice of occupation. For a herder accustomed to organizing his own activities on rangeland in summer — on a one-on-one basis with the flock in the high mountain environment and sometimes facing inclement weather — working all year round down in the plains with a NAC team that knows little about animal husbandry may give rise to serious difficulties. He is bound to be disoriented at best, and may have reason to adopt behavior that some NACs describe as "uncouth." Under those conditions, it's impossible to forge a relationship of mutual confidence.

When the relationship deteriorates as a result of each party's inability to understand the other, it is useful to resort to a mediator from the livestock production sector. At Champlitte in Franche-Comté, for example, contact and discussion with a local sheep farmer proved highly useful in resolving a deadlock. Sometimes the necessary human resources have been identified and applied within the ranks of the NAC team itself. In Burgundy, a NAC employee who was a qualified senior technician in animal husbandry was mandated on a half-time basis to liaise with the farmer-herder, while a NAC scientist was in charge of grazing management oversight and natural resource monitoring.

In order to establish confidence, both parties must make an effort to abandon their preconceptions. In many cases, the herder takes it for granted that the NAC is "incompetent" in matters of animal husbandry and grazing. That is *his* field of competence, which he is not necessarily eager to share. NACs, for their part, have sometimes found that a person who applied for employment claiming to be a herder was actually incompetent at herding a flock of sheep on rangeland, having previously worked only for industrial operations, tending sheep in barns, grazing them on seeded pastures, and feeding them large quantities of concentrates.

Administrative and Financial Aspects

The herder's status remains a thorny issue. When a NAC employs a herder directly, a series of administrative difficulties ensues, as staff members of this kind do not fall into any of the usual employment categories within an association. The French administration is equally perplexed as to the working conditions to which the herder should be subject. Should he contribute to the farmers' mutual credit association? What sort of working hours are appropriate, given the constraints inherent in herding work on the one hand and the rigid legislative framework governing labor law on the other? What can be done about frequent periods on call, with surveillance sometimes of a low order, but for which the herder must be available none the less? What is the proper way to consider the need for brief actions in the course of a day, but spread over the entire year, when the herder is checking to make sure that all is well with the flock? Daily, weekly, or annual time schedules can be adapted to some extent, but much less so in the case of a NAC than in the case of an employer who is a farmer. Under the annualization system adopted by the Upper Normandy NAC, a herder is allowed to work up to forty-five hours per week during the lambing season.

Replacing a herder during his periods of leave or absence due to illness is another sensitive matter. Sometimes his NAC colleagues take over for him, but this could be risky should a difficult situation arise, as for example during the lambing season. This solution is more convenient when there are a number of herders working for the NAC who can replace each other when necessary. A NAC may also hire a herder on a temporary basis, but this is unusual. In Lorraine, the regular herder's wife, herself a herder, is employed for a few hours per week to complete the necessary number of hours worked. At best, the management of temporary or replacement herders entails many additional administrative formalities.

In view of these difficulties, a contractual arrangement with a farmer-herder is sometimes preferable. The latter may be attracted by the prospect of additional pasture at his disposal, but also because the NAC team may be able to help him comply with the administrative formalities concerning eligibility for agri-environmental contracts each year. Sometimes demand is strong, and the NAC has a number of farmers competing for the job. A loan contract for the use of land free of charge, for a term agreed upon by the two parties and with negotiable specifications, is a common arrangement. But this solution is not always satisfactory, as many NACs have found that farmers had difficulty observing the conditions of the contract. Sometimes this is the fault of the contract itself: its provisions may be too inflexible, or it may be worded in administrative language unintelligible to the farmer, thus preventing him from negotiating satisfactory terms. But sometimes it is the fault of the farmer's insistence on giving his own objectives priority over the objectives set forth in the contract.

Herders' wages are paid from public subsidies to NACs for the most part, and it is not certain that these funds will be renewed from year to year. Thus, it is also essential to use a portion of agri-environmental contracts in so far as possible, but this is not always feasible due to limited funds and unpredictable payment dates. Sales of products of the sheep-raising operation may be an additional source of income. A collective trademark to facilitate the marketing of lambs was introduced in 2001 by the Burgundy and Franche-Comté NACs. Unfortunately, this initiative failed because butchers were still not used to lambs raised on rangeland. They claimed that the lambs from NACs did not have the required carcass conformation. A final possibility is that the herder may decide to supplement his wages by engaging in other activities, either in the immediate vicinity during the herding season (e.g., market gardening) or further away during the rest of the year (e.g., winter sports instruction).

WORKING WITH HERDERS: WHAT IS THE OUTLOOK?

In a mere twenty-five years, a great deal of progress has been made. The "free grazer," a kind of semi-wild animal, has given way to more conventional livestock; heavy, power-driven shredders and volunteer work camps are being progressively replaced by grazing with hired herders or farmer-herders working under contracts. Some projects made with talented sheep farmers and herders have proved recently to be very successful in terms of both biodiversity conservation and animal production (e.g., Pasto'Loire project in central France).[8] Even so, NACs still have limited experience using grazing for site management. The learning process involves a good deal of trial and error, especially in the initial stages, due to the lack of shared references.

At present, the greatest challenge is how to ensure that good practices will continue once they have been established. This is because sources of funding tend to shrink each year. In plains regions and in the northern half of France, NACs can keep herders only if they receive public funding. Funds from the European Union for implementation of the Habitats Directive and the Natura 2000 network of sites bring hope, but the money is often slow in coming and the amount more and more disappointing in time of global economy crisis.

Another difficulty arises from the small size and dispersal of sites. The idea of extending grazing to new sites, either close at hand or further away, is one that is frequently expressed. Abandoned fields, of lesser intrinsic biological interest than the present sites, could be used to construct strings of sites forming "ecological corridors" where a full-time hired herder could then graze an itinerant flock. This project is taking shape in Franche-Comté. In contrast, the Lorraine and Limousin NACs, having practiced open grazing with itinerant flocks for several years, are now abandoning pastoral husbandry to manage more distant sites in favor of mowing or mechanical brush-clearing.

The issue of herders' origins is currently controversial within the NAC network. It is not their nationality that is giving rise to argument, but their skills. For some years, NACs have been surmising that they might be better advised either to begin with young persons who have acquired a solid naturalist culture and train them to be herders, or, conversely, to enlist competent herders with experience in managing flocks of sheep and seek to interest them in nature management concerns. The Lorraine NAC has opted for the former solution, while the Ain branch of the Rhône-Alpes CEN is trying the latter. The instruction currently given by shepherding schools (see chapter 12) emphasizes the herding of large flocks on mountain rangeland, a context quite different from a NAC site. One solution might be to suggest that they add some courses taught by NAC personnel to their programs. To supplement such courses, trainees could be offered hands-on experience with qualified herders already working for a NAC.

Is it not conceivable that a job market for herders with "flock and biodiversity resource management" qualifications might become a reality, in France and Europe, at some future time? The size of that market would have to be determined. It might be adequate if all the networks concerned — national parks, regional natural parks, nature reserves, NACs and so on — were to join forces. This would make it possible to offer attractive job prospects for young herders who could be sure of retaining their mobility, an aspect most seem to value. In addition, given coordination among the networks, this approach would make it feasible to recognize and provide fair remuneration for "ecological services" rendered by herders and farmer-herders (see also the introduction chapter).

In the future, pastoral husbandry on NAC-managed sites will continue to be characterized by diversity. No site is exactly like any other, even in a small country like France. No "magic bullet" should thus be sought or advocated, either for relationships among the various parties (of which herders are an important one), or for a specific choice of modus operandi. The experience of all parties should be used to best advantage, and every site, with its distinctive features, examined so an appropriate approach to management can be selected. Is it not thanks to systems of varied activities that our predecessors have bequeathed us the "cultural landscapes" (including what German authors refer to as *Kulturlandschafte*) that are recognized for their outstanding natural interest in contemporary Europe?

ACKNOWLEDGMENTS

We extend our thanks to the persons whose invaluable contributions provided us with much of our material, listed here in geographical order, from north to south:

Michel Ameline and Pascal Vautier: *Upper Normandy Natural Sites Conservancy*

Véronique Corsyn, Carine Crosnier, Mathieu Millot, Laurence Properzi, Sandrine Schwey and Yves Vincent: *Lorraine Sites Conservancy*

François Hergott: *Central Region Natural Heritage Conservancy*

Sylvie Caux, Romain Gamelon and Rémi Vuillemin: *Burgundy Natural Sites Conservancy*

Pascal Collin and Laurent Delafollye: *Franche-Comté Regional Natural Areas Conservancy*

Arnaud Six: *Limousin Natural Areas Conservancy*

Hervé Coquillart, Nicolas Greff and François Salmon: *Rhône-Alpes Natural Areas Conservancy*

Guillaume Pasquier: *Agency for the Improvement of Outstanding Natural Areas in the Department of Isère*

Many of the grazing activities described here could not have been conducted without the assistance of European LIFE programs supported primarily by the European Union and the Ministry for Ecology and implemented by Natural Area Conservancies and/or their Federation.

NOTES

[1] LPO, 2007.
[2] Lecomte et al., 1995.
[3] Meuret et al., 1995.
[4] See in particular Dupieux, 1998.
[5] Colas et al., 2002; Agreil et al., 2008.
[6] Agreil and Meuret, 2007.
[7] Meuret and Agreil, 2006.
[8] Rosoux, 2013.

CHAPTER 10

When a Shepherd and Natural Area Manager Work Together

Mathieu Erny & François Salmon

THE site of our collaboration between a shepherd and a natural area manager is La Valbonne, a contiguous area of nearly 3,340 acres in the Ain plain. It is a military training camp established in 1875. Apart from a few patches of woodland and isolated groves, it consists of seminatural dry swards that are becoming overgrown with brush, as they have not been grazed for several decades. The little bustard, an emblematic species of protected birds in Europe, has not been seen since 1990, and the habitats of a number of other rare bird species, including the European stone curlew, the Eurasian curlew, and the European quail, are all being jeopardized by the increase in brush. The French government, which owns the site, has entrusted the task of conserving its natural resources to the Rhône-Alpes Natural Area Conservancy (RANAC). A project to have the site grazed again by sheep tended by a herder was finally implemented in 2005, ten years after it had first been suggested.

In this chapter, both of us first presents his personal history, prior to our collaboration, to convey some idea of our initial expectations and the terms of our collaboration, which we then discuss. We conclude with a joint effort highlighting what we see as the keys to success in such collaboration. This description of our experience, written at the editors' request, is a supplement to chapter 9.

ORIGINS OF THE TWO PROTAGONISTS

The Shepherd

Mathieu (age 42): I was born in the Alsace region of northeastern France. My father is a professor of ethnology, specializing in the education of young people in Africa, and my mother is a nurse. Between the ages of four and ten, I lived in tropical Africa. When I returned to Alsace, I felt somewhat out of synch, and my schoolwork suffered as a result. At the age of fifteen, I opted for a three-year training course in woodcarving, followed by six years at a school of decorative arts; my ambition was to become a creative sculptor. But at the age of twenty-four, I had to go to work to earn my living. I spent three years in the field of the education working with mentally challenged young people. I found the work interesting, but not enough to spend the rest of my life at it. I then tried to live from the works I produced as a sculptor, illustrator, and writer of stories and legends, but I found it difficult to earn enough. I was not inclined to do just any kind of work, and in 1996 I set off on a pilgrimage to Santiago de Compostela, thinking about the matter while en route. Wide open spaces, walking, the outdoor life . . . the experience introduced me to a form of freedom I enjoyed. Upon my return home, I thought of becoming a logger or fruit-picker, but a friend suggested I spend a summer as part of a team herding dairy cattle on mountain rangeland instead. I sent in a job application, but it was some sheep farmers who replied: "We have 1,200 sheep, and we are looking for a herder." I was impressed with this proposal, and wrote back saying that I had no training in herding sheep. "We have not been able to find any trained shepherds, and would be prepared to employ you anyway," was their reply. I waited too long and didn't get the job, but the experience made me think: we all know what shepherds are from children's stories and novels, but nowadays we don't really think of herding as something done in real life. Now, looking at a firm offer, I said to myself, "I'd better do this properly!" So in 1998 I enrolled at the Merle Herders School, in Provence. Subsequently, I worked as a hired shepherd in the Crau steppe for four seasons, where I was fortunate to have as a neighbor an experienced Italian herder who loved to talk about shepherding and gave me a lot of useful tips. An ethnologist who specialized in shepherds also helped me realize the full depth and complexity of the herding profession and enabled me to gain more confidence.

I have always worked as a hired shepherd — in the Crau steppe, in the department of Bouches-du-Rhône, and on high mountain pasture during the summer, in the departments of Alpes de Haute-Provence and Alpes-Maritimes. For ten years, including seven years on the same stretch of mountain rangeland, I made a point of ensuring I wouldn't spend 365 days a year herding sheep, because of the hazards of loneliness. Thus, I went back to Alsace every winter to look for a shepherding job, but under different working conditions. As an internet enthusiast, I created a sheep blog and became an advocate for pastoral husbandry due to its contributions to keeping natural areas in good health from an ecological standpoint. I contacted the Ballons d'Alsace Regional Natural Park, which was developing a project where an outstanding cultural and natural site would be managed with grazing. I would become a shepherd, and perhaps a storyteller, on "Witches' Hill" (*Bollenberg*); it would be a dream come true! Unfortunately, the park decided to use fences instead of a herder. I then decided to create my own home page on the internet as a way to offer my services. I had sent my contact information to the National Federation of Natural Area Conservancies, and the federation sent it on to François Salmon, who was looking for a replacement herder for the La Valbonne flock. I was hired in the spring of 2007 under a three-month contract as a replacement herder, and then, after a summer spent herding another flock on a high mountain pasture, I was offered an open-ended contract.

The Natural Area Manager

François (age 45): I was born in the Anjou region south of the Loire in western France. My father is a senior executive with an industrial firm, and my mother is a psychologist. I had a conventional education, culminating with a degree in biology and biochemistry from the University of Paris-Orsay. I had no interest in becoming either a teacher or a research scientist. I was looking for more practical training that I could turn into a career. At the age of twenty-one, I successfully passed the examination for admission to the School of Agronomy Engineers in Nancy, but neither conventional agronomy nor "test-tube research" attracted me in the slightest. Rather, with my urban background, I was curious about nature and the countryside. Even so, I found the agronomy training interesting, mainly because of the variety of themes. In my third year, I decided to specialize in soil science and ecology, including a final-year practicum on the hydrobiology of a marsh, which entailed analysis of invertebrates as water quality indicators at the Lorraine NAC (that was the first I had heard of NACs). After graduating as an agronomy engineer, I decided to take an additional year of training in business administration and microeconomics. INRA (French National Institute for Agricultural Research) then hired me for three months to conduct farm surveys, after which I had a contract with a research firm analyzing the environmental impact of quarries and gravel pits. Finally I landed a three-year job with the Upper Normandy Center for Rural Economics, which provides farmers with advice on economic and tax matters. The work was not rewarding, as the people at the center thought exclusively in terms of individual commercial performance.

At that point I contacted the Upper Normandy NAC. I wasn't thinking of working with an NAC because I was not a naturalist and didn't possess the necessary skills. Even so, in 1992 I answered a vacancy notice from a small nature conservation association, the Rhône-Alpes Regional Natural Heritage Conservancy. Few naturalist skills were required for the position, as it involved advising farmers about the practice of mowing hayfields late in the season. I was hired, and being the only regular employee among a number of volunteers, I was responsible for managing a number of sites, purchasing land, looking for sources of funding, and acting as treasurer. In 1994, the small association became the Rhône-Alpes Natural Area Conservancy (RANAC), with ten regular employees, recognized and supported politically by the region. Until 1997, I was project director, but I was also in charge of the organization's finances, which was a heavy responsibility. What I really wanted to do was design and execute natural area conservation projects. On a regional scale, that is an activity that cannot be left to a single person. I therefore decided to focus on one department, Ain. In 2005, I was appointed chief of the Ain branch of RANAC, just when the La Valbonne grazing project was finally beginning. When I received a copy of Mathieu's job application, I contacted him immediately.

RESPECTIVE EXPECTATIONS AND TERMS OF COLLABORATION
As Seen by the Natural Area Manager

François: When Mathieu was hired in April 2007, RANAC acquired a flock of four hundred Thônes-Marthod sheep (a breed that originated from northern Alps). We had just completed an inconclusive two-year experiment with a hired herder who had a background in formal technical agricultural training and experience on a conventional sheep farm in the region, one based on the industrialized livestock production model, with the sheep kept indoors. She thus had little experience of grazing, and none at all of herding a flock on rangeland. As she saw it, brush-covered land was worthless in nutritional terms, so she frequently gave the sheep additional feed. Mutual incomprehension and frequent conflicts between RANAC and the shepherdess became such a problem that we decided to let her go.

After this unsatisfactory experience, we took the time to think about suitable criteria for hiring a new shepherd. That is why we hired Mathieu on a temporary basis. The contrast with the shepherdess was apparent from the first. Mathieu was not disconcerted at the idea of herding sheep on this kind of pasture. He confirmed matter-of-factly that a flock could sustain itself adequately in an overgrown, brush-covered environment. As regards care the sheep might require, he did not propose to resort to medication on a regular basis. He was determined to minimize the practice of giving them additional feed, and he would seek to avoid losing lambs, but without bottle-feeding individual lambs. What seemed impossible to the shepherdess, a system of management where sheep lived outdoors year round, was credible and desirable to Mathieu.

One aspect that was important for RANAC was that Mathieu saw his job as part of a team effort. His first contact with the "work team," the members of which help the herder when there are jobs to be done that require a crew, was highly favorable. From when he was employed on a temporary basis, Mathieu chose not to stand aloof with his professional skills, which no one else in the team possessed. Rather, he communicated with the other team members, even about his uncertainties, which the others appreciated.

We have now hired Mathieu under an open-ended contract. He has technician status, and is under my responsibility as I am the "project director," which is roughly equivalent to being a farm operator in the agriculture sector. Mathieu is assigned to the La Valbonne site, but his job description states that he may also work at other sites as backup for other sheep farmers or herders working under contract, for example, or as a RANAC expert for other pastoral husbandry operations. We wanted to make sure Mathieu would not be confined to the site, but would be a full member of the team. In order to keep his private life and working commitment as a herder separate, we asked him to find his own accommodations off-site. That is why there is no herder's cabin on the La Valbonne site, just a small cottage team members can use if necessary.

From an administrative standpoint, Mathieu is a "staff technician," which supposedly means I design and organize tasks and he performs them. However, I do not possess the skills of either a herder or a pastoral sheep farmer. All my knowledge comes from technical guides dealing with grazing management. Mathieu, for his part, is like most shepherds in that he is not at his best when following orders. What I need him to do is keep a sharp "herder's eye" on the flock and the grazing resources and help me negotiate with other users of the site, including the army and hunters. So he and I comanage the operations. In practice, Mathieu manages the grazing end of the operation, based on a few general principles we agreed on together. He reports to me regularly, sometimes several times a week. In less than a year, he has gone from a technician to a de facto department head, which is as it should be in a climate of mutual confidence.

As Seen by the Shepherd

Mathieu: My first contract to work at La Valbonne was for three months, and it never occurred to me that I might stay longer, even though I was looking for a year-round job. There were three reasons for this. First, I knew that RANAC could find people with better qualifications in animal husbandry and botany. Second, when I first arrived and saw this plain, all littered and strewn with industrial plants, field crops, and superhighways, to say nothing of an army base, my first impression hardly made me think of this as an ideal life setting. Third, a year-round job would have meant saying goodbye to the high mountain pasture, giving up shepherding on summer range. François encouraged me, highlighting the positive aspects: clearly, with the RANAC flock, I would be starting from scratch, with a whole environment to create, or re-create. I quite often have doubts about my skills, and I soon realized that RANAC was looking for just that kind of person, a shepherd who was not mentally committed to a particular model of animal husbandry, as had my predecessor. My comparative lack of experience of sheep farming thus worked in my favor as I was expected to share my new adventure with the rest of the team.

What motivates me now is the experimental aspect of the project: keeping a flock of sheep well fed and at the same time keeping the brush under control. Leaving the flock outdoors 365 days a year, twenty-four hours a day, is a practice that frightens many sheep farmers. It's essential to introduce technical innovations, to invent solutions, for example, to ensure that the ewes lamb successfully. I am determined to produce lambs I'm proud of: ewe lambs for replacement and expansion of the flock and ram lambs for slaughter.

Another thing that motivates me is the good working atmosphere in the RANAC team, and to an even greater extent the fact that I will soon be invited to give expert opinions on projects at other sites where management by grazing is under consideration. My job is to learn with the flock on "my own site," but also to learn from contact with other sites and other sheep farmers or herders who are collaborating with a NAC.

I enjoy working on sites that are somewhat unusual, sites with "personality." Sites like that are not uncommon, but in many cases farmers today pay little attention to them. On La Valbonne, I find myself confronted with the challenge of upgrading an area that at first sight seems pretty ordinary, just dry grassland and bushes, but is actually highly

PHOTO 1: Peaceful late afternoon grazing scene at La Valbonne military camp.

interesting. It is one of the last places where you can see what this plain was like before the advent of industrial agriculture and urbanization (see Photo 1). So my artistic spirit is awakened, even when I'm listening to my RANAC colleagues talking in code language about community habitats, Corine code, Znieff, IBAs. . . . But this particular artist is decently paid, €1,275 a month, and I have weekends off and vacation leave. Anyone who has been a hired shepherd in the Crau steppe knows these benefits are a good deal.

I have one wish that hasn't been fulfilled. I would like to know more about ecological restoration and maintenance objectives for this site. I am working with a colleague at RANAC who is mandated to prepare the Natura 2000 "objectives document" for the site, but all we talk about are technical aspects of grazing for site management; I haven't learned much about the ultimate object of the exercise. The members of the RANAC team, who have impressive qualifications in the field of ecology, probably never imagine a shepherd would like to know about these things. I once tried to study botany on my own, but all I learned was the names of plants. Anticipating vegetation dynamics more effectively is part of my job now, especially processes impacted by grazing. So I need some training, partly to learn more about the natural "treasures" I'm supposed to be guarding, and partly to make sure that I can adapt my grazing practice to suit RANAC's ecological objectives.

MICHEL MEURET / INRA

PHOTO 2: François (on the left) and Mathieu at La Valbonne.

KEYS TO SUCCESSFUL COLLABORATION

1. **Don't expect individuals to collaborate if they have no desire to do so from the outset.** Institutional guidance, funding, and an offer of stable employment are not enough to constitute a basis for confident, effective collaboration. The collaboration must get off to a good start as soon as the shepherd is hired. It is thus essential to look at each individual's motivation rooted in her previous experience. We think two people who have "knocked about" are more likely to develop a successful collaboration than two very young people, one just out of herding school or on-the-job training at a sheep farm and the other fresh from a course on nature conservation and agriculture.

2. **Make sure the shepherd is not isolated on the site.** It is crucial for the herder to be integrated into the team as soon as he is hired. He, like his colleagues, should be given a small office and a computer with internet access. Subject to the requirements of work schedules and provided the distances involved are not too great, it is important to organize frequent meetings between the herder and the rest of the team. In our case, Mathieu frequently joins the others for lunch at the RANAC headquarters, which are only a few miles from the site. These are occasions for instructive discussions on

personal as well as professional matters. Mathieu enjoys these opportunities for a close-up view of how RANAC functions, and his colleagues like to hear him talk about his ewes and lambs. These discussions make the herder's work less mysterious, which is important because the idea that farming is necessarily an environmentally damaging activity still lingers here and there. In addition to these meetings, the members of the team should lend the herder a helping hand on occasion, for example when he is setting up fencing. The project director should be involved too, needless to say.

3. **Don't wait until an emergency has arisen to discuss matters.** There should be an ongoing dialogue between project director and shepherd (see Photo 2). This affords an opportunity to take stock of a series of themes, even when everything seems to be going smoothly.

4. **In a crisis, don't blame each other.** When a serious problem has arisen and stress levels are high, quick concerted action is essential, with the herder and the project director on site together if possible, and not merely in contact by telephone. The project director should drop whatever he is doing and cancel other appointments if necessary. Afterward, they should take time to work things out, learning from the emergency and developing a shared diagnosis. This will enable them to agree on a new set of rules, such as, "Under what circumstances should the vet be called, and which of us should make the call?" In our case, Mathieu now calls the vet, on his own initiative, to ask for advice. We have decided to deal with a vet who favors preventive practices in organic farming.

5. **"Network" the shepherd.** When the herder has demonstrated his skills on the site assigned to him, he must also be involved at other sites in an expert capacity. Otherwise, you get a mental differential between the herder and the rest of the NAC team. One excels in the management of a single site, while the others travel to a number of sites every day, each with its own unique issues and characteristics. The collective objective is to put the shepherd's skills to good use in developing new projects and to arrive at stable management rules valid in all cases. The shepherd benefits in that he can learn more by comparing different situations. One typical example is the use of grazing for brush control: it is instructive to compare the results of long-standing grazing practices organized differently depending on the seasons and the plant species on different sites.

6. **Associate the shepherd with the NAC's thinking about management objectives.** The shepherd himself is able to set management

objectives for his sheep and ensure they are adequately nourished. In addition, it is essential to inform him of the natural resource management objectives the NAC is mandated to pursue: identifying species to be protected, favorable habitat areas and structures; understanding the dynamics of plant communities to be directed by means of grazing; and appreciating life traits of plant populations expanding on the site or that seem likely to do so, including species sheep do not consume. Armed with adequate information, the herder can adjust his grazing practice appropriately.

CONCLUSION

In other conservancies, national parks, or nature reserves, the expression, "It's all a matter of [the herder's] personality" is frequently heard. This is undeniable, and luck is a factor when the herder is hired following a one-hour interview. But there is a better chance of success when both herder and natural area manager have fairly extensive experience in their respective fields. In that case, they know they possess the necessary skills. They are ready, and sometimes eager, to confront an outlook different from their own with the same management objectives. There are thus two implications: the grazing comanagement procedure must be organized fairly rigorously, and the exact natural resource management objective(s) must be formulated in unambiguous terms.

Are there any advantages in working as a hired herder for a NAC rather than for a sheep farmer? We suggest one: the job description of a NAC herder may include looking after a flock of sheep that will become his own in a sense, like any herder who tends the same flock on rangeland every summer, but also the opportunity of working at other sites with different flocks, farmers, and herders. He thus capitalizes on "his site," but in addition he accumulates other experiences. He is in the same position as a herder who works at a different location each year but without having to worry about wages or job insecurity. That is sometimes an attraction, even in the somewhat unusual context of an army camp in the middle of a plain.

ACKNOWLEDGMENTS

We wish to thank our own readers, and also those enlisted by the editors, for helping us finalize this chapter. We extend special thanks to Michel Meuret, who turned up with microphone in hand and thereby enabled us to embark on the preparation of the text with sincerity and enthusiasm.

CHAPTER 11

Shepherding Practices in the Alps Convulsed by the Return of Wolves as a Protected Species

Marc Vincent

PASTORALISM AT THE CONVERGENCE OF AGRICULTURAL AND ENVIRONMENTAL POLICY

B Y the end of the twentieth century, the peasant mode of life as a component of the social fabric of rural France had been in decline for some decades,[1] a result of the combined impact of industrialization, urbanization, and the globalization of agricultural markets. Just then, however, a paradigm shift occurred that unexpectedly gave some apparently outdated approaches to livestock production a new lease on life. Up to that time, two policies had been in effect more or less independently: while agricultural policy promoted industrialized farming, nature conservation policy, which tended to regard any productive human activity as potentially harmful, was in force in nature reserves and national parks designated as sanctuaries. But in 1992, European policy reached what may be termed an "agri-environmental turning-point."[2] Successive reforms to the Common Agricultural Policy (CAP) had led to adoption of the Agri-Environmental Measures (AEMs), while the 1992 European Community Habitats Directive was designed to promote biodiversity and to protect the habitats of plant and animal species, not only in sanctuaries, but also in the "ordinary nature" of agricultural land (see chapter 1).

In this context, as pastoralism has endeavored to maintain its primary function as a food-producing activity, it has simultaneously been recognized and financially rewarded for its contributions to nature conservation in the areas where it is practiced. These contributions include forest fire prevention, maintenance of open land, and, in general, preservation of biodiversity in sensitive natural environments. Since 1992, these new functions performed by sheep farmers and herders have been acknowledged in several generations of European agri-environmental statutory instruments.

Crau Plain and Queyras Mountains: Two Typical Areas of Pastoral Grazing Land

We conducted our surveys on two areas of pastoral grazing land emblematic of sheep farming in southeastern France. The first is the Crau plain and the surrounding hills, a small region in the department of Bouches-du-Rhône where flocks of sheep have grazed for millennia. The other is the mountainous region known as the Queyras, in the Alps, nearly 180 miles away in the department of Hautes-Alpes. The Queyras is a long-range transhumance destination for flocks from Crau, but it also harbors a number of local sedentary sheep-farming operations.

In both these areas, the landscapes reflect the age-old presence of sheep farmers, herders, and their flocks. Crau and the Queyras are linked together by the ancient practice of long-range summer transhumance, which involves moving flocks up from the plains and dry hills of Provence into Alpine pastures in search of young, fresh grass. Long-range transhumance is feasible only with sheep comfortable in a variety of environments, including cultivated grassland, arid steppe, land overgrown with brush, and steep, rugged mountain rangeland. Breeds of sheep with this capability are the result of a long selection process, and the most noteworthy of them is the Mérinos d'Arles,[3] a small breed that is highly gregarious and very adaptable. But long-range transhumance is also a practice that marks the high point of the year and is dear to the heart of every person in Provence. In particular, it is a welcome event for the shepherds, who find it a restorative experience indispensable for their flocks' well-being after the long winter down in the plain.

Ability of Sheep Farmers and Herders to Respond to Change

Each year, sheep farmers and herders must adapt to constantly changing living and working conditions. Furthermore, this adaptability is not merely required in the context of a particular year's activities or in response to short-term conditions. It is comprehensive, structuring and structural, and it entails an ongoing reorientation process. As sheep farming has endured and evolved over the centuries, the practices associated with it today are inevitably the outcome of a succession of changes, in some instances radical changes, introduced in response to changing conditions in the agricultural sector and society at large. This system of sheep production has repeatedly and successfully adapted to meet new challenges while remaining primarily pastoral in its approach.

Both in the Crau plain and in the Queyras mountains, transhumant sheep farmers have confronted numerous far-reaching changes since the nineteenth century:

- lamb production for meat has replaced wool production;
- rural depopulation has resulted in a significantly reduced labor pool, especially within families;
- in mountain regions, sheep farmers have given up irrigating and mowing fields too steep for the new farm machinery designed for use on flat land;
- long-range transhumance on foot has been prohibited and replaced first by the use of rail transport and later by trucks;
- in high mountain pasture areas, herders are no longer supplied by means of pack donkeys, but rather subsidized helicopter flights;
- the bulk of farm families' income was formerly obtained from lamb sales; at present, over half of their income consists of European subsidies now largely independent of lamb production; and
- until the end of the nineteenth century, wolves were regarded as vermin and systematically exterminated, but by the end of the twentieth century they had reappeared as a protected species under an international convention.

However far-reaching, frequent, and even sudden some of these changes may have been, to date none of them has jeopardized the main characteristic of pastoral sheep husbandry: the forging of complex, emblematic linkages among the land, natural resources, and herding practices.

Producers of Outstanding Biodiversity

These tectonic changes might have led sheep farmers in mountain regions to break with tradition and rely exclusively on their arable land's resources to maintain their flocks (i.e., to adopt highly intensive production models designed for plains-based livestock operations. This has not happened, or seldom happened, and mountain pastures by and large have not become overgrown with brush or trees, as would have been the case had herding been abandoned. High mountain pastures and a good many hilly areas have remained open grassland or semi-open scrubland, thanks to the persistence of pastoralism.

Today, those environments are seen as particularly noteworthy and in need of protection for their outstanding biodiversity. The shepherding that keeps them open and diversified is now encouraged by various nature managers. Without even realizing it, herders and their tending practices, in some instances for several generations, had been creating ecological habitats suitable for the establishment and survival of various forms of outstanding biodiversity, including various "red-listed" rare or endangered species, not only on high mountain pastures but in lowland areas as well.

For that reason, agri-environmental policy managers are currently receiving funding under European Union budgets to make contracts with livestock farmers that maintain or orientate their grazing practices to favor a host of species, including flowering plants, insects, reptiles, birds of prey and other rare bird species, and small mammals (see chapters 9 and 10).

PROTECTION OF WOLVES OR OTHER FORMS OF BIODIVERSITY: CONTRADICTORY PUBLIC POLICIES?

The contribution of pastoral sheep husbandry to agri-environmental policies was abruptly called into question by the unexpected return of a species emblematic of biodiversity: *Canis lupus* L., the European grey wolf. By mere chance, the first sighting of a wolf in the French Alps, in 1992, coincided with the conclusion of the first agri-environmental grazing contracts. Wolves had been absent from France for nearly a century, but now they were returning, spilling over the border from Italy as the wolf population there expanded. However in France, unlike in other European countries such as Spain, wolves are fully protected, and consequently no attempt to manage the expanding wolf population is being contemplated. This has created a favorable context for the return of wolves enhanced by rural depopulation, the abandonment of farming, an abundant supply of prey in the form of wild ungulates, and the reversion of what were formerly cultivated fields to brush and tree species. The wolf's status as a fully protected species is enshrined in a binding legal instrument named the "International Bern Convention on the Conservation of European Wildlife and Natural Habitats." That treaty was signed in 1979, ratified by executive order in 1990,[4] and came into force in France two years before the official announcement that wolves had returned to France. On May 21, 1992, a few months before the first sighting of wolves in the Mercantour National Park in the extreme southern part of the Alps, the treaty was reinforced by the adoption of the European Commission's Habitats Directive, the aim of which was more effective conservation of outstanding wildlife species within EU, including *Canis lupus*.

The presence of the first wolves was revealed to everyone in France by the magazine *Terre Sauvage* in the spring of 1993.[5] Until then, it had been kept secret. The revelation took the form of a rallying cry on behalf of wildlife: "The Mercantour [National Park] is in a state of grace this day. The return of the wolf has been achieved without a fight. It has returned timidly and silently, as is its wont. . . . This issue [of *Terre Sauvage*] is dedicated to those who are willing to join us in making every effort to ensure that that state of grace will continue, to those who consider, as we do, that the disappearance of the wolf was the outcome of a long-continued injustice, and that with its return, nature has come to life again."[6] For militant conservationists, wolves were grounds for closing ranks, a new cause worth fighting for. The president of *France Nature Environnement*, the French federation of associations for nature conservation and the environment, wrote at the time that the fight was of crucial importance: "The fight for free, wild wolves is a fight against all forms of confinement, all walls, prisons of every kind, it is a fight against the impoverishment of biodiversity. . . . Were it not for this super-predator, our mountain and forest ecosystems would become denatured, they would turn into open-air chicken coops. Life needs wolves, and human beings need life."[7] At a time when France's wolf population consisted of no more than a few scattered individuals, these warlike utterances were the opening shots in an ambitious campaign of territorial reconquest: "France will have to learn to live with a population of 1,000 to 1,500 wolves."[8]

Within nineteen years, wolves had expanded their range to include the whole of the French Alpine arc (see Figure 1) and had moved through the southern part of the Massif Central into the eastern Pyrenees, shielded by what was virtually blanket legal protection. They attacked sheep, in most cases with deadly effect (see Photo 1 and Figure 2), goats, and more recently cattle and horses. Predation by wolves has always been traumatic for sheep farmers, herders, and their flocks. It has jeopardized the fragile political balance between pastoral husbandry and nature management.

Farmers and herders were unprepared for the sudden onslaught of a fully protected predator and at first could do little but count their losses, report them to the local authorities, and claim compensation. Conflict soon broke out between the friends of wolves and the sheep farmers confronted with predation. For the former, wolves meant a return to the natural order of things, a keystone species for the ecosystem, a wilderness icon and a national heritage. The latter, calling stridently for elimination of the wolves, found their occupation stigmatized as incompatible with the dynamics of an "authentic" natural order, which the presence of large predators showed was in a healthy condition.

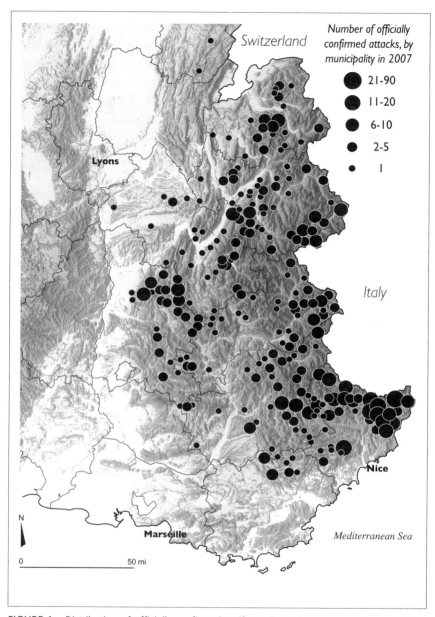

FIGURE 1 – Distribution of officially confirmed wolf attacks in the French Alpine arc during 2007, by municipality (adapted from: DIREN Rhône-Alpes, DDAF-DDAE data, March 2009. Topographic data source: NASA/NGA/USGS public domain - adapted by: GIS data base staff, INRA URFM Avignon).

MARC VINCENT / INRA

PHOTO 1: A sheep killed by a wolf on a high mountain pasture in the Queyras (Hautes-Alpes) in August 2005.

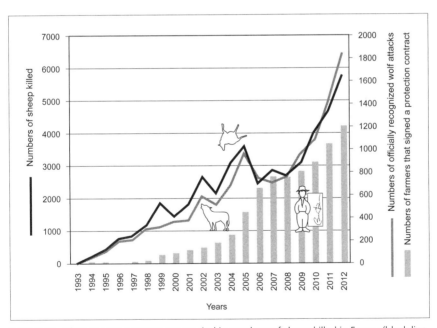

FIGURE 2 - Change over a twenty-year period in numbers of sheep killed in France (black line, left y-axis), numbers of officially confirmed wolf attacks (grey line, right y-axis) and numbers of farmers that signed a five-year protection contract (grey bars, right y-axis) (Source: Rhône-Alpes Regional Bureau of the Ministry of the Environment).

Is pastoralism facing a new and painful crisis? Is the policy of encouraging the recovery of the wolf population a contradiction within France's public policy on nature? In protecting wolves in the name of biodiversity, is France not simultaneously jeopardizing the known benefits of shepherding in natural environments, an activity now recognized and promoted through funding under agri-environmental grazing contracts? These questions were the starting point for our research.

OBJECTIVE, EXPERIMENTAL DESIGN AND RESEARCH METHODOLOGY

We undertook our investigations in 2005 and 2006, conducting individual interviews and gathering and analyzing printed documents.[9] The interviews were conducted in the mountains of the Queyras and the Crau plain. Our aim was to understand how the return of these protected predators to mountain regions was affecting the practices of sheep farmers and herders, and how shepherding, bearing the brunt of predation, was attempting to adapt to this new and difficult situation. Approximately thirty interviews were conducted with farmers, herders, and specialists in various aspects of sheep production, including representatives of farmers' associations, administrators of the Queyras Regional Natural Park and the Coussouls of Crau Nature Reserve, and technical staff members of both, including rangeland technicians, public service advisers, instructors at herding schools, a consulting veterinarian, and scientists. We also attended a number of court cases involving sheep farmers who were being prosecuted for killing wolves. We analyzed some cultural practices and museum exhibitions relating to the history of wolves, human beings, and sheep. In addition, the results of our interviews were compared with statistical and cartographic data, technical and scientific studies, articles, dissertations and reports, symposium proceedings and court records, official documents, statutory instruments, and several hundred press clippings with a bearing on the subject.

CONFRONTED WITH WOLVES: THREE GOVERNMENT-SPONSORED PROTECTIVE MEASURES

Action to protect flocks of sheep from wolf predation began in the 1990s, with two LIFE (European Financial Instrument for the Environment) programs managed in France by the Ministry of Ecology. In response to the findings of a parliamentary Commission of Inquiry,[10] the French government decided to replace those programs with a more comprehensive Wolf

Action Plan for 2004 to 2008,* to be administered jointly by the Ministry of Ecology and the Ministry of Agriculture.[11] The latter is in charge of the "loss prevention" component of the plan. It provides funding, under five-year contracts, to farmers who have sustained losses from predation or are likely to do so soon, to enable them to hire assistant herders and undertake capital outlays for guard dogs and movable fencing to protect their flocks. Four levels of funding are available under a contract of this kind, depending on the size of the applicant's flock; the choice of protective measures is left to the farmer. Rural municipalities fall into two categories: those in which predation is already a reality and those anticipating the arrival of predators in the near future.

For the time being, farmers are not required to institute flock protection measures to be eligible for compensation for losses resulting from predation. Any farmer can sign a five-year protection contract. In 2002, 138 farmers signed such a contract in France. In 2012, they were 1,182 (Figure 2). Regardless of the level of protection selected, however, the farmer will receive compensation if the official investigator certifies that a sheep was killed by a wolf rather than having died from a natural cause (such as disease) or an accident (such as a lightning strike or panic caused by stray dogs). In uncertain cases, the farmer usually gets the benefit of the doubt.

These protective measures, with the exception of guard dogs, were applied in the Alps before the reappearance of wolves. None of them is simple for sheep farmers, transhumant sheep farmers in particular, to implement. They are more than mere technical adjustments in practice; their impact is structural and goes to the very heart of shepherding, affecting not only the effort it entails but also relations between herders and other users of Alpine areas.

There is a hierarchy of flock protection techniques viewed as complementary. They are based on three assumptions about the behavior of wolves, which are cautious animals that avoid humans. These assumptions derive from research on wolf behavior in sparsely inhabited regions, mainly Canada,[12] and in some European countries (Romania and Poland) where herding is more labor-intensive than it is in France.

Assumption 1: An assistant herder, who is constantly with the flock and has had specialized training in flock protection, should be sufficient to keep wolves from approaching.

Assumption 2: If a particularly bold wolf were to succeed in approaching the flock, despite the watchful human attendants, it would encoun-

* The Wolf Action Plan for 2008 to 2012 followed this; the current plan is for 2013 to 2017. Additional information, available in English, is posted on the French official website about wolves: http://www. rdbrmc-travaux.com/loup/index.php?lang=en.

ter a formidable obstacle from guard dogs, which are specially bred to live constantly among sheep, move at their pace, and keep any intruders away, including wolves, stray dogs, and would-be sheep-rustlers. A properly trained guard dog must distinguish between a stranger up to no good and a harmless tourist. It must also devote all of its time to the flock and not chase rabbits and the like.

Assumption 3: A flock that is shut in for the night in a special pen attended by herders and guard dogs will not be subject to predation. On summer range, where secure sheds are not available, the flock should be put into an electrified movable enclosure, known as a night pen, located in close proximity to the cabin(s) where the herder sleeps.

HOW ACCEPTABLE AND EFFECTIVE ARE PROTECTIVE MEASURES?

Assistant Herders and Ecovolunteers: Skilled but Insecure Jobs

Living and Working with an Assistant Herder

Since the appearance of wolves in the French Alps, the occupation of assistant herder, which had been all but forgotten in France for decades, has been reactivated (see also chapter 2). Assistant herders were formerly unskilled, general-purpose hired hands. In some instances the assistant herder might be a young apprentice who did various chores that the herder would otherwise have to do himself. In practice, it was the assistant who was responsible for obtaining supplies and preparing meals. When the old teams consisting of sheep farmers and their herders became progressively fewer over time, disappearing altogether when transhumance came to consist of transporting sheep by truck, the function of assistant herder went the same way. Today's assistant herders are employed on a seasonal basis, they perform tasks associated with the presence of predators, and they are paid out of the French government budget.

In the parliamentary commission's report,[13] this protective measure was described as one that was "greatly appreciated" by sheep farmers. The report emphasized the additional constraints and the effective management of "pastoral units" (see definition in chapter 2) resulting from the presence of wolves, including the extra work associated with prevention: transporting movable night pens, transporting equipment from one grazing quarter to another, and feeding guard dogs. The assistant herder, in addition to his or her specific duties, also helps look for lost sheep or sheep killed or injured, working in cooperation with official investigators who certify losses resulting from predation.

The commission's report noted that in 2002 funding had been made available for 107 assistant herder posts in the six Alpine departments. This was not adequate to meet the need, as there are approximately one thousand high-altitude pastoral units grazed by sheep in the French Alps.[14] However, a trend in the direction of more assistant herder posts is discernible: in 2005, 414 assistant herder contracts were concluded for the Alpine arc, representing approximately 1,000 work-month equivalents.[15]

But there is a problem: shepherds' cabins are small, and in many cases two persons who had not previously known each other find it difficult to get along when they are thrown together in close quarters for a summer alone. As one herder put it to us: "[In a cabin] there are no separate bedrooms, one for the herder and one for the assistant. It's all right for a man and wife . . . but it's very difficult to find two guys who can get along under those conditions! By the time they've been up there for two weeks . . . they're not on speaking terms any more. You can feel the tension."

Sometimes assistant herders have been perceived as natural hewers of wood and drawers of water, so to speak. The original intent was that the assistant camp beside the flock for an immediate response in the event of a nocturnal marauder. The idea that an unskilled worker in a temporary job, being paid the minimum wage (in 2007, gross pay of €8.44 an hour for 152 hours of work per month), should be assigned to such a task met with an unexpectedly hostile reception on the part of many herders. The following comment is by one herder who was infuriated at this new form of exploitation: "No way is anyone going to be required to camp out beside the flock. We ourselves demand decent cabins to live in, don't we? So sending someone to camp out beside the flock, sleep in a tent, it doesn't make sense. It would be a step backward!"

The problem of inadequate accommodation was also raised by a farmer-herder who himself had a "state-of-the-art" cabin with a usable roadway leading up to it so that he could drive in. His cabin proved to be a neat little cottage with every modern convenience . . . but only one room. Under these conditions, the unsatisfactory nature of the design was apparent: how could two workers from different backgrounds and with different tastes and different characters possibly endure such a lack of privacy?

> I have been offered an [assistant herder] . . . but it's not feasible. I told them as much. See for yourself! This cabin is fine, but it's not designed for two people. Well, yes, perhaps it would be all right if it were your son or your wife! But sharing accommodation [with a stranger] is very difficult. People's characters are too different. You can't live like that.

Prior training, suitable accommodations, responsibilities, and job descriptions, remain to be worked out before a menial job can become a genuine skilled occupation. Professionalization would transform every assistant herder into a sort of "neo-herder" possessing flock protection skills.

Ecovolunteers Discover Shepherds' Living Conditions

At the initiative of associations that actively advocate the return of wolves, another category of workers, known as ecovolunteers, have also provided herders with assistance; they help more fleetingly than assistant herders, and in smaller numbers. They are usually members of pro-wolf organizations, from urban backgrounds, and interested primarily in nature. One of these associations, known as FERUS (Latin word for "Fierce, wild, savage, untamed"), is interested in promoting the conservation of bears, wolves, and lynxes in France. FERUS presents a glowing summary of the work of its *pastoraloups* (approximately "wolf/pastorals"), as they call their volunteers:

> Between May and October of 2006, nearly 60 ecovolunteers carried out two- to three-week missions with 16 sheep farmers, after taking an awareness course lasting a week. In the aggregate, they accounted for over 900 presence days (compared to 300 in 2003)! They had very few interactions with wolves. Only five flocks sustained losses, amounting to 10 ewes in all, out of flocks containing a total of 15,000 sheep and goats!"[16]

Some of the *pastoraloups* themselves give more nuanced accounts. The statements reproduced in this chapter were provided by volunteers who took part in the campaign organized in 2003 and 2004:

> Anne-Catherine (an actress from Paris): "I had never realized how difficult a shepherd's job is. I had no idea that there had been so many wolf attacks."[17]

> Hervé (background and occupation unspecified): "Late in the day, the fog came rolling in. 'Wolf weather': wolves take advantage of the poor visibility to slip past the guard dogs unnoticed. . . . At all events, Jérôme [the farmer-herder] seems to have had a good many adverse encounters with wolves in the past: he has a stack of approximately 300 certifications at home. He explained to me that he is generously compensated for immediate losses, but not for the two years needed for a ewe lamb to grow to adulthood. The problem with wolves is that they aren't satisfied with picking off a sheep from time to time: a wolf always kills several sheep, even if it only eats one of them, and this creates panic that sometimes

results in collective suicide among the sheep. One day, Jérôme found 25 of his sheep dead on a scree slope, and several more that had been killed at the top of the slope. . . . In cases like that, as a pro-wolf activist, it's best just to keep quiet."[18]

Stéphane (twenty-five, a humanitarian, department of Loire-Atlantique): "I hope I'll be able to handle the work! . . . But I'll have to be careful. Especially since I'm not in the best of shape. Last night, my team was standing guard over the flock, and this morning we were falling asleep on our feet. Before I started on this training course, I used to laugh at popular superstititions about wolves; I had heard about wolf attacks on sheep, but I didn't take them too seriously. But last night, every sound, every crack of a dead twig took on a different meaning. . . . Would I be up to the challenge in a dangerous situation?"[19]

Some who have chosen to become ecovolunteers are discovering not only the fairly rigorous conditions under which shepherds live and work, but also the semipermanent stress of having to be constantly alert for wolves. It is a lot for them to handle. Accordingly, it would be advisable to steer these persons in the direction of professionalization by integrating them into what might become a kind of "nature police," administered by France and its Ministry of Ecology. The present situation will ultimately generate specialized occupations relating to the task of protecting flocks of sheep from predators that enjoy the status of protected species. In France, as elsewhere (in Canada and the United States in particular), those occupations will not be able to rely exclusively on the good will of farmers and herders. They will have to be organized by other agencies, including those responsible for nature and wildlife management.[20]

Guard Dogs: An Old Technique in a New Context

According to associations concerned with the protection of wolves, the use of specially trained guard dogs to protect flocks of sheep would be a simple and effective solution.[21] As we shall see, however, the accounts of those who have tried dogs suggest this method may entail substantial disadvantages.

A Forgotten Technique

In continental Europe, guard dogs were the only dogs kept in association with flocks of sheep until the seventeenth century, or the twentieth century in the case of some countries. Subsequently, guard dogs became increasingly uncommon, partly as a result of the decline in the wolf population that occurred during the nineteenth century.[22] Farmers gradually

PHOTO 2: A Great Pyrenees guard dog (patou) on duty on a high mountain pasture in the Queyras (Hautes-Alpes).

lost interest in the use of guard dogs to protect their flocks, especially in the Alps. In the Pyrenees, on the other hand, guard dogs continued to be used to protect the sheep from bears and wolves as far as Asturias on the Spanish side, and to protect them from the few remaining bears on the French side.[23]

In France, a breed native to the Pyrenees, the Great Pyrenees (known familiarly as the *patou*) (see Photo 2), was reintroduced in the 1990s to guard flocks on Alpine summer pastures. The breed had been preserved by fanciers, but most living Great Pyrenees never had any contact with a flock of sheep. This led, and still does lead on occasion, to behavioral difficulties. In 2005, a survey found approximately twelve hundred guard dogs protecting flocks of sheep in the French Alpine arc (see Figure 3). Great Pyrenees account for 77 percent of these, the others being Maremmano-Abruzzese, Anatolian Shepherds, Caucasian Ovcharkas, Tibetan Mastiffs or assorted crossbreds.[24]

The guard dog's function is to deter any intruder from approaching the flock. It is neither a herding dog nor a pet, much less an attack dog. A guard dog must display four behavioral characteristics: attentiveness (to remain permanently with the flock); trustworthiness (not to molest the

276

flock); protectiveness (to keep the flock safe from predators); and sociability (or tolerance and indifference) toward humans, without being friendly with them. These characteristics are the outcome of a combination of genetic makeup, introduction to the work situation, and training.[25] Studies suggest few guard dogs display atypical or dangerous behaviors.[26] However, interviews with herders in the Queyras revealed that difficulties can arise, and there have actually been court cases involving owners of aggressive dogs.[27]

It might be imagined that thanks to his ever-watchful guard dogs, a shepherd could go to bed and sleep without a care. This is not the case. All the herders we interviewed told us that living semipermanently in a situation when the alarm might be raised at any moment made them apprehensive and was much more fatiguing because it is more difficult to

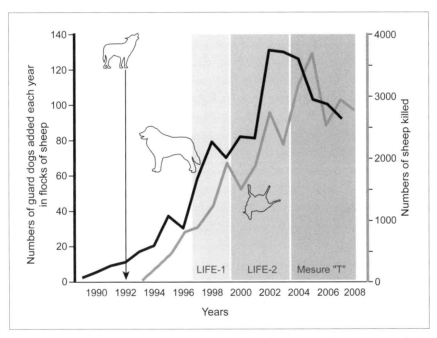

FIGURE 3 - Change over time in total annual numbers of patou guard dogs put with flocks of sheep in the French Alps and numbers of sheep killed by predators. Guard dogs were introduced in progressively larger numbers beginning in 1992, the year in which the return of wolves to France was officially announced, followed by the implementation of the LIFE-1 and LIFE-2 programs, with their financial incentives for sheep producers to purchase guard dogs. The decline in numbers of new dogs brought in since 2004 may be attributable either to a saturation effect or to the possibility that producers are now purchasing dogs without applying for financial assistance from the relevant authorities. More recent data are not available. (Sources: Departmental Directorates of Agriculture and Forestry, National Office for Hunting and Wildlife and Ministry of Agriculture).

return to a normal state following an alert at night, when the herder expects to get some rest. Herders become light sleepers, awakening as soon as the dog barks. As the summer wears on, emotional fatigue is added to physical fatigue, and a state of nervous tension sets in, exerting a progressively stronger grip and preventing the herder from working effectively during the day as well.

> Because when you're herding sheep from June 20 to October 20 and you don't get a good night's sleep [in all that time], well, by October you're tired. It's all very well saying we've got dogs now, they don't eliminate the danger entirely. At the slightest bark, all of a sudden you're wide awake, you get up, you go to see what's happening. By the time fall is over, you've had it. You're worn out.

Another factor is that on high mountain summer pastures, dogs represent a problem in terms of managing for "multiple-uses." Shepherds and farmers have their own immediate and direct interest, while hikers are not always prepared to share what they regard as a recreational environment. All must now come to terms with a new reality in the form of these great white dogs with their characteristic behavior patterns. The same applies to wildlife species, such as marmots, which have become tame in natural parks, partly because they are a protected species and partly because hikers feed them.

A Guard Dog Can't Live on What It Can Catch, It Needs Dog Food

Guard dogs have to be adequately fed, and because of their body size, they have hearty appetites. Feeding them on a "sort of hit-or-miss" basis, as one herder put it, may have unexpected consequences for the surrounding biodiversity:

> A: With the new [guard dogs] that I've got now, things are working out pretty well. They stay with the flock. I know they won't go wandering off at night. They're fed regularly every evening, even during the day sometimes. That's essential. Of course, when they see a marmot close at hand, near the woods, they'll take off after it. Or a deer, they'll go off chasing a deer for a quarter of an hour or half an hour at a time. But then they'll come back to the flock, no problem. They won't go off hunting for an entire day unless they're hungry. When that happens, up on a mountain pasture like this, it's because the farmer hasn't behaved responsibly and looked after his dogs the way he should.

Q: You think that's the reason, it's because they're hungry? They're not being looked after properly?

A: Yes, I do! Apart from taking off to chase animals that come past right under their noses, of course. . . . *Patous* absolutely have to be fed every evening. The problem is that in some areas the herders don't do that, so the dogs go off hunting in search of something to eat.

However important it may be, the task of keeping the dogs adequately fed is sometimes perceived as yet another daily chore for the shepherd, who is overworked as it is, especially if there is no assistant herder: "Now I not only have to carry electric netting and medications, but dog food as well."

On occasion, guard dogs that do not get enough to eat have been known to regard passing hikers as an inexhaustible source of food. In such cases, the herder must be able to make his dogs obey.

If the dogs begin to follow tourists, you must call them back, and don't hesitate to take food out to them when the resting-place isn't next to your cabin. Not everyone is willing to do that, but if the dogs aren't properly fed, they're useless. They won't stay with the flock if they're being fed out of hikers' backpacks. They'll follow them for miles. They'll hardly stay with the flock at all, and they won't be of any use. That's the main thing right there. If you want to have effective dogs, you have to feed them properly.

Unfortunately, providing the dogs with adequate quantities of food is not always enough. One farmer told me that when he took his sheep into the mountains for the summer, he had to leave his two guard dogs behind, in the Crau plain, because they would no longer stay with the flock. They preferred to follow groups of backpackers because the backpackers gave them tidbits they found much tastier than dog food.

The Multiple-Use Concept in the Mountain Setting: The Difficulties of Coexistence between Backpackers and Guard Dogs

While pastoral husbandry evolved in the French Alps in the absence of wild predators, tourist activity in that region has grown at a rapid rate. Since its origins in the 1960s, mass tourism has developed considerably, beginning with a winter season oriented toward the snow industry, soon followed by a summer season made feasible by the establishment of marked long-distance walking trails.[28] By now, it is not unusual for a popular stretch of mountain terrain, one accessible from a point on a convenient road, to be used by several hundred hikers every day during summer. The arrival of guard dogs on the scene has not gone unnoticed.

When a group of hikers sets out along a mountain trail, the first "guard dog" they meet is a picture on an information panel at the starting point of the marked hiking trail that crosses the high mountain pasture area (see Photo 3). For some years now, the tourist information services of rural municipalities have been posting information placards containing warnings in three languages about the possibility of encountering livestock guarding dogs. These virtual *patous* are accompanied by detailed messages meant to be reassuring. Their function is to explain, for the benefit of the uninitiated, how guard dogs behave. These signs include advice like "Avoid making sudden movements," "Keep your distance," "Get off your bicycle," and "Keep your dog on a leash." Clearly, this sort of thing is more alarming than reassuring and stands in jarring contrast to the hiker's memories of previous leisurely walks along mountain trails.

When a hiker approaches a flock of sheep while they are grazing near the trail, he may not notice the dogs at first. They are the same color as the sheep, and they keep pace with them. In cases where a flock has several guard dogs dispersed among the sheep, one may be virtually invisible in

MICHEL MEURET / INRA

PHOTO 3: An official information board warning other users of high mountain pasture areas, including hikers, that they are likely to encounter guard dogs.

the midst of the flock, while another may be acting as a rear guard. One of the dogs may approach the hikers and sniff at them or their dog. As a rule, these interactions are uneventful, but conflict sometimes occurs.

All the sheep farmers and herders we met had tales to tell of altercations with hikers who found the attitude of their dogs alarming, fights between a guard dog and a passing dog, or, worse yet, a summons from the police following a biting incident, in which case the dog must be examined by a veterinarian. The most serious situation, which fortunately does not occur frequently, is for the farmer to be hauled into court as a result of a complaint. One experienced herder was startled to find that his dog had bitten a hiker who had gone into the night pen among the sheep. The hiker meant no harm, but he sustained a nasty bite. Without taking the time to discuss matters with the herder, he went to the nearest police station and lodged a complaint. The result was the farmer who owned the dog had to make several round trips between his home in the Crau plain and the municipality of the mountain pasture, 180 miles away, in the middle of the haying season to consult a veterinarian to make sure the dog was not rabid.

> So far, these dogs have caused us more trouble than wolves. . . . The *patous* are supposed to protect the flock. But three people have been bitten by our dogs this summer. When that happens, things go from bad to worse: calls to the mayor's office, calls to the police. . . . There was one fellow who wanted to lodge a complaint. I explained matters as best I could. I told him that livestock guarding dogs were not your typical suburban pets, they had a job to do, and actually he had been lucky, because our dogs were comparatively friendly, they came from a place not far from a city, and there was no way that we could keep really fierce dogs. He was bitten, but if the dog that bit him had been a really fierce dog, an attack dog, it might have eaten him whole.

When these regrettable incidents occur, local officials tend to take a somewhat negative attitude toward the sheep farmers because they are anxious to avoid issues that might adversely impact the tourist trade, a substantial source of income for small businesses in mountain villages:

> The mayor is upset, because she's the one who catches the flak. She asked me to make sure my sheep didn't graze along the hiking trail! I told her that the trail cut right through our August grazing quarter, from one side to the other, and that it ran squarely across the *biais* [i.e., the tendency of the flock to move spontaneously in a particular direction while

grazing]. There's no way I can prevent the flock from grazing near the trail! Some day someone is going to lodge a complaint, and then there'll be a real problem.

As the tourist sector has flourished, especially in regional natural parks, guard dogs have occasionally had an adverse impact even on the flocks they are supposed to be protecting: "A hiker comes along with his dog and walks right through the middle of the flock. The *patou* spots them and makes a beeline for the hiker or his dog, causing the flock to break up into three or four separate groups. As a result of this kind of thing, *patous* have a serious disruptive impact on a flock of sheep."

The Results of Practical Experience with Night Pens

Another technique is to confine the sheep during the night in a catch pen placed near the herder's cabin (see Photo 4). This practice has been in use for a decade now in the Queyras mountains during the period of transhumance. Wolf advocacy associations have called for its adoption but have not necessarily foreseen the impact either on herders' workloads or on mountain ecosystems.

Far from being an innovation, penning the sheep overnight by means of portable fencing has been in practice since the 1970s for many herders tending flocks on high mountain pasture. It is a management technique, sometimes a sophisticated one, that takes into account the configuration of the range where the sheep are grazing, the date, weather conditions, the *biais* of the flock, the importance of ensuring that some unpalatable plants are grazed, and more recently the presence of wolves.

Beneficial or Harmful for Pasture Resources?

One farmer told me, "[Night] pens, if properly used, are helpful to the herder in his work." To understand why, I had to look into why different herders used electroplastic netting, which is often difficult to set up and invariably requires a good deal of time and sometimes considerable agility as well.

One herder was tending on summer range a flock consisting of sheep from eight different farms. This system is economically advantageous for local farmers, as they share the cost of hiring a shepherd. One undesirable aspect is that during the first weeks on the summer range, the combined flock tends to break up into its component parts, the members of each original group staying together. In order not to have to "tend several flocks at once," the herder uses movable fencing to shut them in at night. This useful technique promotes flock cohesion as the sheep from the vari-

MICHEL MEURET / INRA

PHOTO 4: A night pen made of portable electroplastic netting, located near the herder's cabin on a high mountain pasture.

ous farms are compelled to spend the night penned together, thereby facilitating the herder's work.

Another herder cited different reasons for using a night pen. One had to do with the configuration of the particular summer range where he was herding. It was long and narrow, with the grazing quarters for the beginning and end of the season close to the village. This situation created constraints that the herder had to manage, partly in the interests of the sheep when they had to be penned because of weather conditions, and partly because it was important to keep the sheep away from the approaches to the village.

> I have to pen them at the beginning, when we're near the village, so that they'll stay together at night, because otherwise they'll disperse. But higher up, there are August grazing quarters with natural *couchades* [i.e., nighttime resting-places for the flock]. And then toward the end of September they have to be penned again, because it's not a good thing for them to set off too early in the morning, when the grass is covered with frost.

On occasion, concern for grazing resources outweighs the chore of setting up night pens. A number of herders told us how those pens could become powerful mountain pasture management tools, provided they were carefully positioned, regarding the condition of the pasture and the season:

Another function of the pens is to improve the grazing. After a few years, I noticed that I was applying too much manure, I was killing the good grass. It was becoming more abundant, but less palatable. So I tried putting the pen at a place where the grass was really not very good. The next year, it was definitely better, so I was careful not to put the pen in the same place the following year.

One herder who had been tending sheep for over ten years on the same mountain pasture was proud of his "rotating portable pen" system:

> You can't imagine what this grazing sector used to be like. There was nothing here but patches of *Queyrel* [*Festuca paniculata* (L.) Schinz & Thell. subsp. *paniculata*], so it was inedible. But what I do is, even after two or three years, I pen them [the 1,200 sheep] in overnight for a maximum of four days, not longer. And I rotate the pen . . . four days here, four days there. But the thing is, there is always a little room in the pen for them to graze. Sometimes in the morning, if I'm late getting started, or sometimes in the evening, if some of them are still a little bit hungry. And the pasture has changed beyond recognition. It's all good grass now. In some cases I might even say that it's the best grazing anywhere up here. Or nearly so.

In this account we see an illustration of benefits accruing thanks to the practice of an experienced shepherd who has chosen to shift his night pens every four days, sometimes to a location quite far away from his cabin, for reasons that are unrelated to wolf predation. The dung produced by the flock, properly distributed, is improving the condition of the pasture. As a rule, however, the reverse is the case. When a flock is kept for too long in its night pen, located near the cabin for convenient surveillance, the pasture becomes severely degraded. Repeated deposits of excessive nitrogen and problems of polluted springs and streams appear, since the dung is no longer collected and used as fertilizer, as it formerly was: "Assuming the sheep are kept in their night pen for 13 and a half hours (the average duration observed during the summer pasture season), a flock of 1600 animals deposits 3.63 tons of fresh excrement (feces and urine) on the ground every night, representing, on average, 1386 lb of dry matter and containing 46 lb of nitrogen."[29]

Penning Sheep to Protect Them from Wolves Proves Harmful to Good Grazing Management

As we read in chapter 4, to manage a summering flock effectively a herder must first structure the available area into separate grazing quarters and sectors, taking into account the seasonal nature of the resources and the way the natural configuration of the terrain will affect the movement of the flock. Shepherds' cabins should be located at lower altitudes or down in sheltered small valleys where they will not be exposed to bad weather. When on their August grazing sections, those located at the highest altitude, the sheep use natural bed grounds, which may be a long way from the herder's cabin, far up on a high ridge or steep mountainside. The herder may have to walk for over an hour to rejoin his flock before sunrise. Few experienced herders complain about this, for they are applying two of their main rules: (1) minimal interference with the flock's natural activities and spontaneous directions of movement, and (2) ensure that the flock does not spend too much time on previously grazed areas.

Now that wolves have become a threat, protection night pens have come into widespread use. They are located in the immediate vicinity of the herder's cabin for convenient surveillance. As a result, almost all areas featuring natural bed grounds have been abandoned. It is difficult to make higher-altitude pastures profitable when the flock sets off at the crack of dawn for its day's grazing from a much lower altitude, far from the August grazing quarters.

> In August, penning the flock near a cabin every night when the sheep are supposed to go up to the high ridges makes no sense at all! . . . Some pastures are just too far away, the sheep don't graze there very much, if at all. And the reason is that they're not allowed to go the way they would naturally go, because of the pen.

The question then arises: in order to use high-altitude grazing quarters, is it feasible to provide accommodation for the herders, so that they can sleep near the night pen? A building program aimed at erecting small supplementary cabins is currently being implemented on most high mountain pastures, but the cost of this initiative is substantial. For that reason, in the early days of wolf predation, rural municipalities had to develop ad hoc solutions: trailers, where a track usable by motor vehicles allowed them to be brought in, helicopter flights to ferry in temporary shelters of the kind used at construction sites, and—for those who were exceptionally brave, exceptionally poor, or exceptionally subject to wolf predation—tents, a most uncomfortable form of accommodation at high altitude.

Sheepwagons are not a viable option because of the extremely steep mountainsides of the Alps and Pyrenees. Consequently only a small number of night pens can be used at high altitudes. The herder thus has no choice but to take the sheep out to their grazing sectors every morning and bring them back in the evening in order to pen them overnight. As a result, it is now not unusual to find that constantly traversed areas of high mountain pasture show signs of deterioration or even outright soil erosion. This negative impact of an unavoidable pastoral practice is currently being investigated by the Queyras Regional Natural Park:

> The Park is monitoring the consequences of the return of wolves for natural meadows and soil conditions. Damage is occurring. Previously, the sheep could be left out to find their own overnight rest area. Now, the herder has to bring them back to the cabin every night. That means erosion. You can see it in some places with your own eyes! It's not a matter of an assumption, it's really happening!

Inevitable Implications for the Health of the Flock

For the sheep, poorly maintained or overused night pens may cause various foot disorders (e.g., foot rot) that farmers and herders dread. Natural bed grounds and "rotating portable pens" would avoid the prospect of having to treat epidemic outbreaks. When the flock has to be brought back and penned overnight in the same place, the health of the sheep may be seriously at risk, especially in rainy weather. "I try to ensure that the sheep spend the night under healthy conditions so that they won't have problems with their feet. It's healthier to rotate the pens in any case."

Being constantly moved out and back may affect the health of the sheep, which are supposed to be in better condition when they are brought down from the high mountain pasture than when they were taken up there early in the summer. This is particularly challenging as by the end of the summer most of them are heavy with the lambs that they will bear in the fall, shortly after their return.

> When the sheep are left to themselves, they go on grazing late into the evening and start again early the following morning. But now they're penned in. The herder has to live, after all. So he pens them in at about 8 p.m., and then lets them out at 7 or 8 o'clock the next morning. . . . This means they lose grazing time and a lot of weight. Those hours spent not grazing when they should be grazing are inevitably going to affect their body condition at a time when they're at a late stage in gestation or beginning to lactate.

CONCLUSION

The presence of wolves in the French Alps is a recent phenomenon that has violently shaken the practices of sheep farmers and herders. It is forcing them to alter their practices in ways that are not yet known to be functional, effective, or even relevant.[30] A summer of ease and plenty on upland pasture—an essential restorative season for men and animals alike—can no longer be taken for granted. Even worse, the new situation is bringing about a far-reaching reassessment of the image of shepherds in the eyes of other users and managers of high mountain pasture areas.

The pastoralist approach to sheep husbandry has consistently demonstrated its adaptability and its capacity to evolve in response to changing situations in the Alps. Beginning in the 1990s, European agri-environmental policies encouraged it because of its contribution to the restoration or conservation of resources originating from biodiversity. In various regions, including the Alps in particular, natural environment managers now frequently search for experienced professional herders who are known for their competence. For other users of mountain areas, including hikers, the herder and his flock have become one of the attractions of the outdoor experience, as many a tourist information brochure will attest.

Now that wolves are back and a protected species, sheep farmers and herders have become a constraint, especially in the eyes of the wolf defense activists. The latter like to point to instances of poor management resulting in overgrazing and erosion. Accounts of flocks put out to pasture without a herder appear regularly in the militant naturalist press, as though that has become the general rule for an archaic occupation that has lost its skills and its sense of responsibility. "Good shepherds" are those who apply protection measures to the letter without complaining, and who do not make a fuss in public about wolf predation and the losses they sustain.

Flock protection measures are also significantly altering the image of herders in the eyes of other users of mountain areas. Herders with their flocks and dogs have become a potential hazard to them. To be sure, herders may be irritated by throngs of lighthearted, heedless backpackers, and they are quite happy to see them give the flock a wide berth. However, herders decline to be regarded as a public menace for doing what they have to do to protect their charges from predators. Some herders are honestly ashamed of the unsanitary conditions resulting from the required night pens, for they value their professional ethic with its tradition of conserving natural resources.

In view of these contradictory forces acting on pastoral sheep husbandry, we may ask whether sheep producers and herders should have to bear the burden of reorganizing their occupation by applying passive protective measures (assistant herders, guard dogs, and night pens) so as not to jeopardize the healthy growth of the wolf population.

In an effort to resolve the contradictory aspects of public policy, we propose a policy of active management of France's newly reestablished wolf population. This policy might be termed one of "lupotechny": "The concept of regulation [is gaining ground]. . . . Successful implementation of a plan of action of this kind in Europe, not only from a technical standpoint but in terms of social acceptance as well, would require the recruitment and training of Wolf Control Officers, whose actions would be structured on a 'lupotechnically' sound basis."[31] The aim of this policy would be to modulate the growth of the population and discourage wolves' opportunistic behavior toward domestic animals. We suggest that respect for wolves demands an environment that affords them living conditions where they are encouraged to exercise their skills as large predators on wild prey species. The objective would be to ensure that wolves continue to be protected, without putting pastoral sheep husbandry at risk. The disappearance of herders, or a substantial reduction in their numbers, would have a severe negative impact on other attributes of mountain ecosystems.

A precondition for a flourishing population of *Canis lupus* in Europe is that its conservation is compatible with other natural area management objectives and the activities of other users. The protection of nature cannot be reduced to full protection of a single species, regardless of its legal or political status. In the present situation, wolves are an emblematic heritage species that enjoys full protection no matter what, including the degradation of other natural resources which are protected under the same public policies.

Lupotechny, however demanding financially and in specific human skills, and however difficult to implement, would be preferable to the existing situation, consisting of (1) a laissez-faire approach to the growth of the wolf population, with its fully protected status; (2) no effort to develop means of distinguishing delinquent individual wolves or problem packs that have developed opportunistic predatory behavior targeting livestock, despite an abundant supply of wild prey; and (3) government action focusing exclusively on flock protection measures and compensation for losses.

The wolf population in France consists of (as of winter 2012) about 250 adults and sub-adults, with an increasing trend of +27 percent per year on average.[32] The annual budget is €8,000,000 (€7 million for protective measures and €1 million to compensate farmers for losses). This substantial slice of the pie is quite exceptional compared to other budget allocations for wildlife species conservation in France.* According to L. David Mech, an authoritative US biologist who is deeply committed

---

* Editors' note: The salaries of the forty agents (Wildlife Services and other) working full-time on wolf recovery at national scale (M€2/year) must also be considered. The total cost of wolf recovery in France is not less than €40,000 per wolf per year (US$53,000). It seems that the wolf is on its way to becoming another of France's luxury brands.

to protecting wolves, "As the cost of compensation increases, the public may very well begin to demand that conservation associations assume the burden instead of government. In any case, unless wolf populations are controlled, people may express opposition to compensation payments for losses caused by wolves."[33]

Once an active wolf control and population management policy has been implemented, it will be feasible to contemplate a pacified state of coexistence among livestock farmers, herders, and conservationists. This is a necessary condition for breaking the deadlock resulting from the application of two contradictory public policies, with adverse consequences for the pastoral way of life and the conservationist movement.

ACKNOWLEDGMENTS

I should like to extend my special thanks to all the sheep farmers and herders who were willing to humor me by participating in my field survey and describing their experiences with various methods of protecting their flocks from wolves. Christine de Sainte Marie and Jean-Paul Chabert, both agricultural economists with INRA, encouraged me to take on this controversial subject single-handed in the field and then accompanied me every step of the way. I am indebted to Jean-Pierre Olivier de Sardan, director of studies at the École des Hautes Études en Sciences Sociales (EHESS), for my training in socioanthropological field survey techniques. François Sigaut, director of studies at EHESS in Paris kindly agreed to serve as my thesis adviser. Lastly, Michel Meuret helped me identify the material in that thesis that was most relevant for the purposes of the present collective book. I am deeply grateful to them all.

NOTES

[1] Mendras, 1967.
[2] Alphandéry and Billaud, 1996b.
[3] Fabre and Lebaudy, 2004.
[4] Décret, J.O. 198, 1990.
[5] Peillon and Carbonne, 1993.
[6] Adam, 1993.
[7] Brard, 1996a.
[8] Brard, 1996b.
[9] Vincent, 2011.
[10] Estrosi and Spagnou, 2003.
[11] MEDD and MAAPAR, 2004.
[12] Hénault and Jolicœur, 2003.
[13] Estrosi and Spagnou, op. cit.
[14] Landrot, 1999.
[15] Jallet and Fabre, 2007.
[16] Life-Coex, 2006.
[17] Degioanni, 2003.

[18] FERUS, 2004.
[19] LCI/TF1, 2004.
[20] Meuret and Chabert, 1998.
[21] France Nature Environnement, 2005; FERUS, 2007.
[22] Planhol (de), 1969.
[23] Bobbé, 2000.
[24] Moret, op. cit.
[25] Ibid.
[26] Le Pape et al., 2001.
[27] Vincent, 2005; Calendre, 2007.
[28] Lamour, 1980.
[29] Lapeyronie, 2000–2003.
[30] Garde, 2007.
[31] Chabert et al., 2004.
[32] Kaczensky et al., 2013.
[33] Mech, 1995.

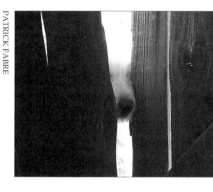

Herding Schools

CHAPTER 12

Herding Schools:
Upgrading Herding as a Skilled Occupation

*Michelle Jallet, Marie Labreveux
& Olivier Bel*

A LTHOUGH herding has been practiced in France for centuries, until the 1950s or so skills were passed from generation to generation within families. The advent of modern herders schools in France has brought a new respect and recognition to the skills of this occupation, and an increasing number of French guys and gals from urban areas with no agricultural background have become interested in herding as a profession. Training currently available at all herding schools in France shares a primary objective: professional skills development. In this chapter, we will outline the four long-cycle training programs offered at public establishments run by the Ministry of Agriculture; we will not consider the various short, practical-training courses organized by herders' associations or the livestock sector. We will also describe in-depth the two cases with which we are most familiar: namely the schools of the Provence and Rhône-Alpes Regions, which we ourselves manage. Although these various training programs may have different methods, many share similar objectives and concerns.

A CONCERN TO UPGRADE THE OCCUPATION OF HIRED HERDER
Historical Background
Until the 1950s, a local "master herder" (a *bayle*, to use the local term) managed "his" mountain pasture, organizing the work of a number of hired shepherds. He set up a hierarchy within the group of herders based on each individual's experience, age, and state of health.[1]

Shortly thereafter, livestock production techniques began to evolve at a rapid rate in response to the spread of intensive agriculture in plains areas and in the mountain valleys as well. Following a visit to the rugged upland region known as the Queyras in the department of Hautes-Alpes, the renowned French agronomist René Dumont commented, "[Agriculture in this region] is about as productive as it is in the most backward provinces of pre-revolutionary China."[2] He advised the local people to move down to lowland areas and take up intensive crop production; this, he argued, would be a more economically advantageous way of utilizing the region's agricultural workforce. According to Dumont, steep, dry terrain downslope from high mountain pastures should be planted with pine trees to avoid runoff and erosion problems. His advice was heeded: today, there are virtually no local sheep farmers left in the region. In the Alps, only transhumant sheep producers, mostly from Provence, continue to use the upland summer ranges, in some cases herding local flocks in addition to their own.

The 1970s saw the advent of the first European agricultural support payments, some of which went to sheep producers, and the "back-to-the-land" movement of people seeking to escape urban living conditions. Both developments created new jobs for herders, many filled by young persons from urban backgrounds who had moved to the countryside. Most of them were self-taught, and the most determined of them were able to learn the job simply by doing it. Ultimately, they succeeded in rehabilitating the occupation of shepherd, thanks to their experience and professionalism. They acquired the practical skills required not only of herders, but of sheep farmers who herd their own flocks, making use of a blend of traditional practice and modern technical knowledge. In contrast to their predecessors, these young people learned to apply their skills in a number of areas (sheep production, natural resource management, and others, in addition to herding), thereby refurbishing the image of an occupation that had become many-faceted and complex. Today, the self-taught shepherd from an urban background, who thirty years ago was regarded as a marginal figure if not something of a social outcast, has forged an identity based on the value and social recognition of his or her occupation.

Sources of an Enhanced Image

Such recognition is a recent phenomenon. For rural young people in the mid-twentieth century, the image of a herder condemned to tend a flock of sheep had only negative connotations: it was associated with boredom, hardship, isolation, and unsociability.[3] The situation is quite different today: the image of the shepherd has become a source of fantasy as well as profit. Plains regions have witnessed the development of what might be termed "pastoral tourism" — staged but colorful transhumance drives in many cases consisting of little more than a flock of sheep driven through a village. For their part, mountain tour operators now offer what they called "shepherd encounters."

Today, fortunately, the occupation of shepherd has much to recommend it, quite apart from this folklore aspect:

1. A shepherd fits rather neatly into the sustainable agriculture model, as it has come to be known: he consumes little fossil fuel, makes little use of motor vehicles, uses renewable energy, recycles his waste products, and buys nothing that he does not need. Regardless of his level of ecological awareness, a herder appears to be an eco-citizen and enjoys a positive image in the eyes of young city-dwellers.

2. He is important in the economic viability of the sheep-farming operation for which he works, contributing to the quality of the flock's nutrition on pasture, the ewes' reproductive success, the quality of the lambs or cheese obtained from them, and monitoring the flock's state of health. Most herders today are more than persons who tend flocks: they perform a variety of tasks, and this upgrades the image of their work.

3. Their work and presence on rangelands serve important environmental functions: maintaining open landscapes, controlling brush, preventing forest fires and avalanches, contributing to biodiversity conservation, and protecting the habitats of rare or endangered wildlife species.

4. Lastly, herding is central to multiple-use issues in rural areas. Both in the mountains and in plains regions, pastoral grazing lands are increasingly popular with tourists, some of whom are not as careful as they should be about leaving the herder and her flock undisturbed (see chapters 2, 11, and 15). Some herders are willing to welcome visitors on occasion during the winter, or even while on summer range. They are practicing a form of agro tourism, as they explain their work to visitors and offer suggestions for acceptable behavior in a shared mountain setting.

Over the past twenty years, these various forms of recognition have improved living and working conditions for herders. At the local level, progress has come about mainly due to the work of three stakeholders: (a) regional or departmental pastoral service organizations, such as the Pastoral Service Bureau for the Provence-Alpes-Côte d'Azur Region (CER-

A Herders' Association that has Helped Upgrade Its Members' Occupation

The Hautes-Alpes Shepherds and Cowherders Association was founded in 1978. Its accomplishments include drafting a collective agreement for hired sheep- and cow-herders who tend flocks or herds on mountain pastures to improve their living and working conditions. The association also promoted the establishment of a radio communication network between livestock farmers and herders to facilitate their work during the summer pasturing season.

The association originated and regularly updates a "summer season record" based on information supplied by herders, including the characteristics of flocks of sheep being summered at high altitude (size of flock, breeds, physical condition, and so on), pasture quality, number and comfort level of cabins, herder's wages, and quality of relations between herder and farmers. The association also organizes short, inexpensive training courses on various subjects such as botany, veterinary care, and shearing that also allow herders to get to know one another.

Nowadays the association is devoting its efforts to the task of ensuring that the previously mentioned collective agreement continues to provide good working conditions for shepherds and cowherders, including adequate wages.

The association has been recognized as speaking on behalf of sheep- and cow-herders working in the department of Hautes-Alpes. However, it has not become an institution with full-time representatives and salaried secretaries, and the membership would be very much upset if it did!

PAM) and the Ariège Pastoral Federation; (b) shepherds' and cowherders' associations (see inset); and (c) public corporate bodies and local officials (national parks, regional natural parks, departmental councils, communities of municipalities, and the like). These improvements have included the renovation or construction of cabins on summer range, complete with running water and solar panels; herding facilities such as access tracks, sorting pens, and rainwater catchment basins, helicopter transport, and radio and telephone equipment. These efforts provided herders with greater employment stability by reducing their isolation and making their work less labor-intensive.

At the national level, a professional upgrading operation on herding was launched in 2001 by the Savoie Alpine Economic Development Board.[4] Their aim was to assess the situation of pastoral sheep and cattle husbandry in the Rhône-Alpes region, and to submit suggestions to the

Interministerial Group on Pastoralism, whose mandate was to examine pastoralism in France (see details in chapter 2).[5] Outcomes of this initiative included recognizing the multiple tasks that the herder occupation entails and developing an employment scale for hired herders with a number of skill and competence levels, and associated wage differentials, for different degrees of responsibility (see Figure 1).

The proposed three levels of qualification cover progressively broader segments of the range of tasks entrusted to herders. This is a useful approach that should help upgrade their occupation. The problem facing young novice herders, however, is how to acquire the skills to qualify for levels 2 and 3, as shown in Figure 1. That is the mission of the herding schools run by the Ministry of Agriculture. These institutions offer skills development and/or certification courses that take the growing diversity and complexity of herding today into account.

Working herder - "This level includes the tasks of surveillance, tending and milking (where summer range activities include milk production)."

Skilled herder - "This level is appropriate where indicated on the grounds of substantial experience or formal qualifications, and includes the tasks of herding livestock and pastoral resource management. Employment at this level would comprise two categories, the higher of which might include such functions as receiving visitors or managing environmental constraints… This level is a prerequisite for management of a flock or herd consisting of animals owned by a number of different farmers."

Highly skilled herder - "This level also includes rangeland management and multiple use (visitor management) and environmental constraint management in addition to the tending of livestock."

FIGURE 1 – Proposed three levels of qualification for hired herder employment as developed by the Interministerial Group on Pastoralism (MAPAR, 2002). Summary of subgroup 3: Employment, training, professional activity (joint Chairs: P. Aubert and R. Tramier).

OVERVIEW OF LONG-CYCLE TRAINING PROGRAMS AVAILABLE FROM HERDING SCHOOLS

Five long-cycle training programs have been established in France. The earliest one, which was located in Rambouillet, near Paris, is now closed, but the other four are operational. All of them are offered at public establishments belonging to the Ministry of Agriculture. The programs are all located in the southern part of the country (see Figure 2).

The National Herders School in Rambouillet

The National Herders School in Rambouillet was established in 1794 on a tract of land located twenty-two miles southwest from Versailles and forty miles from Paris, which the King of France, Louis XVI, purchased

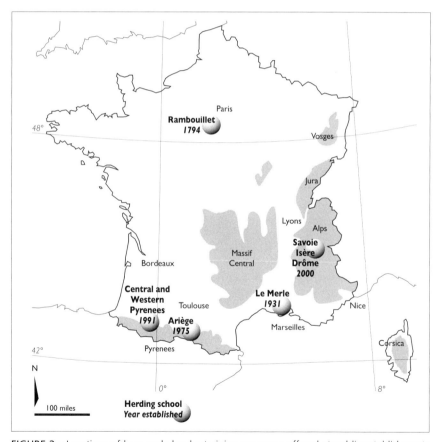

FIGURE 2 – Locations of long-cycle herder training programs offered at public establishments run by the Ministry of Agriculture. The Rambouillet Herders School, which was founded in 1794, has been closed since 1989. The other four, all of which are located in the southern part of the country, are operational.

eleven years prior. The late eighteenth century was a period when cities were expanding rapidly, but it was also a time when a return to the "natural order" and an agrarian economy was fashionable among European elites. Accordingly, in 1783 the king decided to create an experimental agricultural establishment in Rambouillet, to be known as "the King's Farm." In the following year he purchased from the King of Spain a flock of Merino sheep for the quality of their wool, which was the main product of sheep-farming in that age. The effort to improve wool breeds ("Merinization") was pursued in France and internationally until the First World War. Other types of livestock besides sheep were produced in Rambouillet, including Swiss cattle, African sheep, Angora goats, and later, under Napoleon Bonaparte, horses and water buffalo for use as draft animals. Numerous sheep farms, dubbed royal or imperial depending on the period, were established until 1870; they are now historic monuments.[6]

In 1939 the National Herders School in Rambouillet became a combined national sheep production school and learning center. The latter awarded an occupational certificate in sheep production after a nine-month training course. In subsequent years, the establishment came to specialize in general instruction in animal production, offering a variety of training courses, including technical courses for producers. The course on herding skills was discontinued in 1988–1989, although a specialist certificate in sheep production was offered for another four years.

Today, the Rambouillet National Sheep Farm receives 80,000 visitors a year. It conducts a number of sheep-related activities, some historical, some educational, and some cultural, such as the Wool Art Festival held in 2007. In 2010, the World Merino Conference was held there.

The Four Existing Establishments

The four long-cycle training programs currently available are presented by chronological order of establishment in Table 1.

The main characteristics of these programs as they stood at the time this chapter was written are summarized in the four following subsections. The origin and development of training programs available from the Merle Herders School (in Provence) and from the departments of Savoie, Isère, and Drôme (in the Rhône-Alpes region) are discussed at greater length in the following pages. The Pyrenees Mountain Transhumant Sheep/Cow Herder training program is presented in detail in the next chapter.

The Merle Training Program in Provence

The Merle Herders School was founded in 1931 in Salon-de-Provence (department of Bouches-du-Rhône), in the heart of a farming operation in

TABLE 1: Brief Descriptions of Currently Available Long-Cycle Training Programs

Year Established	Present training program title	Institution or organization	Type of attestation	Duration of course (months)	Maximum enrollment	Subjects
1931	The Transhumant Hired Herder	Merle CFPPA* & Monepellier SupAgro†	Level 5 National Diploma	12	15-20	Sheep, meat breeds
1975	The High Mountain Pasture Herder	High Mountain Herders Association & Pamiera CFPPA	Certificate of successful completion	10	10	Sheep; Cattle
1991	The Pyrenees Mountain Transhumant Sheep-Cow Herder	Oloron Sainte Maria LPA,‡ Lannemezan CFPPA & Etcharry AFMR§	Level 4 National Diploma	24	12 to 15	Sheep, dairy breeds; Cattle; Cheese
2000	The Alpine Mountain Pasture Sheep/Cow Herder	La Motte Servolex CFPPA, Die CFPPA & La Côte St André CFPPA	SIL** certification of successful completion	7	8 to 12	Cattle; Sheep

* CFPPA (Centre de Formation Professionnelle et de Promotion Agricole): Agricultural Extension and Professional Training Center
† Montpellier SupAgro (Centre International d'études supérieures en Sciences agronomiques): International Center for Advanced Studies in Agricultural Science
‡ LPA (Lycée Professionnel Agricole): Agricultural Vocational School
§ AFMR (Association pour la Formation en Milieu Rural): Association for Training in Rural Areas
** SIL (Spécialisation d'Initiative Locale): regional certification in a specific field of specialization, a regionally recognized qualification

the Crau plain. The training program, currently titled the Transhumant Hired Herder, is organized jointly by the Merle CFPPA and Monpellier SupAgro, an agricultural engineering institution, and is supported by funding from various sources, including the Provence Alpes Côte d'Azur (PACA) Regional Council. Every year, fifteen to twenty selected trainees attend the school for twelve months based on a training schedule that reflects the Provençal sheep meat production cycle, beginning in October with autumn lambing for sheep farmers in the Crau. The diploma is an occupational certificate in agriculture confirming that the trainee has completed ten "capitalizable units," each relating to one of the practical or theoretical subjects included in the program.

The school's 2007 information brochure concludes with the following passage, written by a well-known French novelist whose work has inspired many young people from urban backgrounds to pursue pastoralism:

Herder – This is a skilled occupation, not something that just anybody could do. No one would dream of deciding overnight to take up the occupation of locksmith, shoemaker, tailor, mason or whatever, but it seems perfectly natural to decide to take up the occupation of herder (just as it seems perfectly natural to decide to become a novelist or a poet or an artist). The person says to himself or herself, "Herding, why, there's nothing to it. Looking after sheep is something that by definition anybody can do. Instead of continuing to go to my bank, my insurance company, my government office or whatever every morning at 9 o'clock and sitting at a desk until 6, I'll go and herd sheep among the Provençal hills, surrounded by thyme and savory."

That's thyme that sheep won't eat.* Nothing is easy.

Jean Giono, 1962

The High Mountain Herder Training Program in Ariège

The high mountain herder training program in Ariège was established in 1975 in the central eastern Pyrenees (see Figure 2). Since 1994, it has been organized jointly by the High Mountain Herders Association and the Pamiers CFPPA. It is intended for persons who want to become cowherders or shepherds or, more generally, practice an occupation in a mountain setting. It is funded by the Midi-Pyrénées Regional Council, and every year it accepts ten trainees who have some experience herding sheep or cattle.

The program extends over a ten-month period. It consists of two modules:[7] (1) initial training on an individual basis during the winter (January to May) with a "tutor" who is himself a transhumant sheep or cattle farmer. This module enables the trainee to acquire a basic knowledge of livestock, herding, and the transhumant mode of husbandry as practiced in the Pyrenees; (2) following validation of the first module, the summer component of the program (May to October) takes place on a summer range, where the trainee is constantly supported and guided by a veteran cowherders or shepherd. The training is thus essentially one-on-one and hands-on. During the program, however, eight week-long sessions are organized in which the trainees are brought together, usually in a mountain chalet, for instruction by qualified experts in a variety of subjects: veterinary care, dog training, weather, botany, first aid in the mountain environment, and the like. The High Mountain Herders Association monitors each trainee to determine how well he has mastered the material and to help him make appropriate vocational and life choices. An individual

---

* Editors' note: The original French expression is, "*Ne pas manger de ce pain là.*" Jean Giono poetically altered this expression to "*Ne pas manger de ce thym là.*" *Pain* (bread) and *thym* (thyme) sound very similar in French. The original expression literally means, "He won't eat that kind of bread," and an equivalent English expression would be, "He would not stoop to that."

report is prepared by the trainee and submitted to an ad hoc board that decides whether he should be awarded a certificate of successful completion of the program.

In this department in the Pyrenees, where herding activity is still actively practiced despite far-reaching changes in the collective use of high-mountain summer pastures,[8] this program receives nearly 150 applications each year. Over 80 percent of the graduates find jobs, in most cases as cowherders as there is more demand for them at the present time.

The Training Program in the Western and Central Pyrenees

Since 1991, a second training course for herders has been available in the Pyrenees at a location somewhat further west than the high mountain herder training program in Ariège (see Figure 2). Its present title is the Pyrenees Mountain Transhumant Sheep/Cow Herder. The course is organized jointly by three organizations: the Etcharry AFMR, the Oloron Sainte-Marie LPA and the Lannemezan CFPPA, the latter two having authority to award diplomas. The course straddles two regions (Aquitaine and Midi-Pyrénées) and three departments (Pyrénées Atlantiques, Hautes Pyrénées, and Haute Garonne) and obtains funding from a variety of sources. Twelve to fifteen trainees are admitted, and their training continues for two years.

This program is organized in a "work-study" format, two-thirds of it taking place in the field and only one-third in the classroom. The "tutors" are livestock farmers who do their own herding (see chapter 2 for a discussion of this category of persons), and they are associated with the training at every stage: applicant selection, summer and winter practical skills acquisition, instruction in various subjects in a classroom setting, assessment of trainees' progress, and final validation. The program begins in May. Each trainee is assigned a tutor, and in mid-June trainee and tutor set out together for five months of real herding on high mountain pastures. In the fall, the trainees attend the agricultural vocational school in Oloron Sainte-Marie, where they compare notes on their individual work experiences. In addition, part of the school instructors' task at this stage is to relate the theoretical component of the course to what the trainees have already learned from actual practice.

In the western Pyrenees, it is still fairly common for dairy ewes to be herded on high-altitude pastures during the summer, and for the herder to milk them and make cheese right there on the range. Thus one of the objectives of the program is to train "herder cheesemakers." At the same time, trainees must also acquire other occupational skills, since pluriactivity is still the rule in these high valleys. Over the two-year period of the program, the task of validating trainees' mastery of the various subjects proceeds through a series of individual assessments, usually in work situations. The outcome is an "individual skills record" containing all the trainee's own written remarks and assessments. This record is the basis for the trainee's final defense of his performance before the board that determines whether to award a diploma. The diploma (level IV) is certified at the national level, making it the only one of its kind awarded to herders in France.[9]

The Training Program in the Rhône-Alpes Region

The training program in the Rhône-Alpes region, which is the most recent of the four, was established in 2000. The training is provided at three adult training centers: the Savoie and Bugey CFPPA, located in La Motte-Servolex (department of Savoie), and the CFPPAs in Côte Saint-André (department of Isère) and Die (department of Drôme). Here again, the objective of the program is to train both shepherds and cowherders, bearing in mind that they will have to find other jobs over the winter. Most of the program's funding comes from the Rhône-Alpes Regional Council, which realized that a need existed following an "Operation occupational enhancement" initiative aimed at herders with events organized in Chambéry in 2000 and La Motte-Servolex in 2001. The three departmental training centers work in close cooperation with their respective pastoral service bureaus. Between eight and twelve applicants are selected every year for seven months of training.

The program begins in August with an initial group training period on an Alpine summer range, supervised by school instructors. This is followed immediately by five weeks of individual practical training as the summer range season draws to a close. Next come five months of training in a wide variety of subjects, distributed over all three centers. In the midst of this part of the program, the trainees take another period of hands-on training under the guidance and support of a livestock farmer who practices winter transhumance in the southernmost part of the country. The program ends in February, when livestock farmers are hiring herders. The trainee uses his individual summer season record to make a final presentation before the board that decides whether he passes. The evidence of graduation is an SIL (regional certification in a specific field of specialization), which is a regionally recognized qualification.

FIGURE 3 – Graduating classes at the Merle Herders School in 1940–1941 (top) and 2009–2010 (bottom). Photos by: Le Merle Teachers' Archives (class of 1940–1941); M. Meuret (class of 2009–2010).

A CLOSER LOOK AT TWO TRAINING CENTERS

The Merle Herders School

Origins of the School and Its Herder Training Program

The story of the Merle Herders School begins in 1925, when the widow of prominent local banker Félix Abram bequeathed a thousand-acre estate known as Le Merle to an organization mandated to promote agricultural modernization (the Southern Regional Farm Bureau). The estate was located west of Salon-de-Provence, in the Crau plain (in the department of Bouches-du-Rhône, Provence). The bequest was accompanied by a number of stipulations in Mme. Élisa Abram's will: the beneficiaries were required to (1) establish an experimental farm at which research of relevance for the agriculture of the region was to be conducted; and (2) train young farmers interested in specializing in the cultivation of the Crau's hay meadows and herding flocks of sheep. In 1941, the Southern Regional Farm Bureau conveyed the bequest to the Montpellier National School of Agriculture, which in 2006 became SupAgro Montpellier, the International Center for Advanced Studies in Agricultural Science.

The Merle Regional Herders Training Center was founded in 1931. Its original target clientele consisted of young people between the ages of fourteen and eighteen. The training was divided into two parts: theoretical courses given at the center, with the estate's flock used for practical exercises, and ten months of practical learning at the farm of a sheep producer. Once trainees had completed these two periods of instruction, they had to take an exam, and if they passed, they were awarded diplomas certifying that they were qualified herders. From 1931 to 1935, the diploma was awarded by the French Sheep Producers Union; subsequently, it was awarded by the Ministry of Agriculture. The center operated in this way from 1931 to 1942 (see Figure 3 [top]: class of 1940–1941), when the German occupation was extended to southern France, putting an end to the training program. The center started up again in 1947, but in 1950 its work was interrupted once more by training-related difficulties.

The complications that arose at Merle at that time have been described by M. Fayn, president of the Mérinos d'Arles Breeders' Union:

> Between 1931 and 1950, 136 apprentice herders were trained at the Center. Unfortunately, serious difficulties tended to arise during the ten-month training periods at the farms of traditional sheep producers in the region. All too often, the learner found that he was working with a farmer or farm employees who had a good working knowledge of their trade but were not interested in trying to put the center's fine theories

into practice. So either the trainee adopted the farmer's or herders' methods and forgot all about the lessons that he had learned at the center, or he stood his ground, and the result was conflict, in which case he had to find another employer. The problem became serious enough that, in the view of Irénée Denoy, director of the Le Merle estate, and Jean Blanc, who at that time was the regional agent of the National Sheep Producers Federation, a new approach to professional training for herders was warranted. Denoy and Blanc decided that as an initial step, sheep farmers themselves and their employees should be provided with up-to-date information and acquainted with current thinking. Accordingly, an adult education course on the subject, billed as an "information and skills development session for sheep farmers," was introduced in 1950.[10]

Beginning in 1950, in accordance with the provisions of the 1925 will, training and skills development sessions for sheep farmers were held concurrently with the training courses for novice herders. By 1969, over a thousand sheep farmers had taken courses at the Merle school.[11]

In 1969 the Ministry of Agriculture introduced a new category of continuing skills development institutions known as agricultural extension and professional training centers (CFPPAs). This term is still in use today: the official title of the Merle school is the Merle CFPPA.

Until the 1990s, two training sessions for future herders were held per year, each featuring an eight-month cycle; a total of approximately twenty-four herders were trained every year. By 1995, however, the number of applicants had begun to decline, the image of the school was losing some of its luster, and the program was in difficulty. Sheep farmers in particular were expressing disillusionment that the training no longer met their expectations. Accordingly, CERPAM was mandated to conduct an in-depth study of working relations between farmers and herders.[12] One of the problems identified by the farmers was, "We need competent workers who won't leave!"[13]

Following two years of investigation, CERPAM suggested it might be able to make a useful contribution to a review of the content of the Merle training program and the way it was organized. Accordingly, a working group was mandated to prepare a list of activities entrusted to herders. The working group's steering committee was made up of sheep farmers, herders, union representatives (including the Southeastern France Regional Sheep Federation), and livestock sector support bodies. Once the working group had completed its task, CERPAM joined forces with the Merle CFPPA to overhaul the training program to develop course content that more adequately reflected recent changes in herders' job skills and the expectations of the region's sheep farmers. This was the origin of the Transhumant Hired Herder Occupational Certificate in Agriculture, a qualification first awarded at the session that began in October 1999; it continues to be awarded to this day (see Figure 3 [bottom]: class of 2009-2010).

How the Training Program is Currently Organized

The new training program is organized along entirely different lines from its predecessor. The latter was criticized primarily on the grounds that it comprised two sessions per year: one from March to October (S1) and the other from July to February (S2), with a period of practical work/training experience herding a flock of sheep on summer range common to both sessions. Under these conditions, the trainee, who in many cases was not from a farming background, found it difficult to orient within the year-long sheep production cycle. To illustrate, during S1 the rams were being prepared for the spring breeding period, while lambing took place during S2! Similarly, trainees in S2, who arrived in July and were immediately sent up to the mountains to learn herding at firsthand, frequently behaved as though they were on holiday; equipped with little more than shorts and sandals, they tended to run for their lives at the first thunderstorm. Many of them dropped out of the program, mainly because they were inadequately prepared.

Another criticism leveled at the earlier program was that it was designed more for farm owners than for employees. Many hours were devoted to the fundamentals of business practice (management, accounting, tax law, and the like), at the expense of practical skills. A trainee might graduate from the course knowing how to prepare an accounting statement but not how to tend a flock of sheep!

In the light of these charges, the new training program introduced at the Merle school in 1999 runs for an unbroken period of twelve months, from October to October. It was designed to correspond to the production cycle of the region's transhumant sheep, which as a rule lamb in the fall. It comprises six periods of attendance at the school and three periods of practical experience, as seen in Figure 4):

- October–November: six weeks of practical work on a sheep farm during lambing and the following period, caring for the young lambs;
- February–March: six weeks during shearing and herding in an area of hills or wooded rangeland in Provence, using shepherd dogs;
- July–September: fourteen weeks herding and tending a flock on summer mountain pasture.

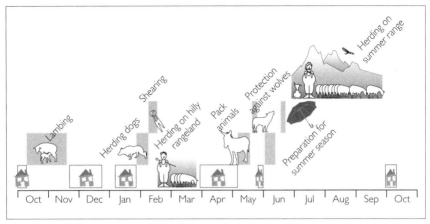

FIGURE 4 – Schematic presentation of the twelve-month training program in effect at the Merle Herders School since 1999, comprising six periods of classroom work and three periods of hands-on practical work.

The school decided to offer a course with the award of a diploma certifying that the recipient was a "highly skilled worker." The course comprises 1,760 training hours, a total adequate to train competent hired workers that regional sheep farmers require. They are highly professional, thanks to repeated sequences of practical hands-on learning activities; they possess specialized knowledge in transhumance and shepherding on summer range; and they are also capable of working in all other capacities on a sheep-farming operation.

The school's present staff members are all from farming backgrounds, and all of them have direct experience with sheep production as farmers and/or herders. For specialized technical subjects, such as guard dog training, the school brings in outside experts. During periods of hands-on practical training outside the school environment, which afford opportunities for transmitting knowledge, skills, and self-management capabilities, all trainees receive individual support and guidance from a sheep farmer or an experienced herder. At the same time, they have continued supervision from in-house staff members, each of whom undertakes feedback and assessment visits to one or more of the various field sites.

Applicant Selection

From 1999 to 2008, the numbers of applicants seeking admission to the Merle school have increased (see Figure 5). Most of these would-be herders are from urban backgrounds, as is also the case with a majority of applicants to other herding schools. As a rule, they have discovered the school through the internet and have no personal or family connection

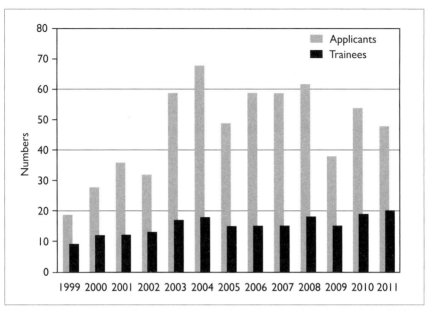

FIGURE 5 – Numbers of applicants and trainees admitted to the Merle Herders School (1999–2011).

with herding sheep on pasture, or even any familiarity with livestock-keeping.

The school accepts only fifteen to twenty trainees per year (see Figure 5) for two reasons. The school cannot accommodate more than that, and the regional council provides funding for only twelve trainees. Funding for additional applicants must be obtained from other sources (fund-raising organizations that support training activities, private firms, and the like). The additional applicants are usually working herders who have learned their trade on the job and who have come to realize that "training at the Merle school would enable me to upgrade my job skills."

Every applicant is required to appear before an admissions board, which looks at his file, including work history and relevance of career plans. Since 1999 the board has functioned as a selection panel consisting of Merle staff members, hired herders, sheep farmers, former trainees, and technicians employed by livestock sector support bodies. Interviews take from thirty to forty minutes and focus on applicants' motivation. Two examples of letters of interest are presented in Figure 6.

Beginning in 2004, the Merle school has also provided training for a separate group of five to seven "assistant herders" each year (numbers not indicated, Figure 5). These are persons who are recruited every year by a group of sheep farmers in the department of Alpes-Maritimes to work for

311

Subject: Request for information about herder training program
To: Michelle.Jallet@supagro.inra.fr

Dear Ms. Jallet,
My name is X. and I live in Belgium. I am 28 years old and hold a BA in History of Art and Archaeology. I have been employed under fixed-term contracts as a site supervisor for a number of archaeological excavation projects, but am now considering a quite different career choice: I am interested in taking training with a view to becoming a herder or herder-cheesemaker. I have given this idea careful consideration, despite the fact that this part of the world is a long way from a mountain pasture region. I have spent every summer in mountain country ever since I was a small child (in the Dolomites, which is where I originally come from), but I have come to regard this type of sporadic contact as unsatisfactory. My interest in herder training is thus not a mere dream, but a deep-rooted aspiration to which I propose to devote all my energy. I am motivated above all by a desire to live close to nature and rediscover the rhythm of the seasons. To date I have been exploring possibilities in this connection on the Internet, and you are the first persons I have contacted.
Before submitting a formal application, I would like to have some information:
1. Is the training program open to "foreigners" such as myself?
2. How much is the tuition?
I look forward to hearing from you shortly.
Yours sincerely,

Subject: Application for transhumant hired herder training program
To: genevieve.andreis@supagro.inra.fr

Dear Ms. Andréis,
I have worked on various occasions with both goat producers and sheep producers in my native region, and I should now like to take the next step by training to become a qualified herder.
I fear that I have missed the application deadline, but I wonder whether I might be allowed to enter the program even though it is already under way. This possibility was suggested to me by the herder of my own village, Mr. Arnaud D., who informed me how to contact you.
My resume is enclosed. If you require any further information, please do not hesitate to get in touch. 04.66.77.XX.XX or 06.14.55.XX.XX.
In the hope of a favorable reply, I remain,

Yours sincerely,
Ms. X

FIGURE 6 – Sample letters of interest written by applicants to the Merle Herders School (identities not disclosed).

a full year, not just for the summer pasture season; they are not seasonal assistant herders hired under "section t" contracts to protect flocks from predation by wolves. The Merle school provides them with seven weeks of training spread over a year. It is not unusual for some of them to apply for the full-scale herder training program the following year.

Validation of Trainees' Skills

The Merle school is an accredited institution whose graduates qualify for a Level 5 Occupational Certificate in Agriculture issued by the Ministry of Agriculture. In validating trainees' skills, the school relies on the national benchmark job description for "Highly Skilled Worker in Specialized Livestock Production" that requires the program to be organized in capitalizable units (CUs, or independent training modules standard for all French professional schools). The trainee qualifies for the final diploma once he has completed a specified number of CUs.[14] The Merle training program comprises ten CUs, of which seven are more or less standard (mathematics, French, animal husbandry, etc.), while the remaining three from the following list are unique and specific to the region:

- sheep dog training
- the use of pack animals in herding activities
- summer range management in areas subject to wolf predation
- preparations for a season herding on summer range: what you will need, coping with inclement weather conditions, mountain plant and animal life, etc.

The regulations governing CU-based validation are not rigid; they leave room for innovative approaches. For example, individual assessments are carried out on high mountain summer pasture: the instructor visits the trainee and his tutor, who is a sheep farmer or an experienced herder, and joins forces with the latter to evaluate the skills the trainee has acquired during the period under review. This will include organization of his daily activities on the mountain pasture, management of the flock and pastoral resources, anticipation of problems, and so on. In addition, a "skills acquisition record" is progressively developed by the trainee as he gains practical experience or attends one-day workshops at a farm and thereby learns the skills outlined in the fifteen task sheets that describe a herder's duties.

During the training program, a panel made up of equal numbers of sheep farmers or working herders and instructors meets two or three times during the year to consider the individual trainees and validate, or not validate, the CUs completed by each of them. The panel recommends

How Much Does It Cost?

While costs vary among schools and regions, we present recent costs for the Merle School to give some indication of the costs for training and who pays those fees.

The annual cost per trainee at Le Merle is currently €9,800 (US$13,000), which corresponds to 1,000 teaching hours. A trainee pays nothing but housing charges, car and fuel, personal dress, mountain shoes, and some daily food for himself and his sheepdog. During schooling, each trainee gets a salary. Depending how long the trainee has worked in France as a professional, and pay contributions at that time to French state and regions, the amount of salary may be 300 to €650 per month (US$400–870).

The French system of professional schooling provides 100 percent monetary support to the school. Support can be obtained by the school if their trainees are either students that quit upper-level studies, working in other occupations who want to change jobs, or adults (up to forty-five years of age) in search for an occupational reconversion, or any other adult in search of a job (not necessarily his first job) who is not already getting unemployment support from France. The Provence region provides support of €4 (US$5.30) per hour of training, and the national support for adult schooling supplements this.

Is it painless for trainees? Perhaps not. Indeed, due to high costs, quite often trainees are unable to pay for their housing at school. They prefer to sleep in a van or at a local sheep farmer.

The editors

trainees for diplomas once the entire program has been completed. This system, which is specific to continuing professional training, is highly flexible, as it affords a means of validating test results over a five-year period. Every year a few trainees who failed a test during their training year get another opportunity to apply for validation of the CU needed to complete the program. The yearly success rate at the Merle school's final examination is not very meaningful, as the rate achieved by the trainees in any year may improve over the following years. Even so, nearly 70 percent of them pass every year, and the rate is improving thanks to a more effective individual trainee monitoring policy.

Transition to the Workforce

Demand for qualified herders is increasing steadily. There is always work for them on sheep farms that practice transhumance, including summer and winter transhumance. Consequently, most newly fledged Merle graduates have no difficulty finding employment. In the first year, they are usually hired under seasonal contracts to summer flocks on mountain ranges. A follow-up study on the school's former trainees since 1999 has shown that nearly 66 percent of them are still working as herders with at least one seasonal contract every year. They are working within the region as well as over the entire length of the Alpine arc. As they have acquired experience over the years, some of them have become sheep farmers themselves and now look to the Merle school to supply herders they can hire for their operations. The wheel has come full circle.

The Alpine Mountain Pasture Shepherd and Cowherder Training Program in the Rhône-Alpes Region

The relatively new Alpine mountain pasture shepherd and cowherder training program in the Rhône-Alps was established at the request of the dairy cattle farmers of Savoie, who produce "mountain-made" milk and cheese. In the northern Alps, producers who summer their cows on mountain pastures refer to themselves as *bergers* (the French term used elsewhere for shepherds only) and not as *vachers* (cowherders — see also chapter 2). Consequently the program is called (see Figure 7) Formation Berger-vacher d'Alpage, literally, "The Alpine Mountain Pasture Sheep/Cow Herder"

An Inconclusive Initial Experiment

An initial training course was introduced in 2000 at the La Motte-Servolex CFPPA, in the department of Savoie. It was only three and a half months long, including a probationary month of hands-on experience at the end of the course, the beginning of the summer range season, with a tutor who was a cattle farmer and potential employer. The farmer and the CFPPA signed a training contract for the duration of the course. If the trainee and the farmer were both satisfied with the outcome, a work contract was signed for the remainder of the summer range grazing season.

For three years this short program worked fairly well, but only as a refresher course for persons from farming backgrounds. However, some farmers did not act as tutors. Rather, they left the trainee to manage as best he could during the probationary period. This situation led to discouragement on the part of the CFPPA and the farmers and trainees. Accordingly, the CFPPA decided to adopt a different approach as a result of the proceedings and conclusions of the Second International Herders Conference.[15]

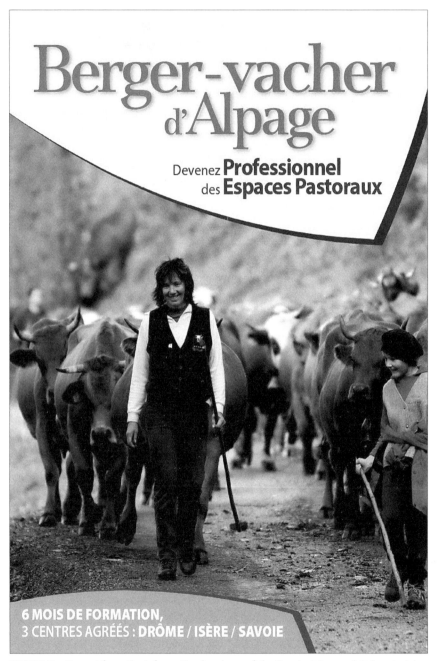

FIGURE 7 – Excerpt from the information brochure of the Savoie, Isère, and Drôme training program.

Designing the Present Training Program

One important change was to enlist partners for the training program from outside the borders of the department of Savoie. The Savoie Alpine Economic Development Board (SEA-73) began by contacting the Pastoral Service Bureaus of the two departments further south: the Isère Alpine Development Federation (FAI) and the Departmental Mountain Economic Development Association (ADEM) in the department of Drôme. As those bureaus were not accredited to offer long-cycle training programs, they approached the CFPPAs in La Côte Saint-André (department of Isère) and Die (department of Drôme). Networking these six structures (three CFP-PAs and three pastoral service bureaus) was a simple matter, as a number of instructors and rangeland technicians already knew one another and shared a common interest in upgrading herding as a skilled occupation. Another factor in the decision to expand the initiative to a more regional scale was that none of the individual departments had either the financial resources or the motivation to organize its own training program.

The design phase for the new training program took up most of 2002 and 2003. The underlying idea was to enable every trainee to translate his interest in a pastoral lifestyle into a viable professional career. Accordingly, it was essential to encourage them to become involved in the life of the region as more than just guardians of flocks or hired milkers and cheesemakers. The region had recently been the scene of a number of "agriculture and rural life" initiatives, and the designers of the training program drew upon experience acquired there to develop a course that enabled trainees to acquire the skills they need to herd cattle or sheep on summer range and to motivate them to engage in other activities, such as crafts, forestry, or tourism in the same part of the country.

Ultimately, it was deemed preferable to offer a training program that would equip the trainee with occupational skills but would not award him a formal diploma, as any institution that offers a diploma is subject to a set of constraints (e.g., it is required to teach general subjects, such as mathematics and French) not readily compatible with training focused on technical skills. There was another and perhaps more important reason as well: the pastoral service bureaus of the three participating departments were committed from the outset to guaranteeing to farmers that the program's graduates would be competent herders, and guaranteeing to trainees that they would be able to find jobs. Accordingly, they decided that the program would award an SIL, a regionally recognized certificate of competence in a specific occupational field.

The training calendar was designed with one primary aim in mind, namely to ensure that trainees would be employable as soon as they completed the program. For an SIL program, regional funding requirements stipulate a total of six hundred hours of theoretical classroom work and hands-on practice combined. Thus, it was necessary to ensure that the trainees complete six hundred hours by the time farmers recruit them for the summer transhumance season in March or April. The timing of the hands-on training period on summer range was a problem, as the designers of the program wished to avoid the aforementioned risk of a farmer who was supposed to provide instruction neglecting his duties and no experienced herder to serve as a tutor. In the end, the following schedule was adopted:

- receive new trainees late in August;
- spend one week as a group on a summer range to learn about the fundamentals of the herding profession;
- do five weeks of hands-on practical work at the end of the summer pasture season;
- complete twenty weeks of classroom work and short-term specialized training, with a break in January for one week of hands-on practical work on an individual or small group basis under the support and guidance of a farmer during winter transhumance;
- finish the training course late in February, at the beginning of the period when farmers are looking for herders for the summer pasture season.

Here, as elsewhere, a trainee is never left alone with a herd or flock on summer pasture. He is under the nearly constant support and guidance of the working herder, whose function it is to act as a tutor. It is equally essential that the farmer take his educational duties seriously. Thus, farmers and experienced herders are asked to sign a formal "training contract" with instructors from CFFPAs and pastoral service bureaus providing oversight services throughout.

Selection Procedure

Since 2003 the Savoie-Isère-Drôme herder training program has attracted approximately fifty applicants a year. The first step in the selection process consists of reading applicants' letters of interest and eliminating those who appear to have an overly idealized view of their proposed profession (e.g., "I love nature, I have always grown flowers on my balcony"). Approximately twenty applicants are weeded out at this stage. The others are considered by a selection board that meets in December and again in April, six months or four months before the training begins. The board consists of one cattle or sheep farmer, one shepherd or cowherder, and one rangeland technician or CFPPA staff member. Applicants are interviewed individually for approximately thirty minutes. The board listens carefully to the applicant's reasons for choosing to become a professional herder, noting in particular the realism of his thinking about the seasonal nature of the work. On occasion, when an applicant clearly has never seen a flock of sheep or a herd of cattle in his life, the board will suggest that he put in two weeks of hands-on experience at the operation of a cattle or sheep farmer, who will then have input into the selection process. In the end, letters of acceptance are sent to approximately fifteen applicants. In practice, only eight to twelve of them are likely to turn up late in August; the others presumably change their minds about their professional ambitions.

The selected applicants come from a variety of social and professional backgrounds. They tend to be from urban areas and are generally between nineteen and fifty years of age (their average age is thirty). Most of them are men, but approximately one-third are women. All of them have held one or more jobs; their aggregate work experience covers a wide range of fields. In some cases, their grandparents or great-grandparents were farmers who produced crops or livestock.

The Summer Season Record: How to Get Maximum Benefit from Direct Hands-On Experience

A central part of the program is the trainee's individual "summer season record." For hired herders in the Rhône-Alpes region, this has become a standard item. The record is designed to connect the herder with farmers and the pastoral service bureau. At the end of the season, the herder submits it to his employers as a summary of the season's work and a source of pointers for possible improvements for the following season.

The individual summer season record, then, is a working document, not something developed expressly for the training program, and the subject headings are the result of input from various pastoral service bureaus and associations. In the case of trainees, it should be used as a logbook, containing an account of the experiences of the individual, fleshed out with notes, sketch maps and personal drawings. The trainee should also use it to jot down questions for instructors when he comes down from the mountain range. In addition, it is an essential tool for the final assessment of the trainee's skills.

Courses: Advantages and Disadvantages of the Use of a Number of Different Locations

Courses are given for two weeks at a time at each of the three CFPPAs in turn, with the result that the trainees are compelled to undertake "trans-

humance" treks of their own at fairly frequent intervals. The idea is to fa-
miliarize them with the specific contexts of the three departments (Savoie,
Isère, and Drôme) with respect to the pastoral mode of husbandry, the
issues confronting them, and their respective job markets. The courses are
given by CFPPA instructors and pastoral service bureaus, which provide
information about regulations governing herding on summer pastures.
Specialists are brought in to discuss dog training, the use of pack mules,
solar energy applications, and the like.

Every trainee learns how to become both a shepherd and a cowherder.
If he takes his summer hands-on training with a flock of sheep, he will be
assigned to a cattle producer in the winter and vice versa. All trainees are
required to take a course on cheesemaking and to take their turns milking
the cows at La Motte Servolex CFPPA.

This practice of providing instruction at different locations brings the
trainees into contact with a variety of instructors, enabling the training institutions to share their respective areas of specialization and workloads.
There are disadvantages as well, including substantial travel and accommodation costs for trainees, while instructors and their partners sometimes find it difficult to arrange meetings and exchanges of information.

The Difficulty of Providing Training to Find Complementary Jobs

A hired herder's work contract expires when he comes back down from
the mountain range. Cowherders' contracts are for a hundred days, and
even assuming good pay, that is not enough to enable them to support
a family. The same applies to most shepherds, although the terms of
their contracts are more variable. For that reason, the program ensures
that trainees are aware of various possibilities for employment and of
job creation initiatives outside of herding in mountain regions. This is
the subject of a ten-day module that gives specific examples of combinations of activities, presented by persons who work that way themselves.
At the present time, the module is too short, and experience has shown
there is little point trying to motivate a trainee to look for one kind of job
when he has signed on for training for a different kind of job. Follow-up
surveys conducted since 2003 have shown that former trainees usually
take the traditional route of looking for short-term seasonal jobs in the
agriculture sector.

Validation of Skills and Prospects for Employment

Trainees are tested throughout the year, and in all cases they are informed of the results. Written tests are given on all subjects, along with
practical assessments in hands-on situations, such as milking cows. At

the end of the program, the main assessment tool is the trainees' summer season records, presented by each trainee orally before the examining board. The ensuing discussion is much like an end-of-season summary presented by a working herder to his employers. Trainees are aware of this, and it strongly motivates them. Every trainee is assessed first and foremost on his account of the overall organization of the summer herding place and how the season went. Each trainee is also assessed on how well he has used theoretical and practical training to deal with issues that arose during the summer herding season. The results have been impressive: only one trainee has failed in the five years that the program has been in operation.

How well has this recently established training program done in terms of its graduates' success in finding employment? Trainees receive close support from the three departmental pastoral service bureaus, with their constantly updated lists of employers. They finish late in February, and are in the job market immediately. Follow-up surveys show that most graduates are hired for the summer pasture season following completion of the training program. Others, preferring not to work alone, become assistant herders. To date, all have become shepherds or cowherders within two years of taking the program, with women tending to prefer working with cattle rather than sheep.

CONCLUSION
Differences in Design but Shared Concerns
Herders schools exist in every region of France in which transhumance is practiced (except the Auvergne region in south-central France), with every school focusing on the sectors in which its region specializes (cattle, dairy sheep, meat sheep). The various training programs differ in lengths and organization but have several features in common.

They are all continuing professional development programs for an adult clientele (i.e., persons at least eighteen years of age). There are no herder training courses within the primary or secondary school curriculum. At most, there are "introduction to pastoralism" modules in the professional or technological sections of agricultural secondary schools.

The body of statutory instruments governing continuing professional training programs must meet both the officially formulated needs of a particular region and the requirements of a profession. Herding schools accept this concept: all the training programs have been initiated in response to demand from livestock farmers seeking to maintain or develop pastoral practices recognized as beneficial for a region as a whole, including long-range transhumance in particular.

All these programs are organized by objective, seeking to inculcate specific skills. While teaching basic techniques appears to be simple enough, it is more difficult to simultaneously teach trainees how to apply those techniques effectively, let alone teach a herder's know-how and self-management skills. A herder has to learn how to adapt, observe and anticipate, to acquire the "herder's eye" through personal experience (see chapter 14). It is not at all obvious if or how such skills can or should be taught and the trainee's progress assessed.

This is why the various training centers emphasize hands-on experience in real-life situations, where knowledge transfer is based on the skills of actual working herders or farmers. Regardless of the name selected for this process ("tutoring," "guidance and support," or some other term), the objective is the same: to maintain herders' know-how, not by providing standardized answers, but by putting trainees in situations where they will discover their own ways to learn and understand. The acquisition of knowledge takes time, however, as herding is a craft that can only be mastered through experience.

The seasonal nature of herders' profession is an integral aspect of most of these training programs. Some devote more attention to it than others, and they adopt different approaches, but all try to help their trainees to become aware of various possibilities for combining herding with supplementary jobs, such as shearing, logging, ski slope grooming, handicrafts, guiding hikers or the like during the remainder of the year.

A final shared concern is the numbers of trainees admitted to these programs. In the aggregate, full-length training programs turn out no more than fifty qualified shepherds/cowherders per year. This is not adequate to meet demand, representing only 2.5 percent of current annual turnover in the shepherd population (see chapter 2). Of course, some young people also try to become herders every year without any formal training (see next section). Assuming approximately as many of these people as there are qualified graduates, the total of new entrants is still only 20 percent of the renewal rate required given that France's herder population is getting up in years.[16] There are perhaps 150 applicants every year who are denied admittance to a training program. Many applicants clearly are not strongly motivated and admissions boards have good reason to turn them away. Even so, it is becoming a matter of urgency to reconsider enrollment limits, which are largely restricted by the funding available for them.

Many herders learn their occupation on the job, either by choice or because they have not been accepted into a training program. We shall not take time to list the advantages and disadvantages of the various ways of learning how to become a herder,[17] nor to compare and contrast different learning methods.[18] An entire chapter would not suffice for that task. However, we may legitimately ask why the same situation recurs each year with two quite different types of trainees taking the same training: the neophyte who "has never seen a sheep in his life," and the experienced herder who decides to "go back to school" after practicing his occupation for a number of years.

Profile of Trainee Herders and Their Prospects for Professional Success

Are herders born or made? Uninformed French citizens think that herding is still an inherited occupation: "Grandpa was a herder, and I am a herder, so you, too, will be a herder, my son!" In reality, this "genetic" route is no longer the way herding is learned. And a good thing, too, for if no one ever became a herder apart from the offspring of livestock producers or herders, or even young people from rural families, the shortage of qualified herders would be even more acute than it is in a country that is now over 80 percent urban. Moreover, the sons and daughters of livestock farmers frequently expect to take over the family farm and prefer to learn how to do the job properly by taking courses for prospective farm operators, which are more advanced than herder training programs.

Most herder training centers report that approximately 80 percent of their trainees are from urban backgrounds, with rural roots increasingly far behind them (see also chapter 13). This situation is not a problem, but it requires trainees to master both technical skills and cultural skills, including the distinctive vocabulary of herders.

When they enter the program, trainees from urban backgrounds have usually been educated up to the same level as the courses they are about to undertake, or even beyond. Most of them have held jobs, and because their histories vary so widely, it is difficult to extract relevant statistics from the available data. A trainee may be a teacher of Latin who has decided to change career, an Air France flight attendant seeking to make a childhood dream come true, or a software developer whose partner has walked out on her, to give a few examples.

Most trainees are in the twenty-six-to-thirty age group, and they tend to be unmarried. A growing proportion of them are women, who account for 30–50 percent of applicants to herder training programs in recent years. These young women are strongly motivated, and in many cases they possess skills the farmers desire, especially for working in sheep barns during the lambing season. They tend to be more "maternal," as well as more dedicated and fatigue-resistant than their male counterparts.

Women graduates have no difficulty finding employment with sheep, goat, and cattle production operations during the summer transhumance season as well as the rest of the year.

For trainees who intend specifically to work with breeding ewes, a common denominator is perceptible: they are making an career choice, of course, but they are also looking forward to a way of life, a "quality of life," as the trainees themselves put it, that will offer "some peace and quiet," at least during the summer pasture season, and will enable them to escape from "being dependent on the consumer society." They are making a life choice, with implications for their relations with other people and with material possessions, first and a career choice second. In most cases, the appropriateness of their career choice has to be validated, or invalidated, after the training and once they get a job in the profession.

Over the past decade there has been steady growth in the number of applicants with some form of nature conservation-related training. These persons have no difficulty accepting new practices arising from European agri-environmental policies. Indeed, they are sometimes quite creative in the way they, for instance, alter a grazing circuit to include areas not usually grazed by the flock.

These "herder-naturalists" are keenly observant of animal behavior, and their more holistic approach gives them an advantage over their fellow herders in the form of a more intuitive and, more importantly, a quicker awareness of how a flock of sheep is likely to respond to the characteristics of a particular grazing area. However, friction may arise when this approach diverges from more traditional practices of experienced herders, for these young, innovative herders are not necessarily interested in receiving advice from their elders.

In any case, the profile of a skilled herder in the twenty-first century will emerge by degrees from an amalgam of these various approaches and forms of awareness.

ACKNOWLEDGMENTS

We thank all those who helped or inspired us, directly or indirectly, in preparing this chapter, including in particular:

Geneviève Andréïs (co-instructor at the Merle Herders School) and Fabrice Cartier (rangeland technician with the Drôme Departmental Mountain Economic Development Association)

All sheep production sector stakeholders (farmers, facilitators and technicians, economic partners, and presidents of livestock sector support bodies) for their assistance and support for our herder training programs

Each of the successive directors of the CFPPAs that worked to develop effective training courses in the departments of Savoie, Isère, and Drôme

Michel Meuret for his unfailing encouragement and invaluable assistance preparing the text

Guillaume Constant and Marc Bouillon, herders and partners, who devoted time to the task of rereading it

And not forgetting our former trainees who have now become herders and whose passion we share.

NOTES

[1] Mallen, 2001.

[2] Dumont, 1956.

[3] Baumont, 2005.

[4] SEA Savoie et Haute-Savoie, 2001.

[5] MAPAR, 2002.

[6] Association des Anciens Élèves de la Bergerie Nationale de Rambouillet (Rambouillet National Sheep Farm Graduates Association), 1986.

[7] Formation des Pâtres de Haute Montagne, 2005.

[8] Eychenne, 2006.

[9] Répertoire National des Certifications Professionnelles, 2007.

[10] Fayn, 1973.

[11] Ibid.

[12] Legeard, 1996.

[13] Monneyron, 2003.

[14] MAP, 2006.

[15] SEA Savoie et Haute-Savoie, 2001.

[16] Legeard, op. cit.

[17] Moneyron, op. cit.; Tolley, 2004; Baumont, op. cit.

[18] Bachelard, 2002.

CHAPTER 13

The Pyrenees Mountain Transhumant Sheep/Cow Herder Training Program

Pierre Gascouat, Danielle Lassalle & Sandrine Verdier

IN the year 2000, a diploma of qualification as a Pluriactive Sheep/Cow Herder was approved by the French government on the basis of a benchmark job description drafted and applied in the western half of the Pyrenees Mountains.[1] This region comprises, west to east, the three departments of Pyrénées-Atlantiques, Hautes-Pyrénées, and Haute-Garonne (see map, Figure 1). The diploma, which identifies the holder as a qualified "Transhumant Sheep/Cow Herder," is a level IV certification, which in France verifies that the holder is deemed competent to work on an independent basis. At the present time, this national-level certification is in a category of its own in the National Directory of Occupational Certifications.[2] Two training centers are accredited to award the diploma: the Oloron Sainte-Marie Agricultural Vocational School (LPA = *lycée professionnel agricole*) and the Lannemezan CFFPA.

The construction of this training program, the subject of the first section of this chapter, grew out of the Pyrenees Mountain Pluriactive Sheep/Cow Herder Training and Development initiative. This effort, promoted by farming sector organizations, training centers, and herders' associations to ensure the survival of pastoral husbandry in the high valleys of the western and central Pyrenees, was launched as a training program within the department of Pyrénées-Atlantiques in 1991. A multidisciplinary team from a group of institutions* developed and tested a work-

* Etcharry Association for Training in Rural Areas (AFMR, Association Pour la Formation en Milieu Rural), Oloron Sainte-Marie LPA, Pyrénées-Atlantiques Departmental Sheep Production Center (CDEO, Centre Départemental de l'Élevage Ovin), Hautes-Pyrénées Pastoral Service Bureaus.

study training program in which theoretical instruction alternated with hands-on experience under the supervision of farmers and herders engaged in summer transhumance (i.e., driving flocks and herds up to high mountain pastures) in the Pyrenees. We discuss the details of those practices as they shed light on how trainees are accepted into the program, how working farmers and herders are selected to tutor them, and the training calendar, based on the rhythm of the seasons over two consecutive years. We then discuss how fully the instructors are involved in the encounter between tutors and trainees. Under the harsh conditions of summer range, teaching trainees to work independently is essential, and we show how trainees learn to make cheese at a summer cabin, with intervening periods of exchanges and formal instruction. We then focus on trainees' experiences with practical herding based on their knowledge of flock/herd behavior, a theme addressed in a specific training module. We conclude by summarizing the aim of this effort to construct professional identities: to train individuals who are not from the local society without breaking with the distinctive features of a pastoral husbandry sector that must adapt or perish.

THE MAIN PHASES IN THE TASK OF CONSTRUCTING THE TRAINING PROGRAM

The Pioneering Phase: The Late 1980s

The initial phase was highly experimental. For the two main originators, a technical sheep production institute (CDEO) and a national training center (AFMR), investing in a program to train sheep-/cowherders meant accepting some risk. The professional, economic and technical context of the day was dominated by a measure of indifference, even condescension, toward what was regarded as the obsolete practice of pastoral husbandry. Yet that phase, which lasted until the mid-1990s, determined the main working lines of emphasis and all of the instructional tools, which are still being used today.

The training structure design features a work-study format lasting two years. Trainees alternate between hands-on practical work (in summer and winter) and classroom instruction (in spring and fall). Their time is distributed as follows: two-thirds in the field, with the support and guidance of a "summer tutor" on high mountain pasture and a "winter tutor" for the supplementary winter activity, and one-third at a training center, where they receive training adapted to the distinctive aspects of their prospective occupation. Tutors are involved at every stage. Most of these are farmer-herders, and their summer ranges are recognized as training venues in the fullest sense of the term. During those two years, every trainee

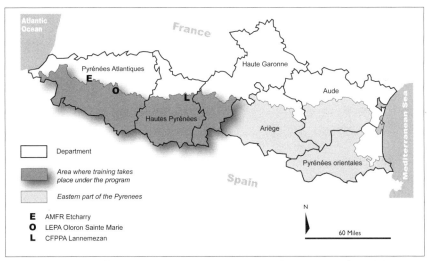

FIGURE 1 - Location of the Pyrenees Mountain Transhumant Sheep/Cow Herder Training Program.

thus enjoys the benefit of individual support and guidance, ensuring that his vocational preparation meshes seamlessly with the array of activities specific to the Pyrenees valley in which he takes his practical training.

A trainee's successful completion of the course is validated on the basis of an instructional tool of Canadian origin, the "portfolio of skills,"[3] and evaluations in work situations. The final examination is an oral one, taken before a panel of instructors, rangeland technicians, and working farmer-herders. The trainee has to demonstrate that he can describe his experience and show his peers what skills he has acquired in the course of the past two years. In fact, the quality of the dialogue among trainee, working farmer-herders, and rangeland technicians is a major component of the training program. Heavy emphasis is placed on complementarity between the herders' practical knowledge, which is empirical in nature, and the more theoretical scientific knowledge of the instructors. The latter type of knowledge is taught gradually to the trainees as they acquire practical experience.

The Integration Phase: From 1995 to the Present Day

By 1992, the context in which pastoral husbandry was practiced in France had begun to change under the combined impact of the revised European Common Agricultural Policy and the rise of environmental policies. Increasingly, livestock production practices that did not degrade the environment and its resources were attracting attention (see chapter 1). This trend is legitimizing the sheep-/cowherder training program.

While the program's visibility has been heightened, it is inevitably being affected by national political debates over the recruitment and remuneration of hired herders. The French government and local and regional authorities are prepared to provide funds for hiring herders, but only subject to various conditions, such as the adoption of practices aimed at conserving biodiversity (habitat for rare or endangered species). Most farmers in the Pyrenees, including those who practice pastoral husbandry on mountain rangeland, have reacted fairly strongly. All of them have insisted that the aim of their activity should continue to be primarily productive (i.e., the output of food products). In this climate of tension, a more sociological reading of the Pyrenean pastoral culture has proved essential. It is now clear that the aim of the training program must be to ensure that would-be future herders, mostly from urban backgrounds, are satisfactorily integrated into that culture. To that end, they must acquire specific knowledge and practices indispensable for herding in the Pyrenees.

BRIEF HISTORICAL SURVEY OF THE ORGANIZATION OF HERDING IN THE WESTERN AND CENTRAL PYRENEES

The conditions in which transhumant pastoral husbandry has been practiced historically in the Pyrenees have generated a distinctive way of life. Close proximity to the mountains and livestock has bred characteristic habits of thought and modes of action, as may be seen from the Pyrenean approach to cow and sheep herding.

In the Pyrenees, pastoral husbandry is exclusive to a society of very small landowners whose economic and political organization is based on a village community of "households." A household is a complex entity comprising farmland, a dwelling, farm animals, equipment, and access to various goods and services, including high-altitude common pasture.[4] The Basque word for a household is *etxe*, its Occitan equivalent *ostal*. The household is always passed from one generation to the next. It entails the cohesion of the entire family with respect to the distribution of goods, activities, and beyond into the realm of economic, social, and political rights. The kingpin of the whole system is primogeniture: the household goes to a single heir, as a rule the eldest son, who follows in his father's footsteps by assuming responsibility for the family group. This highly unequal mode of inheritance thus defines a category of "younger sons" (*cadets*) occupying a secondary rank among their siblings. Generally speaking, younger sons who remain in the household are primarily responsible for looking after the livestock (with the assistance of the farm laborers, if any, who are also included in the household). In many Pyrenean valleys, these younger sons play a key role in herding sheep and cows on summer range.

The organization of this herding activity has long been, and continues to be, the keystone of a specific system of pastoral husbandry. It entails developing skills expressly tailored to the grass and the livestock as well as the ability to work independently in a demanding context. This type of organization originally arose sometime between the twelfth and fourteenth centuries,[5] and subsequently spread to most valleys in the Pyrenees. In conjunction with the distinctive features of the various local contexts, it was the starting-point for what is today the broad diversity of Pyrenean pastoral practices.[6] Over the centuries and down to the present day, a farmer may adopt one of two approaches to the task of grazing his livestock on summer range: simply put, he may have the animals herded by members of his household, or he may have them herded by someone else. In the latter case, either he enters into an "equal shares" contract with the farmer(s) who will be herding his stock, or he and other farmers combine their animals and join forces to hire a herder. The term "herder" (*berger*) is used generically to designate either a cowherder or a shepherd.

From the late nineteenth century onward, and with accelerating momentum since the 1950s, the household system has been breaking down as a result of the decline and near-disappearance, of a labor supply consisting of family members. The result has been a major disruption of the pastoral society, and this has directly impacted herding activities. Not only are there not enough hands to do the work, but owing to the very nature of summer rangeland and the specialized tasks that it entails, the traditional division of labor is no longer feasible.

The local society must thus seek to attract and integrate persons from outside. It is also being compelled to become more open. Now that farmers and their households are no longer the dominant social group, they are finding that they have to share the mountain rangeland with other users. This is the socioeconomic context in which our experiment in training prospective herders has been conducted since the 1990s.

A SHARED ADVENTURE: THE TUTOR, THE TRAINEE, AND THE INSTRUCTOR

We begin our discussion of the training program by describing the would-be herders who sign up for it. We describe the preparatory stage and the two-year training schedule.

The Trainees

Officially, the French "continuing vocational development" system is intended for persons who are over the compulsory school attendance age of sixteen. There is no upper age limit. In practice, our trainees are usually

TABLE 1: Characteristics of Transhumant Sheep/Cow Herder
Program Trainees (Class of 2007–2009).

Women	6
Men	9
Type of qualification	
None	1
Vocational	4 (Farm worker, plasterer, plumber)
General	4 (Secondary)
Postsecondary	6 (MA in sport, tourism, recreation; audiovisual technician; nature management and conservation technician; agricultural technician; BA in Occitan language and ethnology)
Age group	
18-28	11
29-38	3
39 and over	1

between eighteen and thirty-five years of age. In 1991, the first graduating class was essentially male. Since that time, women have been a steadily growing fraction of the total. In 2007, the ninth graduating class was 40 percent women. The average number of trainees is twelve, but in some years there have been fewer, in accordance with an educational policy validated by the experience of professional herders that may be summed up as, "Better one good herder than a bunch of incompetent ones!"

Most of the trainees are from urban backgrounds, and they come from every part of France. Some of them have grandparents who are farmers. In the early years, many of them had little education, but the average educational level has risen steadily. The class of 2007, with fifteen trainees, is characteristic of this trend (see Table 1).

The typical class includes no more than one or two trainees from farm families. Applicants who feel that herding is their vocation are fairly unusual, although a majority of them say they want to work in a "natural environment." Of the fifteen trainees comprising the class of 2007, only three said they enjoyed working with livestock and were looking forward to life in a mountain setting regardless of the associated constraints.

The growing numbers of better-educated trainees are undoubtedly due to the highly insecure situation of young people, who are having great difficulty finding jobs. Most of them have no settled place of abode and as often as not live in an RV with a dog as their only companion. Some of them have serious health problems, probably because of inadequate health insurance coverage, with the result that they are unable to look after themselves properly. This situation is being observed in all branches of the continuing vocational development system in France.

We have to devote progressively more time to solving these problems at the expense of our educational mandate. There are substantial prerequisites, both physical and psychological, for a commitment to a career as a cow- or sheep-herder, and, increasingly, trainees from backgrounds other than farming in a mountain environment do not meet those prerequisites. As a result, they find the training extremely arduous. The following example is a letter written by a prospective shepherdess in a writing workshop during her training:

May 3, 2002.

Dear A. and J.,

I want to tell you about my occupation, namely herding. You know, it's not always easy, even though the weather has been fine this year.

My hands became all cracked, they wouldn't heal up. Every time I milked a ewe, my hands hurt.

I had moments of fear and panic.

What am I to do? I'm an incompetent, even the ewes don't want to have anything to do with me. What am I doing here?

I cry, I lash out at things, I scream. And then, when I have purged myself of hatred, my courage and determination return, and I realize that I can do it after all.

What happiness I feel once I've succeeded, and yet how exhausting it is too.

Those moments of fear . . . I wouldn't cry, I wouldn't speak, I felt as though my life were being played out in a card game. It was a very lonely moment too.

It seemed to me that I hadn't seen my parents in a long, long time.
In the evening, when I returned to the cabin, I was hoping for a little understanding, a sympathetic ear. But no, what I got was the same questions as always:

"Where are the sheep?"

"I don't believe it!"

"You didn't!"

"Yeah, yeah, but you managed it in the end!"

And that was the end of the discussion. He wasn't interested in hearing the details.

On the other hand, there were always rewards. Walks when there was time to enjoy the surroundings, the animals, the flowers, the bells, the changing landscapes. There were times when I found myself singing at the top of my voice when I was with the sheep. Feelings of safety, solidity, an impression of strength and insignificance simultaneously, a feeling that I had grown up.

There were some unforgettable times, in the morning while milking, a sunrise that opens all the doors of your heart at once. A moment when all you can do is enjoy the present moment. Looking back on all that now, all of it at once, and blending it all together, what I get is a nice thick, firm, delicious mayonnaise.

The positive aspect has come out on top. Tomorrow, if I can, I'm going back up the mountain.

H.
(Class of 2001–2002)

Happily, we also have some pleasant surprises every year. For example, we had a nineteen-year-old lad who started his training in 2007. He did a stint herding dairy sheep on summer range in the Béarn region. It was very demanding in terms of working hours, but he threw himself enthusiastically into the work of milking the ewes and making cheese. Then, with his tutor's full approval, he went off to herd the flock over by the Spanish border, spending several nights in a cabin that was primitive in the extreme (see extract, Figure 2).

Choosing Tutors and Summer Herding Places

For the trainees, the tutor frequently represents the initial anchor point in a new career. Accordingly, we expect tutors to become integration vectors, a mandate that goes well beyond that of teaching herders' knowledge and skills.

We make a point of offering every trainee a "summer herding workshop" tailored to his training, taking into account his previous skills levels and geographic preferences. The training program does not make use of professional tutors, meaning the program doesn't use the same people as tutors every year, but all of them have some teaching experience already. For every class, we prepare a number of new tutors and new areas of summer range. We are supported in this endeavor by the departmental pastoral service bureaus and other livestock production technical support services, as well as farmers' and herder's associations. We thus have a repertoire of sites that can be used for current and future classes of trainees, and that repertoire is solidly established and expanding each year.

Tutors, in turn, have various reasons for accepting trainees. The tutor may be a sheep- or cowherder who decides to give up his job, perhaps because he is setting up in business on his own account or retiring, but wants to train a successor before he goes. Or the tutor may be a "younger son" working as a herder for his household but is no longer in a position to do so on a full-time basis (see example 1). Or, lastly, "the tutor" may be a group of farmers who were previously taking turns tending a combined herd every summer and are hoping that hiring a herder will yield more competent herding, better time management, and better pasture management (see example 2).

Example 1: A Summer Range in the Ossau Valley

J., a "younger son" of the H. family, has herded the family livestock all his life, milking the animals and making cheese. But now he is over seventy years old, and eventually the family, which now consists of only a young couple with small children, will have no one who can spend all summer on high mountain pasture. J.'s nephew, who inherited the household, is thinking of a new approach that raises a number of economic and sociological issues. How is the person who replaces J. going to be paid, and how are they going to work together without the old herder feeling that he is being pushed aside? This situation is typical of the traditional system, once there are no longer any "younger sons" or farm laborers to do the herding.

Example 2: A Summer Range in Vieille-Aure

In the fall of 2006, the president of a local breeders' grazing trust (see chapter 2) contacted us. This is a trust of five farmers who run a combined herd of 300 to 350 beef cattle on summer range. Prior to 2006 each farmer had looked after the herd in turn, in addition to performing his other tasks in the valley, including growing forage crops and cereals. As three of the five farmers schedule a summer calving, they must travel to the mountains two or three times every day to inspect the herd during calving. The area of summer range is a nine-mile drive over a rough track from the home farms, and in most cases the cattle will be grazing a long way from the track, so that a visit to check up on the herd means from one to four hours' walking. In addition, as the farmers put it to us, these visits entail "vehicle expenses, fatigue, and a feeling of a job poorly done." That is why they decided to take one of our graduates and train him to work as a cowherder.

I have just turned the sheep around at the Spanish border. They seem to have understood for the rest of the day.

FIGURE 2 - Extract from the account of a trainee who went to herd sheep near the Spanish border.

We are always looking for opportunities to conduct summer herding workshops, although we do so more actively in late winter and spring. When someone offers to hire one of our trainees, we meet with the farmers who manage the summer range. Our immediate objective is to identify the needs, but our longer-term objective is to help create a job for a sheep- or cowherder.

We assess the advantages and constraints of this prospective workshop: its geographic location, the configuration and ruggedness of the terrain, the kind of flock or herd, the number and type of animals, the available facilities and the various tasks that the novice herder will have to perform, the tutor's personality, the farmers involved, potential sources of conflict, and so on. We then explain, in detail, how the training will be organized, who our trainees are, the importance of the tutoring, and the commitment required of all participants (trainee, tutor, and instructor) in this "shared adventure." Not all sites are deemed acceptable: inadequate support and guidance, dissension between farmers, excessively harsh herding conditions (isolation, work that is too demanding, etc.) or, conversely, conditions that are not sufficiently challenging.

Once selected, summer herding workshops are placed on our list, but assignments depend on the availability of appropriate trainees. Workshops are identified before we know our trainees or their previous experiences and plans. Once the trainees have been selected, we must be very careful to match each trainee with a suitable tutor.

The Two-Year Training Program

During the process of developing a benchmark job description, farmers and herders wanted more time in the field as a prerequisite for qualification. The transhumant farmers and herders of the Pyrenees like to project a highly professional image of their trade firmly rejecting anything that might downgrade that. Their initial concern was that at least three years of practical experience herding on summer range should be validated, although that period was ultimately shortened to two years.

Every two years we accept approximately fifteen trainees. Every trainee receives financial support from the French government or the region in his first year. In the second year, he signs a work contract with a group of employers who function as part of the training program. This is practical preparation for becoming a working herder in the Pyrenees.

The work-study training schedule is structured in accordance with the rhythm of the seasons such that a trainee is in phase with the flock or herd with which he is working. Training begins in May with a four-to-five-week period of preparation for the summer herding season. Part of this period is spent at the training center and part on the tutor's farm.

In the course of one week, ordinarily late in May, the trainee meets the tutor's family and learns about their various production activities. He participates in the work of getting the herder's cabin ready and learns how the coming weeks will be organized. If this initial contact is positive, an appointment is made for the date (about mid-June) when the flock or herd that will be taken up to the summer range is put together.

In June, the trainee accompanies his tutor up to the summer range to contribute to the important tasks that must be carried out. At the outset in June, the trainee's instructor goes up to the site to draw up a skills development contract to be signed by all three parties: tutor, trainee, and instructor. This document sets forth the characteristics and distinctive features of the summer range and how it is currently organized. It specifies the trainee's responsibilities and lists the skills that he should acquire in the course of the season: supervision and tending of the flock or herd, monitoring the animals' health, milking them and making cheese, organizing daily life, and so on. Every contract is different, taking into account the distinctive features of the site, the tutor's requirements, and the trainee's skill level at the time he enters the training program.

In the fall, after the flock or herd has been brought back down into the valley, the trainee returns to the training center for another four to five weeks of soul-searching and reflection after what has been, for most trainees, their first experience with mountain herding. This includes classroom instruction designed to supplement the empirical knowledge the trainee acquired during the summer. Courses are structured around a number of modules: care of animals (sheep and cattle), flock/herd behavior and management, familiarity with the summer range, adjustment to life in a high mountain setting, knowledge of the agropastoral environment, and cheese production.

During the winter, every trainee must contribute to the tasks associated with lambing or calving. As a rule, he works with the same flock or herd that he helped tend during the summer. He must choose one or more additional winter activities, in most cases with a direct bearing on livestock production. This is the same approach used during the summer: the trainee is placed in a hands-on work situation, supported and guided by a tutor with his progress monitored by an instructor.

The following spring, once the trainee has officially passed into his second year, the training is organized in the same way as in the first year. The main criterion determining whether or not a trainee passes is the degree of self-reliance that he has attained after one year in the field.

At the end of his second year, the trainee undergoes two assessments in a work situation and his portfolio of skills is examined by a panel consisting of working farmers and herders, instructors, and rangeland technicians. If it appears the trainee has not attained the required level, he is asked to spend a third summer herding on mountain rangeland.

THE ENCOUNTER BETWEEN TUTOR AND TRAINEE: ACQUIRING SELF-RELIANCE IN A WORK SITUATION

Central to the construction of a herder's professional identity is his acquisition of self-reliance in work situations. This is an essential attribute of any herder, as he must react quickly and effectively to any challenges and opportunities.

Under the program, trainees have a choice of three areas of specialization: milking and cheesemaking, sheep–herding, and cowherding—but all of them must learn how to make cheese. This hands-on learning experience teaches them that empirical knowledge and practices with deep historical roots should not be regarded as detracting from modern scientific knowledge and techniques, but rather as complementing them.

The cheese traditionally made in the Pyrenees is a pressed sheep's-milk cheese weighing between 11 and 13 pounds (the version made in the Basque region weighs between 2 1/4 and 6 1/2 pounds). As soon as they begin their training early in May, trainees begin making cheeses in the dairy at the Oloron Sainte-Marie LPA. These cheeses are evaluated in the fall after curing for six months. Knowledge and promotion of this product are an integral part of a herder's training.

Phase 1: Introduction to Cheesemaking Using the Kettle Technique at the Training Center

The trainees make their first cheese together, each of them taking part in one of the steps in the process: milk heating and curdling time, stirring, gathering the curd together and draining it, placing it in molds, and finally pressing it to evacuate the whey.

At the Oloron Sainte-Marie LPA, the sheep's-milk cheese is prepared not in a vat that meets European standards but in a traditional kettle. To be sure, the approved vat technique is regularly used at the school, but the trainees will usually encounter the kettle technique when herding with farmers on summer range. During this time, as the trainees are being introduced to an activity that is economically essential in the Pyrenees; they are learning to gauge the various stages involved using their senses, in particular their sense of smell. Thus, these apprentice cheesemakers are embarking on the complex process of mastering the art of making cheese as they come to understand the successive steps involved and how each step leads logically to the next. They also learn to identify any dysfunctional aspects, analyze them, and devise appropriate solutions.

The cheesemaking technician who comes to the school at this stage provides the trainees with the theoretical basis of this art through demonstration. He is affiliated to the Ossau-Iraty AOC Association.* In addition to his training duties, he spends a great deal of time with professional cheesemakers. He is thus a good source of recent advances in cheesemaking technology.

Phase 2: Working with the Tutor, an Initial Immersion in the World of Pastoral Husbandry

In the western half of the Pyrenees, dairy sheep are still in full production in May and June. On the farms or in the foothills, before the flocks are taken up to their summer ranges, the farmers are busy making several cheeses a day. This is the context in which the trainee, with the support and guidance of one or more skilled herders, first encounters the practices of pastoral husbandry in the Pyrenees.

At first, the trainee is fully occupied absorbing the methods and approach of the farmer-herder who is now his tutor. At the same time, he has not forgotten the initial advice from his instructor at the school. At this time, the tutor demonstrates the successive stages in cheesemaking to the trainee, and then has him go through the process.

This training technique illustrates an essential aspect of the herder's profession: a comprehensive, total approach encompassing an array of interrelated tasks, all of which must be mastered. During the cheesemaking process, the tutor directs the trainee's attention to the productive use of "slack time": it is essential to remain alert, even at a distance, for any contingency, such as a movement by the flock or a change in the weather that may be cause for concern. Such a mental attitude in the work setting, together with the tutor's willingness to trust the trainee, helps him acquire self-reliance, even though he must follow the tutor's usual cheesemaking rules to the letter.

After this period on a farm in a valley, the trainee is abruptly confronted with another new experience: the summer transhumance drive up to a high mountain pasture. Cheesemaking activities will henceforth depend on the length of time required for milking the ewes. This contributes to the rhythm of a trying day, at the end of which the trainee will fall exhausted

---

* An AOC (Appellation d'Origine Contrôlée or Designation of Origin label) is a French legal certification designation of a product's authenticity. Ossau-Iraty cheese also enjoys an analogous EU certification, a protected designation of origin (PDO). It is named for two prominent mountains in the region.

into bed and sleep until sunrise. This learning period, which lasts approximately a hundred days, is always very busy, between the discovery of the mountain environment and the need to learn new tasks. Mistakes are a frequent hazard; trying to keep up with an experienced herder, the trainee, who is inevitably slower, frequently does his work in haste.

Phase 3: The Instructor Comes Up to the Summer Range, and a Period of Joint Introspection Begins

The arrival of the cheesemaking instructor to meet with the tutor and the trainee at their worksite affords an opportunity for introspection. As a rule, the trainee has not yet mastered all the tasks, as he is still trying to cope with the novelty of the situation. The three-way exchange among instructor, tutor, and trainee allows them to compare their respective impressions and exchange notes in a way that fosters progressive knowledge-building. With the tutor's consent, the instructor observes the trainee as he makes cheese. He then helps the trainee write down the details of the cheesemaking process. Last of all, he answers any questions about matters that have arisen since the first days on the mountain pasture. He notes the main difficulties encountered by both the trainee and the tutor. These issues will be reviewed and discussed collectively at the school when the trainees return there in the fall.

This encounter is an occasion for shared knowledge-building, the tutor being a participant as well and, in many cases, keenly interested in the exchange of views. These lead to a joint analysis of any dysfunctional aspects and possible means of correcting mistakes. This situation is familiar to all workers who have little control over the natural environment where they are operating. Cheesemaking on high mountain pasture is an activity subject to the vagaries of cold, rain, snow, and even mud.

Phase 4: Return of the Trainees in the Fall, a Time for Exchanges of Impressions and Formal Recording of Experiences

When their first season of herding on mountain pasture is over, all the trainees return to the Oloron Sainte-Marie LPA. They are not as tense as they were in the spring, for now they are free of the apprehension associated with encountering an unknown and potentially threatening world. Curiosity, a newfound awareness, and interest in the others' experiences are rife with many questions. Trainees will find answers partly through their own experiences, in what their instructors tell them, and also in the accounts of their fellow trainees.

This phase of the program begins with oral reports: every trainee describes the cheesemaking method to which he has contributed. Every method is closely associated with a particular context, primarily a geographic context, but the way the tutor organizes his production, knowledge, skills, and distinctive individual approach are factors as well. This phase reveals a broad range of situations that, due both to their common and to their distinctive aspects, enrich the store of knowledge that every trainee has accumulated since his training began.

The trainees are then asked to produce a careful written account of what they have learned and how they have learned it, giving details of the context: length of time, place, weather events, pace of work, etc.

> Cheesemaking on the Couecq summer pasture in the Aspe Valley (June–September 2003):
> Then I break up the curd, that is, subdivide it into particles (the size of a kernel of corn) that are as uniform as possible, to maximize the surface area available for whey release. I cut the curd by hand. First, I go around the kettle to free the curd, then I try gently to break it up into particles by bringing it up from the bottom of the kettle to the surface, especially around the sides. If I wait too long before breaking up the curd, it will be harder to drain."
>
> *(Xabi I, trainee sheep-/cowherder, 2003–2005)*

At this time, trainees taste their first cheeses, made before they undertook their herding on summer range, and subject them to organoleptic analysis. Each trainee also brings a sample of the cheese she made at the summer cabin back to the school, thereby providing a broader sample for tasting.

During the two years of the training program, practical experience and three-way exchanges among trainee, tutor, and instructor alternate in succession, even during the winter: lambing and calving are among the new technical themes discussed.

Our training course thus engages the trainee in a twofold learning process. It leads to the progressive construction of officially recognized self-reliance through the acquisition of practical skills and integration of the local technical culture. At the same time, it leads to the development of an individual effort of reflection which begins by reproducing the tutor's skills but gradually takes on an individuality of its own as the trainee acquires knowledge and engages in exchanges with his classmates and compares his personal experiences with theirs.

THE CONSTRUCTION OF RELEVANT TRAINING TOOLS: THE EXAMPLE OF THE "FLOCK/HERD BEHAVIOR AND MANAGEMENT" MODULE

Early in the history of the training program, in accordance with the benchmark job description, we introduced a module titled Flock/Herd Behavior and Management (see Figure 3). At the time, it was based on the few scientific studies that had been devoted to empirical pastoral husbandry practices and attempted to model them.[7] This module is taught at the training center when the trainees return there after their first summer's experience herding on high mountain pasture.

Originally, the instructors in charge of the module found themselves learning along with their trainees. The latter remembered a few key aspects, such as the pace at which a flock or herd moves while on summer range during a single day or over a season (see chapter 4), as well as flock or herd patterns, which can provide clues to its grazing motivation on rangeland (see chapter 5). But that is not sufficient to account for trainees' personal herding experiences and to enable the group to learn from them. Every such experience is associated with a specific summer range context (geology, altitude, exposure, relief, nature of the vegetation), a specific flock or herd (species, breed, size, physiological condition), and specific herding practices.

Instructors now ask trainees to include observation of tutors' practices and knowledge and to prepare personal accounts of their herding experiences. Accordingly, during their first summer on a high mountain pasture trainees now enter on base maps, or aerial photographs, their flock or herd's rest areas, salt licks, dangerous stretches of trail, and convenient lookout points from which the entire flock or herd can be kept in view. They plot the routes of the main grazing circuits selected to take advantage of the grass as it grows during the season, and also day-by-day weather conditions. In most cases, trainees keep a "logbook" in which they indicate significant events that occur during each day's circuit. Some trainees use a sketch (see Figure 4), a freehand drawing, or even a photographic montage to illustrate various phases of a day's circuit and issues (see Figure 5).

When the trainees return to the school in the fall, their accounts of their experience are personalized and characterized by great richness and diversity. But use of their feedback for teaching purposes could be improved. The transition from a detailed description of each individual's experiences to a cross-cutting analysis aimed at developing a more broadly applicable interpretation is still very difficult. Trainees highlight their own personal adventures, naturally enough, as each of them was

Module	Herd behavior and management
General objectives	• Know and understand the flock or herd • Analyze the work situation in order to adapt flock/herd management on summer range • Anticipate actions that may be necessary

Sub-objectives	• Know the flock/herd's pace of activity and behavior:
	      from day to day
	      over the season
	• Be able to use the herding dog effectively

Content	• Flock/herd behavior: description, interpretation and analysis, based on field observations
	• Animal behavior variation factors
	• Flock/herd patterns adopted during grazing activities and movement
	• Organization of and rationale for successive actions by the herder in the course of a single day and over the season as a whole: biotic and abiotic factors
	• Dog training:
	      approach to the animal (behavior, feeding, raising)
	      training the dog: practical actions

Participants	Pierre GASCOUAT - *Centre de Ressources du Pastoralisme, Oloron LPA* Jean-François CAZAU - *sheep farmer and dog trainer* Transhumant herders and farmers

FIGURE 3 - The "Flock/Herd Behavior and Management" module.

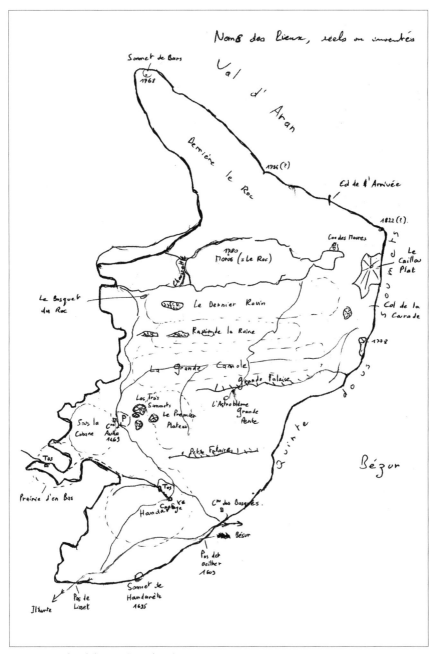

FIGURE 4 - Sketch by a trainee showing a summer range.

FIGURE 5 - Extract from a photographic montage prepared by a trainee to illustrate various phases of a day's herding circuit and the issues that may arise: Handwriting: "Once they are up on the Plateau de la Salière, the sheep will move gradually higher until they reach the saddle of La Pachaou at an altitude of 6,560 feet. If it is raining or foggy, my work consists in preventing the sheep from climbing too quickly, for they are very nervous. As we approach the saddle, we traverse an environmentally sensitive area, and I have to be careful how I handle the flock. This crestline separates the Couecq summer range from those of Banasse and La Pachaou. In fine weather, the sheep will keep to the high ground, feasting on licorice plants, until they come to an area of shade at the foot of the big rock (the saddle of Avroy). I follow them, keeping to the crestline, in order to make sure they stay on my stretch of rangeland. In very bad weather, I keep the sheep in the black hatched sector, where they will be less exposed to the wind (i.e., between the saddle and the plateau)."

plunged into a unique set of conditions. For most of them, the experience was absolutely new and unprecedented.

Regarding the herd management lore they get from the tutor, it appears from instructors' monitoring activities on summer range that acquisition levels are quite low. Trainees lack curiosity about the reasons for tutors' herding practices. At the same time, tutors have difficulty articulating the reasons for their practices. For them, the task of finding words to explain and justify practices they have learned by contact and unconscious absorption undoubtedly represents extra work.

The approach currently under consideration is to encourage trainees to develop as much curiosity about tutors and their practices as about the flock or herd and its behavior. The proposed objective is to identify common herding rules each trainee will subsequently adapt on a case-by-case basis. We do not deem it desirable to adopt a standardized outlook: the variety and diversity of individual situations should be retained, as it is a source of innovative practices.

Our module could thus be given in three phases: (1) firsthand accounts at the LPA by working herders and rangeland technicians to whet the trainees' curiosity and sense of observation; (2) a detailed record of individual summer herding experiences, as is done currently; (3) pooling herding experience feedback, in the future including similarities in management rules applied by different tutors and comparable patterns of behavior observed with different flocks or herds. Two lines of argument could be developed to motivate trainees to proceed in this fashion: our steadfast refusal to train herders who simply carry out orders and our desire not merely to equip young people with a set of skills suitable for a particular context but also to train them to be able to continually adapt to new and changing professional contexts.

CONCLUSION: "TRAINING IN A SPIRIT OF CONTINUITY"

The work of Bertrand Schwartz on the renewal and upgrading of a number of old occupations has been a source of great inspiration to us.[8] Our concern is not "modernizing without excluding," but "training in a spirit of continuity" persons who are not from the agropastoral society of the Pyrenees. Our task is to turn them into skilled "neo-herders" while maintaining close links with the historical, social, and cultural traditions of the age-old occupation of sheep-/cowherder and cheesemaker.

Our approach to instruction entails immersing our trainees in an unfamiliar vocational culture thereby offering them the chance to develop their critical faculties of observation, know-how, and practical skills through in-field work experiences and practices. The idea is not to avoid misunderstanding, or even conflict, between farmer-herders from a specific rural culture (in the social, anthropological, and geographic sense) and trainees from essentially urban backgrounds; such misunderstanding or conflict is inevitable. Rather, the idea is to transcend these tensions as the trainees learn how to function, how to act. Dialogue and exchange in work situations between persons with different histories helps strengthen their personal identities even as the foundations of their professional identities are being laid.

From the outset, this training program has been a continuation of the traditional model of the transmission of knowledge and practices between generations within a family system. Offhand, it may seem paradoxical to emphasize its experimental nature, but a training program cannot help a culture survive and remain vital unless it is an integral part of that ever-changing culture. Accordingly, the program recognizes farmer-herders' right to give consideration to their own thinking,[9] and to be participants in an induced process of change within their working space. This is an indispensable precondition for retaining a recognized place in their society.

At the end of every summer herding season, the distinctive nature of the pastoral world and its workings emerges clearly from instructors' accounts. The behavior of flocks and herds, farmers' and trainees' reactions to unexpected situations, and the psychological impacts of activities carried on under circumstances far from ordinary, all form the subject-matter instructors analyze in common for the benefit of their trainees as the fall begins.

During the summer of 2006, for example, the cows belonging to the community of Buzy left their usual grazing quarters and scattered far and wide over the summer range, much to the despair of the trainee herder, who became exhausted from incessantly running after them to round them up. According to the farmers, it was the first time such a thing had happened in more than thirty years, and they were at a loss to explain their animals' behavior, although the exceptionally cold weather in August may have been part of the reason. In September, in the upper Ossau valley, which was looking strangely green, heavy rains adversely affected the morale of the herders. In addition, a trainee down from his summer's herding on a very steep stretch of mountain rangeland gave us a graphic description of the sound of sheep falling to their deaths over a cliff. Twenty-one ewes dead and eight missing: losses heavy enough to leave psychological scars, an encounter with violent death among the flock evoking inner fears that otherwise, in all probability, would hardly have found expression.

The world of pastoral husbandry is a strange one. Paradoxically, it confronts us with the crucial issue of the nature of learning for recent generations. Young people have been educated in an environment where machines have largely replaced muscle power and the human body. The direct relationship with nature, with its inescapable confrontation with the elements that molded us as human beings, has all but vanished from today's urban industrial societies. Herders, sailors, and a few others are the last representatives of a way of life in which work also implies struggle and self-realization in contact with the forces of nature, in which honing one's sensory capabilities to a fine edge is not only an essential tool for action, but the key to survival.

In our view, the disappearance of pastoral knowledge and skills is as serious a matter as the loss of biodiversity. Our ability to adapt is at stake, after all, and to endure is to adapt.

NOTES

[1] AFMR Etcharry and LEPA Oloron Sainte-Marie, 1995.

[2] Répertoire National des Certifications Professionnelles, 2007.

[3] Robin, 1988.

[4] Cavaillès, 1931; Lefebvre, 1963; Cazaurang, 1968; Soulet, 1974; Taillefer, 1974; Bourdieu, 2002.

[5] Cavaillès, op. cit.; Le Roy Ladurie, 1975; Grosclaude, 1993; Ott, 1993.

[6] Lassalle, 2007.

[7] Landais and Deffontaines,1988; Deffontaines et al., 1989; Landais, 1993; El Aïch et Bourbouze, 1999.

[8] Schwartz, 1994.

[9] Darré, 2006.

Herding Occupation as Seen from Inside

CHAPTER 14

On Being a Hired Herder in the Alps

Isabelle Baumont

"How did you become a herder?" is a question that all herders are frequently asked, myself included, for I practiced that profession in the southern Alps for four summers before returning to university to pursue my studies in sociology.

When they have to deal with that sort of question, sociologists conventionally look at the background of the individual concerned.[1] Personally, I think that in seeking to determine how a person becomes a herder, one must also take into account the specific, practical details of that person's experiences, first in learning how to be a herder and subsequently while working as one.

The analysis presented in this chapter takes practical data obtained from my herding experiences combined with data from approximately fifteen qualitative interviews dealing with herders' thoughts about their profession. I conducted those interviews with hired shepherds in the Provence region of southern France, in the departments of Alpes-de-Haute-Provence and Hautes-Alpes. To protect the privacy of the respondents, I have changed their given names.

A herder's body is his main tool while tending a flock, which is the most demanding activity involved in livestock production in terms of the amount of time it consumes, and also the most prestigious of all such

Based on: Baumont I., 2005. *Berger, un authentique* métier *moderne.* MA in sociological research, Department of Social Science, Faculty of Humanites and Social Science, Université René Descartes-Paris V-Sorbonne.

activities. Generally speaking, the human body has been largely disregarded in the field of social science, apart from the study of ergonomics. Yet a number of authors, including Mauss and Schilder,[2] or more recently Foucault and Bourdieu,[3] have clearly suspected that the molding of the body as a result of an activity—whether vocational, social, religious, or other—is decisive in constructing an individual's identity, representations, and subjectivity. Theoretical underpinning for this insight has been developed by Warnier,[4] and subsequently Julien and Rosselin.[5] It follows that an individual's self-identification as "a herder" is primarily a physical attribute. It is thus useful to consider herding's effects on the body when seeking to understand herders' evaluation of what their profession means to them, and, in particular, the emotional significance of their relationship with sheep and their grazing land.

IN WHAT WAYS DOES THE HERDING PROFESSION INVOLVE THE BODY?
The Human Body in the Pastoral Environment
The shepherd lives in the same space-time as the flock he is herding. Because he cannot leave the flock, he lives in its environment and moves at its pace. His work thus presupposes that his body will adapt, as he must endure the same living conditions as those of the flock. This is a founding experience for the herder, in the sense that it has a far-reaching impact on his body. For hired herders, spending the summer on a high mountain pasture is the very essence of their profession, partly because it involves total use of the body in pastoral life.

Walking, a Necessary Pleasure
The herder's body is primarily a means of locomotion, one that enables the herder to follow the sheep at their pace wherever they go, even up a steep mountain crest at high altitude. As a result, the herder develops the muscles and agility required for walking through mountains or woodland. Walking in rugged terrain is comparable to walking about the deck of a ship: sailors learn to compensate at every moment for the movement of the sea. When I came down from the mountain pasture to obtain supplies, I often had difficulty keeping my balance, and the flat ground gave me the impression that I was flying. At high altitude, furthermore, the body must adjust to lower oxygen content in the air, and it responds by producing more red blood cells. Because a certain amount of time is required to adapt to life at high altitude, a herder always suffers from fatigue during his first days on a mountain.

A herder is always on the move. Walking all day every day, regardless of weather conditions, is a form of training that enhances a herder's endurance and becomes an activity that is essential to his health. If he were to be confined and sedentary, he would suffer. Indeed, it is reasonable to surmise that the production of endorphins resulting from physical effort may contribute to the pleasure some herders take in their daily walking.

Equipment that is Sound and Adequate but Not Fancy

In many situations the herder cannot leave the sheep during the day and thus must remain outdoors with the flock, whatever happens. As herding takes up most of the day, all activities that are "vital" for the herder must take place out of doors, even in the worst of weather. Being able to withstand cold, sun, wind, rain, and snow is thus an important component of the herder's relationship with his body. A misjudgment about approaching weather conditions may result in the herder's having to spend an entire day without adequate protection from cold or rain. I have frequently seen herders who were soaked to the skin after a sudden rainstorm and had no other clothes to put on, and they had to spend the remainder of the day in wet clothing. In addition, it is often necessary to "take the *biasse*," a bag containing the herder's lunch. In setting out to spend an entire day herding, a herder will say that he "eats dry," with reference to food items that are not perishable and can be carried easily: bread, cheese, and cold meat are the essential items in a herder's diet, which is characterized by little variety. Lastly, herding means having to sleep out of doors during transhumance drives on foot, or, more often, taking an afternoon nap in summer, following the example of the sheep, and also getting up in the morning to attend to the sheep at a very early hour, or even before daybreak.

The body should therefore be adequately protected. Going out without rain gear and being soaked from head to foot is to run the risk of falling ill and being unable to go on herding, or, more likely, to have to go on herding with a raging fever. Herders are similarly careful about their choice of footwear. Theoretically, a herder's shoes must not be too heavy or too flimsy, and they must be watertight and comfortable. In practice, herders frequently prefer mountain boots that are made of thick leather and are very heavy. Sturdiness is the most important factor to a herder, as his footwear must be able to withstand intensive use on steep, rocky ground where his feet must be adequately protected. Putting on and taking off a pair of walking boots are actions charged with significance: they mark the beginning and end of the herder's working day. I have seldom met a herder who did not change into a pair of slippers in the evening, once his day's work was over. The same applies to their clothing. For herders, the choice of clothing is an important matter based on practical consider-ations above all. In a mountain setting, herders are readily distinguishable from hikers by their clothing. Once when I was out with a herder, we saw some people in the distance. "Tourists coming," said the herder. When I asked him how he knew they were tourists, he replied that he did not know of any herders who wore white clothing. The main reason for this is that herding is dirty work. Herders lead rustic lives in poorly insulated cabins with nothing but a small solar-powered battery for electricity and no indoor plumbing. Under these conditions, their standards of cleanli-ness are substantially different from those of city-dwellers.

More generally, all their standards of comfort are different. The fact that herders are constantly on the move, as part of their job, requires them to pare their stock of possessions down to a minimum: most cabins have a supply of dishes, pots, and pans, and where that is not the case, the herder gets by with very little. A few books, a few CDs, a small radio, a sleeping bag, and a cellular telephone are the essential components of most herders' creature comforts. One of the basic differences between herders and sheep farmers lies in their respective relationships with their living quarters and their contents. This austere comfort level, which is out of synch with the more usual standards of the age we live in, motivates herders to place considerable emphasis on their relationship with their external environment.

The Human Dimension of the Wide-Open Pastoral Spaces

Herding a flock of sheep induces in a herder a singular perception of the environment unlike that for any other individual in the same setting en-gaged in a different activity. A herder's appreciation of a place is assessed first and foremost in terms of its suitability as pasture for a flock of sheep, primarily on the basis of the quality and quantity of its grazing resources. I have frequently heard a herder speak dismissively of a place that was celebrated for its spectacular landscapes as "poor grazing quarters" be-cause, in his judgment, it had little to offer as sheep pasture.

A herder's perception of space on a summer range is structured by the movement of his flock as the sheep graze. Any flock of sheep grazed on a given type of area will tend to move in much the same way, the *biais*, and accordingly herders perceive space in terms of the various *biais* by which the mountain is structured. The structure imprinted on the ground in the form of a host of small natural paths (*drailles*) made by sheep that have passed that way repeatedly. Broad mountain meadows or stretches of woodland that a neophyte would see as homogeneous are thus perceived by herders as so many spaces differentiated by the way a flock of sheep would use them: here is a preferred transit corridor, there a bed ground or day resting-place, and over there a comfortable area for grazing on rainy days. Indeed, a herder has his sheep to thank for his extensive, in-depth knowledge of the pasture where he is working.

> Alice: "I have said to myself many a time that I would never have come this way if I hadn't had to go and bring in some of my sheep."

Summer ranges are frequently perceived as wide open spaces, but that does not prevent a herder from developing a feeling of intimacy with his working environment. This is due to the fact that he experiences that environment on foot, moving at the pace of his flock. A herder's space is four-dimensional: the three dimensions of ordinary space, plus the time dimension of his movement with the sheep. Regular grazing of the area and repeated transits at the same places little by little make the herder familiar with every nook and cranny. Distances and difficulties gradually diminish. The pastoral space assumes a human dimension, measured by the yardstick of the physical capacities of the herder who has taken it over for his own. This familiarity with the grazing ground and its "affective significance," to use Noschis's term,[6] create a feeling of intimacy that causes a herder to feel "at home" on a high mountain pasture. This feeling is even stronger because the herder is the only person to know and use the area and "take it over for his own" in that unique sense.

The Satisfaction of Having "A Place of One's Own"

In what may seem at first glance a paradox, it is the very simplicity and austerity of the pastoral environment that gives herders a feeling of well-being. The wide open spaces—akin to deserts so vast as to be oppressive for the unaccustomed—are a precondition for that feeling. A sixty-year-old herder reminisces about the years he spent with his flocks in the Crau plain in lower Provence before that area was taken over by industrial croplands, factories and urban development:

> Louis: "I like the Crau. It's a marvelous place, you're on your own, you're undisturbed. Being in the Crau is a decompression experience, there's nothing on the horizon. . . . I had bought an apartment in Salon [a town located on the edge of the Crau; population: 43,152], but I sold it. After fourteen days in Salon, I couldn't take it anymore, I don't know why . . . I didn't feel at ease, I can't explain it. I felt isolated from everything."

The quantitative intensity of the objects and individuals that occupy urban space give rise to a form of malaise in herders. I think that Louis's phrase, "I felt isolated" means that he was not integrated into the urban world because his body was no longer adapted to the objects, rapid pace, and values of that world. Among hired herders, that feeling of exclusion is particularly strong because most of them are constantly on the move during the year. Consequently, the pastures where they herd their flocks are the only place where they really feel "at home." Throughout my interview with Céline, which was conducted immediately after she had come down from a summer spent herding on mountain rangeland, she kept saying that "[her] real house was the outdoors," an expression that is to be explained by the way her body had adapted to pastoral life. She highlighted the distinctiveness of that environment by her use of the expression "herders' world." That expression seems to shed light on the perceived difference between the two worlds, each with its own behavioral logic so radically different from the other's that the logic of the urban world frequently seems incomprehensible to a herder once his season on summer range is over:

> Céline: "When I come down from my summer on a mountain pasture, I have the impression that the world is completely crazy. It seems to me that people are busy with pointless activities, everyone is in a hurry, no one has time for anything, and that money leads everyone around by the nose!"

Up on a mountain, a herder's knowledge and intimate appropriation of the rangeland where he is working grows deeper day by day, month by month, and in some cases year by year. That meadow, that draw, that rushing stream, that ridge, all become as familiar, as highly prized, as emotionally charged, as any "home." The cabin, the mountain, the place where the past four months or six months have been spent, these become geographic and emotional moorings for a hired herder, since as a rule they are the only ones he has. Consequently, the knowledge that he will never see a particular summer range again is often painful, for it is always a place that is an important part of his identity. Who is a herder once he is deprived of flock and pasture?

The Body during Herding Activity

Schematically, herding may be regarded as an ongoing interaction between herder and sheep. The flock is constantly on the move, as the sheep cannot graze for too long in the same spot. A sudden movement by several sheep in a particular direction may be interpreted by the herder as a signal that they want to head for a particular place. To take a step toward the sheep in question is a signal that the herder wants to prevent them from going there, even though he is actually trying to avoid the risk of their drawing the entire flock after them. A herder's work consists of managing the movement of the flock by means of his own movement, with the help of his dog.*

A herder's body is his/her primary means of interacting with his flock, for his mere presence, whether motionless or walking, is significant for the sheep. The herder may be protective or frightening, a guide or a boundary marker. For example, a herder who is leading his flock out to graze in a meadow goes ahead of the sheep to lead the way, and then, when he stops and turns around to face them, he is sending them a signal telling them that they are to go no further. The herder's body thus may convey various meanings, and sometimes the sheep misunderstand. In the previous example, they may continue to follow the herder all the way to the edge of the meadow, having failed to understand the meaning of his change of attitude. The body is a very precise remote-control device: sometimes a gesture or a single step forward is enough to bring the flock's forward movement to a halt. Alternatively, sometimes a shout from the herder, in a tone that the sheep know means they are doing the wrong thing, is enough to cause the flock to make a U-turn. The body is a complex tool that demands great skill if it is to be used effectively. If a ewe needs first aid, for example, the herder first has to catch her, there in the midst of several hundred other ewes. To do so, he must approach her discreetly, without causing the flock to scatter in panic; follow her nimbly; seize her with agility, and then hold her firmly.

The interaction between herder and sheep may be regarded as a form of communication by gestures. Although it may seem inappropriate to speak of two-way communication between human and sheep, the interaction really does involve both parties: the flock and the herder. The herder's body is not merely a means of action, it is also a tool that enables him to obtain information about the flock in order to gauge what his next move should be. This is a form of remote communication in that, as a rule, the herder is not in direct physical contact with the flock. How could he be, as it is made up of several hundred individual sheep? To engage in this form of communication, the herder supplements his body with three extensions, all of which enlarge his field of observation and effectively lengthen his reach:

* The role of the herding dog, and its relationship with the herder is a subject worthy of lengthy, detailed exploration; it deserves an entire chapter to itself. Suffice it to say here that a herder would be unable to do his work without the assistance of one or more dogs.

- **A stick** is the first object that supplements the body. A herder's stick is a veritable third leg that provides him with support both when walking and when standing still, and on steep slopes it helps him keep his balance. It also serves as an extension of his arm when he is at the head of his flock, and as such it enables him to direct the sheep or to slow down their forward movement.
- **Binoculars** are an extension of the sense of sight. They allow the herder to survey a broad expanse of rangeland where he may have to go into action at any time, and to do so without having to keep constantly moving about. An old herder used to say to me, "Better to be without bread than to be without binoculars!"
- **A dog** is the best extension of the herder's body. A herder's dog enables him to expand his field of action and embrace the entire area of rangeland pasture, giving him a strong sense of power. Furthermore, a herder's dog gives him a form of ubiquity, with two faces: good cop and bad cop.

The pastoral environment and interaction with a large number of live animals inevitably entails unforeseen circumstances and risky situations for a herder. In that environment, a herder's observational capabilities are crucial for decision-making. He is constantly in search of information of all kinds, and this effort involves several senses: sight, hearing, smell, and touch. The senses are essential for working with sheep, and all come into play during herding.

- **Sight** is a means of making frequent observations in order to make necessary course corrections and to spot anything dysfunctional. The expression "the herder's eye" comes up constantly in conversation. It designates the ability to notice all the clues that point the way to effective management of the flock. Spotting a lame or sick sheep, one about to lamb, a few ewes that have strayed and are scarcely noticeable among the rocks, all these call for a sharp herder's eye.
- **Hearing** is also useful for herding a flock of sheep. One technique that is widely used in rangeland grazing is putting *sonnailles* (bells) on a number of sheep to provide information about the behavior of the flock as a whole. The bells become an audible signal that may serve as a substitute for sight, or supplement it. The bells form an orchestra, and the integrity of the orchestra means that all is well with the sheep; if one instrument is missing, part of the flock is missing. They also indicate a rhythm. Even if he cannot see the flock, the herder knows from the sound of the bells what the sheep are doing—whether they are peacefully grazing, moving at a more or less steady pace, ruminat-

ing, or sleeping. Lastly, when the herder is working in a place where he does not have a clear view, as in thick fog or dense undergrowth, he can locate the sheep from the sound of the bells and can go and bring them in, or at any rate know the direction and how quickly they are moving. It is also important to be able to hear the sounds uttered by the sheep themselves; some characteristic bleats may be the sign of a problem calling for the herder's attention.

- A herder's **sense of smell** enables him to identify a place where the sheep have recently been. Some herders say that every flock has its own particular smell. Furthermore, some common wounds are not easily detected by sight, depending on their location, and the herder may be able to detect them by their odor. The odor of a sheep's droppings may also indicate the presence of disease in some cases. Lastly, it is frequently by smell that the herder is able to locate dead sheep.

- **The sense of touch** does not come into play for the flock as a whole, but it is useful to the herder as a source of information about a particular sheep. It enables him to assess the sheep's body condition, such as how fat it is or the state of its udder; these aspects are frequently hidden by the fleece, especially late in the summer when the wool is well grown out.

Herding a flock of sheep thus presupposes a form of communication between human and animal, one that mobilizes the herder's body and senses and thereby involves him at a subjective level. All herders speak emotionally about their relationship with their sheep. From that standpoint, the herding profession requires the herder to commit to a substantial personal investment vis-à-vis the flock. The profession keeps you on your toes in the sense that the uncertainty inherent in working with livestock keeps the senses and the mind constantly on the alert.

THE EMOTIONAL DIMENSION OF THE HERDING PRACTICE
From Mutual Acquaintance to Communication with the Sheep

We refer to communication between herder and sheep because their interactions resemble a form of mutual understanding. It is the outcome of a domestication process that enables the herder and the sheep to get to know one another. Little by little, a particular movement made by the herder to encourage the sheep to move ahead, or, conversely, as an indication of disapproval, will be understood progressively more quickly. Once the flock knows its herder, a step or a particular shout or whistle is the only signal the sheep need to respond by doing what the herder wants them to do. The same applies to communication between the herder and his dog: a particular hand signal or whistle is enough to give the dog its orders, in many instances very specific orders. The herder, for his part, learns by degrees to decode the meaning of a particular movement by a particular ewe that is always at the head of the flock, or a certain form of behavior on the part of the flock as a whole (see chapter 5). Consequently, while we cannot properly speak of a "code of communication" based on deliberate, consciously devised actions of all parties, we are undoubtedly dealing with emergent actions performed for a specific purpose, and those actions ultimately become meaningful for the other party, with the result that the intended purpose is achieved.

To an uninformed observer, herding may look like a rather passive way of earning a living, but actually it is nothing of the sort. A herder is constantly on the alert for anything that might attract his attention suddenly and without warning. Herding is an activity where constant vigilance is part of the job description. Anyone who works with livestock must expect the unexpected:

> Céline: "You have to be constantly — I'm not sure how to put it — on the alert, vigilant, so as not to overlook a ewe with mastitis or fail to notice that a lamb is missing, it hasn't come back with the rest of them. I'm always amazed when farmers tell me stories of old herders who knew immediately that a sheep was missing, or that they thought they'd lost her at such-and-such a place. They're really observant; they never miss a trick. Yes indeed, if I decide to go on herding, I would like to become as vigilant as that."

Competence in the herding profession, then, is based largely on observation, which is a prerequisite for action. Action is undertaken only following a decision reached after analysis of the situation; as often as not, action is unnecessary. But at an earlier stage still, the herder must know the nature and significance of the phenomena to be observed, and must be able to anticipate the flock's behavior well enough to decide whether he should take action, and if so, what sort of action. Herding thus presupposes an in-depth knowledge of sheep so that the herder can adapt to ever-changing situations, and such knowledge can be acquired only from experience. That is why herders say, "You're always learning on this job." Competence is attained progressively, and only practice can confer knowledge of a flock's behavior. No herder can ever know everything there is to know on that subject.

Yet it is the herder's ability to decipher the meaning of the flock's actions that is the key to optimal job performance, as only in that way will he be able to anticipate both the flock's behavior and his own. If he learns to do that effectively, he will be the master of the grazing circuit, but if not, he will have to submit to "the will of the flock." Only anticipation at a sufficiently early stage enables the herder to guide the flock by stationing himself at the appropriate spot.

Herding is thus a matter of perpetual adjustment between flock and herder. A herder who used to "tell me about his mountain" by describing his grazing quarters and grazing sectors would frequently say to me, "They don't go over there!" Despite my persistent questions, he never explained clearly whether the sheep didn't go over there of their own accord or whether they didn't go over there because he prevented them from doing so. In the end I came to understand that my question was meaningless: there was no answer, so delicately attuned to each other had the behavior of flock and herder become. Here we see flock management at its best. The difficulty, not to say impossibility, of determining the exact origin of the flock's behavior in any given instance, in this case "They don't go over there!" is a revealing clue to the herder's assimilation into his flock, and, more generally, situations in which each party responds so sensitively to the other that there is no knowing which of them is dominant.

This mutual adjustment, which is the outcome of long acquaintance, requires a protracted reciprocal process of learning. Evidence of this is to be seen in the false moves, even "body language misunderstandings," that can occur among the unskilled body of a novice herder, the flock, and the sheep dog. Céline gave me a description of her first herding job, which she undertook after spending a few days on a high mountain summer range with a herder by the name of Jean-Claude. The detailed nature of her account is due to the fact that I was able to conduct this interview immediately after she brought her flock down at the end of the summer. Despite the length of the following description, it provides a good illustration of the difficulties that may be trying to a beginner, and for that reason I give it here in full:

> Céline: "I spent a week accompanying [Jean-Claude] every day with the flock, trying not to get in his way, staying behind him at all times, observing how he worked. And then, after the week was up, he said to me, 'Well, do you think you can herd the sheep on your own for half a day?' I was absolutely terrified, but I told him yes, I did. Besides, it was going to be easy, because the area was a sort of giant bowl where the sheep grazed in the mornings. I would have to let the flock spread out and be careful that they didn't leave the bowl, that was all there was to it. He lent me his dog, which would obey anyone, and then went off and left me there. In any case, he wasn't going to be very far away, he was going

to be at the cabin. But I was absolutely terrified at having a flock to look after nine hundred sheep. I was saying to myself, 'I can't do it, what if one of them takes off over there, I'll never be able to manage them.' I really had no sense of anything. In fact, all went well until three miserable sheep took it into their heads to go off by themselves, over to one side. I panicked, I said to myself, 'If they go over there, the entire flock is going to go that way.' So I sent the dog after them, whereas what I should have done was go after them on foot and turned them around quietly, without making a fuss. The dog turned the sheep around, that caused the rest of them to panic, they all crowded together, they stopped grazing, and I lost one or two hours of feeding time. Another time, [Jean-Claude] made me try again. But this time he gave me specific instructions: I was to round up the flock and take them to a particular area by a particular route. The first thing that happened was that I sent the dog after them, but he went the wrong way; he did the exact opposite of what I had told him to do, and the next thing I knew, there were the sheep, going off in the diametrically opposite direction from where I wanted them to go. I panicked completely; I had no idea what to do next. I called, 'Jean-Claude, help!' and he came and gave me a hand. . . . But that experience left me under the impression that a flock of sheep was unmanageable, completely uncontrollable."

We may say that the more familiar a herder is with a particular summer range and with a flock of sheep and its behavior, the better placed he will be to anticipate what the sheep are likely to do next. This will make his work easier and minimize his fatigue. Many a herder will tell you, "You don't really know a mountain pasture until your third year up there." When an extensively experienced herder, such as Louis, who has nearly fifty years' experience, is hired to herd sheep on an unfamiliar stretch of summer range, he can expect the unexpected, for he is not familiar with the place:

> Louis: "When you're not familiar with it, you know, an unknown stretch of mountain is a real challenge. I spent an entire day looking for my sheep. I had passed right near them without seeing them."

A herder's skills are thus related to empirical knowledge of sheep in their environment, but that knowledge cannot be entirely transmitted either in words or even through imitation. Consequently, it is not always perceptible to a novice herder. Alice, recalling her early herding days, said, "It looks so simple when you're watching someone else who knows what he's doing."

Reciprocal familiarity between herder and sheep builds recognition on each side. This intimate association between human and sheep is integral to what herders say about their profession, focusing as it does on the hardships endured by sheep and herder, the places they have been together, and the rhythms of their shared existence. Listening to herders talk, an outsider begins to wonder whether they are not part of their flocks, so strongly do they identify with them.

The Herder's Identification with the Flock

The herder's identification with the flock has to do with the need to "stay with the sheep," as the herder must often remain with the flock all day long. Flock and herder are thus subject to the same living conditions: rain, heat, cold, but also, above all, the rhythms of their shared existence, which vary from season to season. Let us look briefly at some facts that show how the welfare of the sheep is associated with that of the herder:

- the sheep graze at times when the air temperature is most comfortable
- in the event of heavy rain during the day, sheep seek out the most sheltered, stony areas they can find in an effort to avoid muddy conditions underfoot
- after several days of rainy weather, sheep love to spend a few hours warming themselves in the sun
- when the night has been cold, they stop grazing in the morning to warm themselves in the first rays of the sun before continuing to graze
- sheep do not like to walk with the sun blazing directly into their eyes
- in summer, sheep sleep twice a day: at night and a long afternoon nap

A herder's close association with his flock also has to do with the sense of smell. A flock of sheep has a strong smell, which permeates the herder's clothing and body. Herders frequently say that they like the smell, because "it's part of the job."

The identification of herder and sheep also appears in herders' speech, in which terminology relating to the herder's behavior is frequently applied to the sheep and vice versa. Generally speaking, the herder should possess all the qualities that enable the flock to behave in the best possible way so that it will do well. The ambivalence of the word *biais* is revealing: herders will say of a flock that is easy to herd because the sheep know where they are supposed to go and where they are not that the herd "has got *biais*," and they will use the same phrase to describe a competent herder. As the herder and flock are constantly interacting, the sheep acquire by degrees the habits the herder gives them; they are said to adopt his temperament. For example, a sheep farmer used to say to me, referring to his herder, "She's a very calm girl, and I've never seen a calmer flock in my life." Conversely, Alice described a farmer for whom she had herded during the summer in the following terms:

> Alice: "She's a woman who is under a great deal of stress! And [since bringing the flock back down from their summer range] I've never seen such a change in sheep's behavior. She's under stress, and merely because of that, the sheep are under stress too."

Among shepherds, human-animal proximity finds expression in metaphors that use human morphology to refer to sheep. A herder who finds a dead sheep, for example, may say, "I see her, she's gone tits up." Another common turn of phrase is, "I've spent all day following their bums around." The human terms frequently used in speaking of ewes have specifically feminine overtones: herders, male and female alike, routinely refer to a ewe as "she." This is partly because the French language has no neuter gender, but there is more to the matter than gender. Sheep are not merely female, they are analogous to women. They are routinely referred to by such affectionate terms as "the girls" or "the ladies," or, conversely, they are subjected to terms of abuse used specifically for women ("bitch!"). This helps establish individual, personalized relationships in which herder and flock engage in what amounts to interpersonal exchanges:

> Camille: "I really feel—I don't know if you have ever felt this, but sometimes I have the impression that the sheep are speaking to us, the way they look at you."

Most herders, even when they have been hired for only a single season, thus come to feel the flock belongs to them:

> Patrick: "It's as though you were a fishing captain, it's your boat, it's your flock, even if it isn't really. It doesn't belong to you, but you come to feel the same as though it did, subconsciously. A sheep that's lame, it's as though it were you . . . and you want your flock to be the finest of them all!"

This feeling of possession undoubtedly trumps actual ownership, for herders frequently designate a flock, not by the owner's name, but by that of the herder who is in charge of it at the time: "That's Fred's flock!" Consequently, a herder sometimes finds it painful to have to return the flock to its owner when the season is over and his contract expires. To illustrate, the day a flock was being sent back down into the valley, when the last ewe was in the truck, the herder said to me, "Well, that's it." He clearly had a lump in his throat as he uttered those words, and that, together with the long silence that followed, made it clear what he was feeling: pride in a job well done, ewes in good health and ready to lamb, but also an acute feeling of loneliness and emptiness.

Responsibility and Commitment

In view of the emotional relationship that binds herder and flock, his personal commitment to the work is readily understandable. "Being a herder means being responsible for your flock, it means looking after the sheep from A to Z," a herder once said to me. A herder takes pride in bringing a flock down from its summer range in good shape (well-nourished) with a full count (no sheep missing). This is evidence of his professional skill, and it can only be the result of constant vigilance—stress, one might say—in accepting to the full the tasks of herding and caring for the sheep. Over and above constant vigilance, most of the choices involved in herding and caring for a flock entail deliberate risk-taking, in what may look like improvisation—but for anyone who works with living creatures, the unexpected is sure to occur.

A herder's assessment of a potentially difficult situation and how it should be handled will be much more reliable if it is guided by personal experience and practice than if it is guided by advice from other herders. For example, it is not enough to advise a novice herder, "When it rains, give 'em plenty of elbow-room!" to enable him to understand what "giving them elbow-room" really means, and how much or how little is appropriate to give them, depending on the configuration of the mountain rangeland and the flock's habits. That is why a novice herder always tends to imagine the worst, and his commitment to the flock is all the stronger on that account:

> Gabriel: "My first year on the job, I stuck to the sheep like glue. I was constantly with them. When it rained, I stayed with them anyway because I was afraid they would wander off or that they would trample down the grass. Claude [the neighboring herder] would say to me, 'Let 'em go, let 'em go, don't worry so much!' But I stayed with them all the time."

As a herder acquires more experience, he becomes less anxious because he is better able to assess risks. He learns how to interpret the flock's behavior, and he understands that a particular behavior pattern is not a cause for concern. He also gains confidence and by degrees comes to leave his charges largely to their own devices:

Alice: "The more herding experience you have, the more you're going to leave [the sheep] on their own. Perhaps because you have gained more self-confidence . . . I really don't know what it is."

While a herder learns to intervene less frequently and less obtrusively, that does not mean that he is less alert for possible trouble, or less vigilant, for even after many years of experience, an unforeseen event can occur at any time. The herder may interpret these contingencies, rightly or wrongly, as the result of his own incompetence or erroneous action, creating feelings of guilt when some misfortune befalls the flock. The loss of some sheep, failure to spot a sick ewe, part of the flock getting into a farmer's crops or becoming mingled with the neighboring herder's flock because it has divided into two groups without the herder's noticing, any or all of these can happen because "the herder wasn't on the lookout" and had allowed his alertness and vigilance to slacken. A flock in such poor health that the herder cannot ameliorate the situation may be reason enough for him to resign, so strong are the feelings of guilt entailed by his commitment to and identification with the flock.

THE SHEPHERD'S "PASSION"

A herder adapts his body to the flock of sheep and the pastoral environment and commits emotionally to his work. This devotion may have significant consequences for his employer-employee relations. A herder who assumes responsibility for a flock that does not belong to him develops a relationship with that flock, and hence to the sheep farmer who hires him. Within the occupational group, the ability most frequently mentioned as essential for a "good shepherd" is passion. I should like to formulate the hypothesis that "passion" denotes an individual's total commitment to his profession in accordance with the discipline required for herding sheep and taking care of them. Like any discipline, it is both physical and moral. It shapes the body and the mind to construct the individual's representation and value system. Applied to a profession, this discipline amounts to a professional standard, one that those who practice the profession are bound to observe:

Isabelle: "What is 'passion'?"

Thomas: "It's when you get up in that morning and that's all you can think about, when you go to bed and that's all you can think about, and all during the day that's all you can think about."

The "passion," which one sheep farmer told me was "a virus," refers to the fact that in practice, a herder has to remain with the sheep every day, all day long. So the term "passion," which is derived from a Latin word meaning "to suffer," neatly expresses the ambivalence that characterizes herders' relationship with their profession.

Pastoral Discipline

Some herders emphasize that herding, and working with sheep in general, assumes progressively greater importance for them in the course of a summer grazing season. It is almost as if the discipline imposed by the sheep is self-reinforcing as it becomes internalized by degrees:

> Camille: "As time goes on I read less and less, I don't do other things; I spend all my time looking at my sheep."

There are a number of internal mechanisms that combine to make the discipline self-reinforcing. To begin with, as we have seen, it is an activity that demands constant vigilance in looking after the live capital that the flock represents. That responsibility is a source of anxiety:

> Jean-Baptiste: "And I was very anxious, I was afraid that they would wander off during July, when the moon was full, and sometimes I was unable to get to sleep, I couldn't even take an afternoon nap."

It appears that a herder's repose requires serenity; he has to feel sure that no harm is going to befall the flock. But such serenity can be found only in the presence of the flock. Consequently, a herder can be in a state of well-being only when he is with the sheep.

> Isabelle: "And you're never away from them?"

> Louis: "No, I can't be, except during lambing, when they're penned up. But all the rest of the time, I'm never away from them. I don't feel at ease when I'm away from them!"

The corollary is the normalization of herding activity as an exclusive activity, as it demands total commitment from the herder. During my interviews, I noticed that when herders said of their fellow herders that they "didn't attend to the sheep," they were invariably referring to the fact that the other herders in question tended to engage in activities that were unfavorably viewed by sheep farmers, such as sleeping too much out of sheer idleness, going down to the village on frequent occasions, drinking or chasing women, or, in some cases, reading, which was thought to prevent them from paying enough attention to their charges. The only legitimate activity is herding.

One clear sign of herders' self-discipline is the fact that they "have to get out there," as they themselves put it, even when they are ill. When I telephoned Daniel the evening after the day I interviewed with him, he was in bed with an attack of gastroenteritis, but he had herded his sheep all day nonetheless and intended to be out herding them again the next day. Similarly, Patrick had gone out to herd his flock despite the fact that the vertebrae in his neck had seized up and he was officially "off sick."

Clearly then herders do not feel this discipline to be something that is imposed on them. They accept it all the more readily in that they think of their profession as one they have chosen of their own free will. Bastien takes a clear-sighted view of the matter:

> Bastien: "Well, I think [staying with the flock] is certainly a constraint. But as a rule, it's something I never even think about, I only mention it now because we're talking about it. As a rule, I spend all my time with my sheep, period. I've really put on blinders. I don't ask myself any questions. What is clear to me, I think, is that it's only since I've been doing this job that I wake up in the morning and I'm happy to get up and go and attend to my sheep. Whereas when I worked in a kitchen or a pastry shop, getting up and going to work, ha!"

Furthermore, the constraints experienced by these herders are felt to be "natural." They are not perceived as something arbitrary, but rather as part of an inevitable natural order of things that includes time spent herding and caring for the sheep. Herders submit willingly to this natural order, especially if they have had other jobs in cities:

> Alice: "The great thing about this job is that you have to live in the present. There's no concept of time, it doesn't matter what time it is. There are no constraints. The only constraint is that you have to live at the pace set by nature, because that's what the sheep make you do. The weather, the sun, the rain, those are your only constraints. You're at one with your environment, you're part of nature. It affects you strongly, because you're trying to adapt to what's around you. At least, that's how I see it."

Compared to a more ordinary job, such as a factory job, herding is perceived as liberating. The herders I interviewed were all paid by a farmer to do a specific kind of work to the best of their ability. But during the summer range season, their daily work is not performed under a boss's supervision, and that seems to be of crucial importance:

Louis: "It's a hard life, but you accept it because you don't have anyone on your back. . . . I couldn't see myself working in a factory, looking at my watch. . . . I wanted to be free!"

A herder does not work for his employer, but for the sheep. The discipline they impose is accepted as an integral part of his being and freedom. Consequently, he is always totally committed to the profession, and the work ceases to be regarded as merely one of the components of his life. Being a shepherd is not a job, it is a way of life.

When working life becomes equivalent to personal life, the former totally displaces the latter. Such a displacement is experienced as acceptable provided it has been freely chosen. Even so, commitment of this order cuts a herder off from all other activities and human contact:

Patrick: "It's a job that requires a lot of you, it's sort of all-consuming. . . . It consumes you without your even realizing. . . . You turn inward, you create a sort of, let's say, parallel universe, and there's nothing else. As long as your sheep are grazing and content, you're content, too. As then your family starts to come apart at the seams, you experience it in a different way; you become separated from it more and more, and the day comes when you say to yourself, "Shit! I'm all alone!"

From the Wide Open Spaces to Confinement

As long as a herder feels content at being with his flock and finds the work meaningful, amounting to a vocation or a passion for the sheep, the associated discipline and constraints are acceptable and accepted, consciously or subconsciously. Once the work ceases to be meaningful in that sense, the herder can no longer continue to do it:

Jean-Baptiste: "As a matter of fact, what I really appreciate is freedom. I thought working as a herder would bring me that, but it's not the case. That's the downside, even though I enjoy being in the midst of my sheep. But I finally realized that the job was taking more out of me than I was getting out of it."

The longer a person has been a working herder, the less he thinks about alternative futures. He ceases to consider the possibility of pursuing a different career, or even of living in a different environment. This may be because to him, herding is the best profession there is, the one that affords the greatest degree of personal fulfillment. Another explanation might be related to the distinctive way herding affects the herder's body, as discussed earlier in this chapter. Whatever the reasons, the herding profession acts as a form of confinement that marginalizes the individual.

Moreover, while herders may adopt the profession because of what it represents, they frequently persevere with it because of the practices it involves:

> Patrick: "I had put myself in chains, because I had said to myself, 'Herding is the only work I know, it's all I've ever done.' . . . It becomes a vicious circle from which you can't escape. . . . It's something of a marginal profession anyway, but if you manage to put yourself on a lower level in relation to your surroundings, if you completely lose confidence in your own resources, you come to be almost afraid of the outside. Up on your mountain, you soon come to feel you're the master of the universe. There's no one to tell you, 'Hey, you have to go back down!' That's the good thing about it, there's no one standing over you [to give you orders]. But in the world down below, there are still people, people who are interesting to meet. That's what's insidious about it; you get into the habit, and you lose your adaptability, in a sense. *You create a world of your own by reading, you sort of drop out.* After a while I really lost touch with reality."

Another source of marginalization is that the herding profession is not practiced in the same places or on the same schedules as most others: the workplace is remote and in many cases not readily accessible; working hours are highly unconventional compared with those of most jobs, especially in summer; and herders are busiest at the time of year when everyone else is on vacation, children in particular. Consequently, a herder's social network is likely to be restricted to people involved in pastoral husbandry, unless he works at other jobs from time to time:

> Gabriel: "One year, I realized I'd absolutely had it. I said to myself, 'What am I doing here?' You know, I never said a word to anyone. I was . . . well, I was completely withdrawn. Because I was always alone, never speaking, there I was, and I said to myself, 'All right, I'm earning some money, but what am I going to do with it? What am I doing with my life? I spend eight months out of the year following Robert's sheep around, and where is it getting me?'"

In other words, the discipline to which herders are subject is constraining, exclusive, and desocializing, and all of that carries an extremely high social cost. Two examples of that cost, worth exploring more fully, are the celibacy the profession imposes on many herders and the more or less destructive escape mechanisms that help herders accept the constraints of their discipline.

Celibacy

The herding profession is frequently incompatible with family life. For many herders, family life has never been an option, or has been one that was short-lived. The commitment that herding demands — working seven days a week, all day long in many cases — leaves little time for conjugal and family relationships. One possible alternative is for the husband or wife to join his/her spouse at his/her place of work. Gabriel's wife recalls her husband's herding days:

> Lucie: "I would take the children to the beach in the evening, and we would go on picnics when it was light until late in the evening, but he could never come with us. The only time I would ever see him was if I went to join him herding the sheep. And I'd see him late in the evening, when his work was over for the day, and he had gone to lend a hand [to another herder]. You don't do anything together. I would really have liked for us to be able to go to the beach together."

Another factor is that if the wife wishes to join her husband at his place of work, she must be willing to share his quarters. The cabins where herders live in summer tend to be fairly rudimentary in terms of comfort, and this is not necessarily offset by the natural beauty of the setting, nor is it ideal for family life, especially with young children. Their accommodations during the rest of the year are seldom comfortable either: in many cases they are located somewhere near a sheep barn, with accompanying flies, manure, noise and the like. This can be inconvenient for a wife, who may not like the smell of sheep, and who soon realizes that she is in the position of a "second wife" who must share her husband with the sheep:

> Patrick: "There you are with your flock, it's the flock that has to come first, not the person you're with. Even if that person has been familiar with the herding profession."

Hired herders sometimes speak of one solution to the problem of establishing and maintaining a family life is to accept "a full-time position" (i.e. a herding contract with a single sheep farmer) as a rule for several consecutive years. However, this is not necessarily a satisfactory solution, as in many cases it means no more days of leave at any time of year, and, even more important, no chance of travelling or meeting people any further away than one day's travel from the sheep-farming operation. Patrick was looking for a measure of stability when he became a father:

Patrick: "When you work full time [for a sheep farmer], you go and you say, 'I'd like to have one day off a week, that's the law.' And you're told, 'There's nothing to prevent you from quitting!' And if you're so much part of the system, like me, that you can't even say 'No' to that sort of thing, you say, 'Well, we'll see about it later.' After fourteen years, you realize that you have had all of a month off, counting your sister's wedding, the birth of your daughter, and your grandfather's funeral, so you've had three days for yourself out of those thirty, you're so much part of the mechanism. My mother-in-law offered to pay for a trip to Senegal for us; she thought it might strengthen our relationship. That was in November, and Robert [the sheep farmer] couldn't get anyone [else, to work as a herder], so I said, 'No, I'm not going to Senegal, I have to stay here with my sheep.' Being a fool, stringing electric netting up there in the snow…"

This explains why many hired herders marry late. When a married couple decides to commit to a flock together, as a rule one of them becomes a sheep farmer.

Escape Mechanisms

Whatever herders may say about their love for their sheep and how much they enjoy spending their time in their company, the work keeps them on the job at all times, with no possibility of recreation. While the herder cannot leave the pasture physically, there are ways of leaving it in spirit. Not all herders avail themselves of escape mechanisms during the day, when they are tending their flocks, but solitary evenings are another matter.

Reading is the first of these mechanisms. Bastien had never been in the habit of reading before he became a herder, but now, in spite of the contentment he says he feels in the company of the sheep, he "devours books." Reading is a convenient form of entertainment for a herder: a candle, flashlight, or oil lamp provides enough light for reading if the cabin is not wired for electricity, a book can be carried without difficulty, and some books are thick enough to keep the reader occupied for hours at a time. For this reason, books are often included on the list of personal effects a herder intends to bring with him up to the mountain range, or his list of things to buy during the season. Other herders carve wood or stone. An activity in which shepherds formerly liked to engage was carving *clavettes* for the sheep's bells. *Clavettes* are small pieces of wood used to hold the piece of leather from which the bell hangs and keep it laterally centered on the wooden collar worn by the sheep; they must be properly adjusted. *Clavettes* are sold at fairs nowadays, but there was a time when they were invariably carved by herders, and there are herders who carry on the tradition of carving them to this day. Other objects carved by herders include sticks, knife-handles, or other pieces of wood that do not serve any immediate practical purpose.

Wine or pastis, and in some cases hashish, may also be regarded as a common evasion mechanism among herders. The status of these items within the profession is ambivalent. Alcohol is relatively accepted for historical reasons. There are many convergent oral accounts that after the Second World War herders' employers would keep them subservient by distributing ample quantities of wine every week as part of their wages. Today, farmers do not use alcohol deliberately or in an organized fashion as a means of holding their herders in submission, but some herders continue to drink in reaction to the confinement resulting from the nature of their work. Alcohol is frequently a festive beverage as well, one that goes down well when neighboring herders enjoy a meal together or when a number of herders meet at such regular events as fairs or on impromptu occasions. A herder may sometimes go for days without uttering a word to anyone, apart from his dog, and gathering with others who have been in the same situation is always an emotional experience. A few bottles of wine enhance the occasion, helping everyone momentarily escape from solitude and the company of animals and relish the company of other herders for a change.

CONCLUSION

Many of the hired shepherds whom I was able to interview replied very thoughtfully to my questions. This, in my view, is because these herders in the Provence region and the Alps have been—and in most cases still are—confronted with two social worlds, which they consider opposites: namely the world of pastoral husbandry and the urban world. By comparing the two, they have become aware of a number of mechanisms that otherwise would have remained invisible to them. Their comments showed that those worlds are inextricably associated, particularly in view of the fact that the urban environment, which some herders had once known very well, had been consciously rejected by many of them. Indeed, that rejection had been part of their reason for taking up herding. No attempt will be made here to distinguish the respective roles of this repulsion effect and their internalization of the pastoral mode of life. To do that, I would have had to question my respondents just before they became herders. What I regard as important is that practical herding experience clearly does nothing to diminish herders' rejection of city life and quite probably strengthens it. Céline states that she became a herder because she found urban existence unendurable. We may reasonably surmise that she is confusing cause and effect: it may be that she finds urban existence unendurable because she is a working herder, for the discipline that she has internalized through her work with her sheep is not compatible with the modes of behavior and the dominant values of present-day city life.

Shepherds frequently refer to their profession as a virus, an environment into which one falls and from which thereafter there is no escape. One herder said to me the first time he saw me, which was on the morning I set off for a transhumance drive on foot, on my very first day as a hired shepherd, "Don't do it, you'll be sorry!" I now think that what he had in mind was that internalized experience of the herding profession, which is irremediable in the sense that it has a lasting impact on the body and mind, in some cases painfully, in others pleasantly, but always intensely, and thereby indelibly marking anyone who has worked as a herder for the rest of his life.

ACKNOWLEDGMENTS

To Vinciane Despret, for reading this chapter and for her interest and advice, to Marc Vincent, for pointing out ambiguous passages and inaccuracies in the text, and to Michel Meuret, for his patient, meticulous contribution, my sincere thanks.

Above all, my thanks to all the herders who made me welcome and were kind enough to tell me their stories.

NOTES

[1] Dubar, 1991.
[2] Mauss, 1950; Schilder, 1950.
[3] Foucault, 1975; Foucault, 2001; Bourdieu, 1980.
[4] Warnier, 1999.
[5] Julien and Rosselin, 2005.
[6] Noschis, 1984.
[7] Salmona, 1994.
[8] Becker, 1963.

CHAPTER 15

An Evening Spent Discussing Our Profession

Roger Minard, Olivier Bel, Émilien Bonnet,
Jean-Do Guyonneau, Pascaline Kropp,
Jean-Lou Meurot & Hervé Tripard

THE seven authors of this chapter, all working shepherds, met at the home of Roger Minard the evening of December 5, 2007, to discuss our profession. Michel Meuret was present as well. Indeed, the meeting had been his idea, as he wished to conclude this book with a chapter based on a discussion among us. We chose the option of recording our discussion and subsequently having it transcribed, for we're more at home with the spoken word, and besides, we are too busy and geographically dispersed to think of attempting to draft a collective written document. For the same reason, none of our fellow herders from the Pyrenees and Corsica were able to join us; it was too far for them to come.

The participants were selected by Roger, Olivier Bel, and Michel. The invitation included information about the general nature and plan of the book and suggested some themes for discussion. At the time of the discussion, none of us had read any of the preceding chapters, and consequently our ideas and arguments should not be taken as responding to their contents. The discussion was late in the evening, from 9:00 p.m. to 11:30 p.m., as once the day's herding was over and we had finished seeing to our sheep some of us had to drive for several hours to attend the gathering. We were not able to discuss all the suggested topics, and we took the liberty of discussing some other issues we considered important. Most of us had never met before. Even so, the discussion was lively and spontaneous, and the two INRA researchers, Michel Meuret and Marc Vincent, had little to do apart from making sure that their recording equipment was working properly.

The entire discussion was transcribed at INRA by Marc Vincent. We read the transcript and subsequently produced the version presented in the following pages. It is more condensed than the original transcript, and clarified in places for the benefit of readers who are not themselves herders, but it expresses our essential ideas.

Our remarks may strike readers as rather pessimistic, giving an impression of a profession that, in the Alps and in the Provence region at any rate, now consists of practically nothing but disadvantages, with no countervailing advantages. It stands in stark contrast with the idyllic popular image of the herder on his or her mountain pasture as presented in other books. And yet we are not embittered. We are fairly diverse in terms of age and experience, and all of us have a deep love for our chosen career. We simply wanted to describe things the way we encounter them day after day, by way of sounding an alarm. As a matter of urgency, all French men and women who appreciate not only good lamb and cheese but also healthy natural environments should make it their business to be aware of our working conditions, even though the picture is not always a pretty one.

THE PARTICIPANTS

Roger – Age fifty-three. Born in Brittany. Farm family (cereals and dairy cattle). From age sixteen to twenty-two, worked on family farm. From age twenty-two to twenty-five, held various jobs, including landscape gardening. At age twenty-six, trained at a herding school. Subsequently, up to the present time: hired herder with flocks of sheep (meat breeds), including ten years of year-round employment with a transhumant sheep farmer in the Crau region (department of Bouches-du-Rhône). Since 1992, worked as seasonal herder: Hautes-Alpes in summer; Alpes-de-Haute-Provence and Bouches-du-Rhône in winter. Since 2004 was elected vice president of the Hautes-Alpes Shepherds and Cowherders Association.

Olivier – Age forty-eight. Born in the Paris region. Agricultural training. Hired herder for over twenty years, mainly on areas of high mountain pasture and hilly rangelands: Isère, Hautes-Alpes, Cévennes, and Alpes-de-Haute-Provence. Also tour leader in mountain regions. Currently herder and sheep farmer in the department of Hautes-Alpes, practicing summer and winter transhumance. Instructor at the Merle Herders School, preparing trainees for the summer season on high mountain pasture.

Émilien – Age twenty-six. Advanced technical studies in agriculture (crop production). In 2003 trained as a transhumant herder attracted to mountain regions. Employed for two years as a hired herder. Since that time, farmer-herder with 350 ewes. Every summer, herder with a collective flock on summer range, including his own ewes.

Jean-Do – Age forty-six. Son of an army man and a mathematics teacher. From 1980 to 2002, hired herder working for private farmers in the departments of Bouches-du-Rhône, Isère, and Var. Subsequently recruited by the Institut National de la Recherche Agronomique as a herder on the Merle Experimental Estate (Bouches-du-Rhône). Also provides guidance and support for trainees attending the Herders School.

Pascaline – Age thirty-two, married, two children. University degree in sport management). Subsequent training in mountain region development, and holds a diploma as a tour leader in mountain regions. Became a hired herder at the suggestion of friends who were herders and farmers. Since 2000, works as a herder for five months during the summer range season every year. Currently also works for a farmer during the winter. Intends to become a sheep farmer herself while continuing to work as a herder.

Jean-Lou – Age sixty-one. Born in the Paris region. Employed first as a seasonal farm worker and then as a hired herder in charge of flocks of dairy sheep and meat sheep (in the department of Aveyron and the neighboring departments) for approximately fifteen years. Subsequently took training at an agricultural vocational school. Since 1987, has been a dairy sheep farmer in the Diois region of the Southern Alps (department of Drôme) with his wife Danielle, a cheesemaker.

 **Hervé** – Age fifty-four. Born in Paris. Late in the 1960s, having broken with his social and academic environment, had several trial periods in communities and practical training with cattle and sheep farmers. At the age of eighteen, training at the Rambouillet Herders School. Training course in shearing and two seasons as a herder on summer range. At the age of twenty discovered Longo Maï, the "self-managed cooperative movement," which at that time was promoting sheep-farming and wool production in the Provence region. Established and managed (with several herders) flocks of sheep in various European countries and regions of France, practicing summer and winter transhumance. Currently occupied with the Longo Maï flock of Mérinos d'Arles sheep and its transhumance drives, wool selection, shearing, and wool processing at the spinning mill in Chantemerle (department of Hautes-Alpes).

THE DISCUSSION
The Ignorance and Thoughtlessness of Tourists in Mountain Regions

Jean-Do: Tourists see us up on the mountain in fine weather, and they say to themselves, "Well, he's certainly got a soft job!" But when it's raining, or foggy, or snowing, the tourists aren't there any more, or they don't see us. So when you're on the road with your flock in bad weather, they'll say, "Those poor sheep!" and not "That poor herder!" That's what the job is really like, and there aren't many people who can see its disadvantages.

Pascaline: I have some friends who live in Briançon [a small city in the department of Hautes-Alpes], as I do. They're natives of the region, and yet, after two or three years, they asked me, "What is it that you do exactly?" They have always lived up there in the Alps, they don't just go there for their holidays. And yet, when I told them that it was hard work and why, they didn't know what I was talking about. "What do you have to do? You spend your time walking, don't you?"

Jean-Do: There's a lot of ignorance!

Hervé: And I believe it's getting worse. There is a widening gap between us and the people who use mountain regions for tourism, hunting, or fishing. The worst aspect is mass tourism and that those people don't know how to behave appropriately. They go to mountain regions and walk right up to herders. No one tells them anything, they're allowed to do as they please. The thing is, they bring money into municipalities in the form of accommodation taxes, and they patronize the local shops. No one wants to subject them to a lot of restrictions. On the other hand, herders and farmers cutting their hay are supposed to be friendly to tourists. This is a hardship for us. Especially since we're on our own, up there on our high mountain pastures, and we tend to perceive the incursion of these hordes of heedless people as something of an aggressive experience. Even if they're not all like that, there are enough of them who are to spoil your morning: an undisciplined dog, a confrontation. . . .

Olivier: It's true that on some high mountain pastures, tourist activity has increased to the point where you may see as many as five hundred people in a day. Needless to say, the percentage of those people who understand the nature of a herder's work is vanishingly small. It's almost a clash of cultures, an encounter between different worlds.

Pascaline: That's exactly what it is: a clash of cultures. This summer I was working on a high mountain pasture that was really popular with tourists. People looked at me as though I were inside a glass bubble.

Olivier: The paradoxical aspect is that high mountain pastures have to be presented as attractive with their stereotyped scenery of sheep and herders. Those are what get prominently displayed on tourist promotion brochures. There can't be anything about what herders' work is really like, with the problems confronting them. To take one example, ever since we've had wolves to deal with, we have had problems with our *patous* [Great Pyrenees guard dogs]. Tourists don't understand that they're not supposed to bring their dogs with them when they're hiking through an area of high mountain pasture, or else that they should keep them on a leash. Some of them say, "But if I can't take my dog with me along these mountain trails, where can I take him?" And when you explain to them that the farmer has to pay rent for the use of the mountain pasture, the grass isn't free for the taking, the herder has a job to do, one that's an important part of the flock's yearly production cycle, they haven't the faintest idea what you're talking about, not the faintest. I don't think it was quite that bad ten or fifteen years ago. But these days it's becoming increasingly blatant.

Jean-Do: That ignorance is mainly the result of the unthinking nature of recreational activities. When tourists get too close to your sheep and break up the flock, it doesn't occur to them that they're doing anything wrong: "We were just coming up close to take a picture, because the trail passes right through them!"

Hervé: It's also this idea of "zero risk" in recreational activities in mountain areas. For example, one day the police turned up and asked me whether it was my flock that had been grazing on the mountain pasture at such-and-such a time. It turned out that an insurance company was trying to determine what had caused a stone to fall and injure one of their clients as she walked along a road. They were trying to determine the cause, with the idea that the owner of the flock might be held liable. I hadn't seen how the accident happened. I was prepared to admit that I was the herder all right, but I was not prepared to admit that the accident had been my fault, even though there was a road there, true enough, and the flock had been grazing the slope above it. But if people who walk along mountain roads aren't capable of judging the risks involved, it's because they don't know any better than to avoid places where they're going to be just below a flock of sheep grazing a very steep hillside. That's what matters have come to. People visit mountain regions just for the beauty of the scenery. But if herders represent a hazard, they're quite prepared to take them to court. I had another problem with a guy who was running and became aggressive because my dogs had alarmed him. He was jogging, he was trying to keep to his schedule, and he was carrying some kind of fancy device to monitor his heart rate. My guard dogs barked at him when they saw him coming in the distance. He was warned! Besides, he had a young dog with him. When I called to him to stop running because he was getting my dogs all excited, he tried to punch me out. Not only that, but he was a local man who was preparing to take training in first aid under mountain conditions. We get some strange situations. What if he has an encounter with a bear someday, who is he going to complain to then?

A Flock of Sheep Drops Manure and Sometimes Clogs Roads

Émilien: I'm a year-round sheep farmer-herder on the hills of a regional natural park [Luberon, department of Vaucluse], it's the same as a high mountain pasture, only 365 days a year. I take them across roads, I have to go into the village with the flock, and invariably there's conflict. People fall into two categories. On the one hand, you have the local guy who's setting off for work. He's chosen to live in the country, but all the same he has half an hour or an hour's drive to get to his job in town. And just at that very moment, there you are on the road with your sheep, and you're in his way. And on the other hand, you have the exact opposite, your basic tourist who has all the time in the world, he wants to take a photograph of the flock, he wants to make friends with your guard dog, and he's an obstacle when you're trying to take your flock through the village.

Jean-Lou: Same thing with us. We live in the department of Drôme, in quite an isolated spot, a tiny village with no more than thirty-five inhabitants, including children. And we're in conflict with the mayor's family, because the mayor wanted to make the village all pretty, with lots of flowers, but there was no way, because of the sheep. And besides, in summer, sheep barns are a source of flies, and they find their way into people's houses. And on top of that, sheep drop manure while going along the street.

Roger: There are some villages where the municipality has passed a bylaw prohibiting farmers and herders from taking their sheep through the village. In the case of Abriès [Queyras, department of Hautes-Alpes], the farmer hasn't driven his flock through the village for over ten years because the sheep nibbled the flowers that were planted in front of people's houses.

Pascaline: There are also local people who live in Alpine chalets that have been converted to secondary residences. They ask you not to come too close, because their grandchildren are going to be coming for the weekend, and they'll see the manure that has been left by the sheep. On the other hand, those same people will turn up, the whole family together, to admire your flock and take pictures of it. There was a time when herders could bring their flocks right up to the outskirts of villages with no problem. Now people complain about manure!

Roger: I think there's a connection with the fact that a lot of the houses in those villages have now been converted to secondary residences, and the people don't want one single sheep getting into their gardens.

Émilien: People in secondary residences, and also "rurbanites" [people who live in the country on a permanent basis but work in cities].

Olivier: It's true that when you're taking your flock along a road, you see how people react. A flock of sheep on the road is no longer something that's taken for granted, it's a completely unexpected sight nowadays. Besides, people never have any time to spare when they're driving somewhere. If you're held up by a flock of sheep for twenty minutes, you're out of luck.

Roger: These days, people aren't accustomed to being around animals any more. You'd think the sheep were going to attack them! Even in mountain regions, they have no idea how to handle a situation in which animals are present. Animals have become something totally alien to them.

Émilien: Because they're used to seeing them behind fences.

Jean-Do: Or on television.

Olivier: There are also local people who are neither farmers nor herders, but make a point of reminding you that they were born here, that they "come from around here," as they like to put it, and they'll tell you that your sheep should never have been there at that particular time. They claim to know something about what you're doing. This is a common occurrence, but that sort of thing is completely irrelevant these days.

Hervé: There's one like that in my neck of the woods, he was telling me off, and I said to him, "You know, I've been herding flocks on these high mountain pastures for seventeen years!" And he said, "Never seen you before in my life, you're not from around here!" It was almost racism, you might say. But he's "from around here," and he can do whatever he likes. In any case, you're always in the wrong: "Those sheep of yours make an awful mess, they're filthy, they degrade the mountain environment."

Jean-Do: Not so very long ago, their parents or grandparents made their living that way. In fact, the present configuration of most rural landscapes was their doing. But since then, there has been a complete break with the rural past; people have rejected their history, even their origins. The reason why some of them look down on herders is that they don't want to admit that they themselves come from herder stock.

Jean-Lou: They don't want to admit that in some cases, they abandoned the land. They were the children of farmers, and they gave up farming because they believed, or someone had led them to believe, that they could no longer make a living from the land. And now they see that farmers, who aren't necessarily from the same place, are successfully keeping livestock and making a living. They can't accept that, because it's proof of their own past weakness.

An Obstacle Course: The Patchwork Quilt of Land Ownership in Hilly Areas

Hervé: In hilly areas, another aspect of the problem is that we have no control over the issue of land tenure! We have to look on helplessly as hill pastures are turned into gigantic playgrounds; all of a sudden we're being invaded by off-road motorcycles, quads, and other four-by-four vehicles. Hunting's a factor too, with its food patches. Those are usually very small plots [sometimes as little as half an acre], or else larger ones but with areas of crops grown on abandoned former farmland expressly to attract game species [e.g., young shoots of winter cereal crops]. This transformation of the landscape into a patchwork quilt of small properties, these cultivated plots stuck here and there in the midst of rangeland, are like so many abscesses, because we're not allowed to go there, even if our animals are dead set on it when the day's grazing brings them there.

Jean-Do: And these days, the business of signing a grazing lease is becoming more and more complicated. A little brush-clearing with the flock from time to time, no problem, but it's increasingly difficult to develop a long-term project. People want to be absolute monarchs of their domains, of their properties, even if they don't spend more than two or three weeks out of the year there.

Hervé: About this issue of land ownership and access by herders, I have the impression that there has been a reversal in the past thirty years or so. The way it was before, public lands [National Forests Authority lands, or common land belonging to municipalities but under NFA management] were completely closed to herders. Then, with the migration to the cities that occurred after the war [in the 1950s], great stretches of land were freed up, but most of it was private land. Since the 1970s, the regional pastoral service bureaus have devoted a considerable effort to reappropriating public lands, even in forested areas. But now, it's mainly private land that is being closed off for tourist occupancy on a seasonal basis, or even year-round residences. My impression is that all the small private properties that used to be available to us—we'd come to some kind of terms with the landowner, we'd supply a lamb from time to time or make some other arrangement—all those properties are being lost. This return of investment in land in regions like this one [department of Alpes de Haute-Provence], which used to be regarded as abandoned as far as farming went, hill country, I suspect it's going to become an obstacle for herders of the younger generation because people will buy a woodlot, even if they're not allowed to build a house on it. They may hunt there, or make arrangements to have some wood produced from the land, and then they'll put a little cabin there, something of their very own. They aren't necessarily people from the region; they may be from the north of France or somewhere else. So there's an offensive under way as we speak, and it's even targeting land that isn't much use for anything but pasture. I see it happening around us where I live because we were left in peace for thirty years, and now the phenomenon is gathering speed. We feel more and more hemmed in.

Jean-Do: I've done a fair bit of herding in the department of Var, within the municipality of Fréjus, in areas that were more or less constructible [on the shores of the Mediterranean]. The grass was free for the taking, but you could find yourself fenced out from one day to the next. So you could never develop a medium-term grazing plan.

Émilien: When it's only a matter of grazing, you can still manage somehow, precariously, maybe, but it can be done. It's much worse when you turn up with your family and your camper, because where there are sheep there are going to be herders, and the herder has to be able to live somewhere, and you don't find decent cabins everywhere. We work in upmarket areas, and in those areas you can't put your camper just anywhere you like.

Jean-Do: You're not accepted.

Émilien: They look at you as though you were a gypsy!

Jean-Do: And they don't like it.

Émilien: Oh no, they value their nice neighborhood! And a camper, or a mobile home, or some other kind of portable housing, is not necessarily attractive to look at. You're a herder, or a farmer, and you turn up with your sheep, and a lot of other stuff as well; your life takes up a certain amount of space, too.

Jean-Lou: There are other people who are in the same boat: housing is becoming a real problem in this country. There's nothing for rent, and building lots are so expensive that there are more and more people who live in campers or cabins all year round. And not only that, but in a national park not far from here, I hear that the local elected officials and the park have adopted measures aimed at what they call the "cabinization" phenomenon. That actually means "Get them out of here!" So we herders, when we're looking for a place to live, we have to weigh in the balance the utility of our flocks to society, the utility of pastoralism and its role in things like brush control and fire prevention. But I think we, along with other people, should also give some thought to the issue of the appropriation of land. I don't mean appropriation in the legal sense of ownership, but the possibility of using the land.

Olivier: The right of use!

Jean-Lou: Because all those private properties that are occupied only during people's vacations, they could be grazed from time to time, provided they weren't fenced. Otherwise, they'd become completely overgrown with brush, and that would be a perfectly good area of pasture gone to waste.

Hervé: Out our way, as long as we could go up into the hill country, we had about 1,250 acres of grazing land available. For the use of it, we paid one or two lambs, depending on the area involved, to a number of owners with whom we had come to terms. And in the middle there was a whole bunch of small plots, and no one knew who owned them, except when one of the owners turned up to cut a little wood. All that land is now considered to be a "natural area," which means it can't be used for building. But it's still privately owned. Some owners cut firewood, which isn't too bad; others come in with campers, or else they want to plow up a former field for a food patch for game or a truffle bed, but without taking any protective measures at all. They're still the owners, and what they're interested in is asserting their rights. So, unfortunately for us herders, grazing a flock is beginning to turn into an increasingly difficult obstacle course. As a rule, we're in charge of three hundred to four hundred sheep every year, and with a flock of that size you can't very well zigzag your way through a maze of unfenced small properties. I really think something should be done. There were those experimental LTGTs [land tenure grazing trusts] a few years ago, but it seems they weren't easy to set up. I wonder if the idea would be more effective now, seeing that landowners are now required by law to clear the land around their homes as a fire prevention measure. Couldn't something along those lines be tried? Consolidated landholdings that herders could use for grazing their flocks? Without affecting their status as private property; I mean, without going so far as to say, "We were here first, and even if you've bought the property, tough!" because sometimes we do tend to react rather like that. But there should be some way of protecting our freedom to graze our flocks, or legalizing an existing de facto situation.

Olivier: That would make the concept of right of use meaningful again.

Hervé: The right of use should be updated on the basis of the community's needs.

Roger: In areas where truffle beds are being established, I'd be surprised if it were feasible.

Hervé: But at the very least, the land could be fenced. I said as much to a landowner. "If your land is worth its weight in gold," I said, "why don't you put a fence around it?"

The Last of the Mohicans behind the McDonald's

Émilien: Grazing land has also been reduced by all those areas in valleys and plains that have been turned into industrial zones.

Jean-Do: The CAZ [commercial activity zone] in Saint-Martin-de-Crau [department of Bouches-du-Rhône] was located on the finest grassland in the district!

Émilien: When I was coming down from the high mountain pasture this fall, the weather had been very dry, and there wasn't enough grass on my usual grazing land in the foothills. So I took the flock into the industrial zone in Apt [department of Vaucluse], because there are some former meadows there. But it has become a very unpredictable business now. I found myself herding between a national highway, a railroad line and a large factory. I felt like the last of the Mohicans on land that was still covered with brush, behind a McDonald's. Experiences like that occur all the time: you're a sort of alien intruder, you feel as though you were on another planet. When you're herding in the Crau plain, for example, you're living in an old cabin with no electricity or running water, beside a four-lane highway with big trucks roaring past at high speed, and factories everywhere. And there you are, anachronistically trying to herd sheep in the midst of all that. It's quite surrealistic sometimes!

Olivier: What place in society is there for the role of nomads, herders? Few people ask themselves that question, even in the case of young farmers who are just getting started. When you're in a grazing system with a great deal of mobility and you are juggling various verbal authorizations, you can't possibly meet the criteria of the CAP [European Common Agricultural Policy], administrative checks, veterinary checks, all that, or the insurance criteria: "Where is your head office located? What acreage is available to you for the next five years?"

Jean-Lou: That's a description of what's happening in France, but it's the same thing elsewhere in the world as well! In Africa, in Asia, pastoral livestock farmers are confronted simultaneously with urbanization and industrialization. Besides, in Africa, competition between nomadic herders and sedentary farmers goes back a long way. Generally speaking, policies tend to promote the elimination of nomadism and herders. Herders have reacted by developing a pastoral code that is valid for a number of African countries. They've translated customary law into legal language. I believe it would be of interest to look into that initiative and try to do something similar. We know a lot about our profession, but our knowledge would have to be systematized, written down in due form, and perhaps, with the help of legal experts, have a number of things that are crucial to our activity adopted into French law. Should be feasible.

A Brush-Control Service?

Olivier: When you work as a herder, you can sometimes keep one foot in private land becoming overgrown with brush. But once you start to think about putting up fences, you've had it. As long as you're herding, landowners' perception of what you're doing leads to a form of tolerance. That may be one reason why a landowner will sometimes come to see you and say, "You can go over there. Have them graze that area over there." That does happen, after all. Whereas if you go and fence off an area where you don't really have permission to do that, you're sure to be kicked out.

Hervé: Or your fences'll be cut.

Émilien: To get back to people who tell you that you should have your flock graze a particular area, you really have no choice but to go and see, just to be obliging. You waste your morning in going to see an area where it turns out there's nothing but coarse grass, overmature and really tall! And since you have agreed to do it, you have to take the flock over there and pasture them on it. It often happens that when people find grass for you, the reason why you haven't already spotted it for yourself is that it really isn't much good.

Jean-Do: In the department of Var, where I've done some herding, I'd sometimes be offered good stuff, in places where the sheep and a herder would open up the landscape a bit, get rid of some of the brush. The village people had finally realized, you see, that when you cut down brier roses by hand, they resprout all over the place! But when they saw that the herder was with his sheep, and the sheep were under proper control. . . . On the other hand, if the herder just opens a fenced area in the morning and rounds up his sheep in the evening—and especially if they start to get into people's gardens—well, that's the end of that. But it's true that a herder pasturing his sheep, "at the head of his flock," is regarded as an asset.

Émilien: It's true that when you become a herder, you think you're going to be left alone to look after your sheep in peace. The fact is that if you want to have grass, you have to engage in social relations on a permanent basis. Sometimes you have be a master of psychology just to be able to pasture your sheep for half an hour!

Hervé: That's the way it is, that social role, because the grazing land available to herders varies depending on society and its concern for its land. For the younger generation, some land is being closed to grazing, but there may be other land that is being made available. So it's essential for us to keep each other informed and for bodies like CERPAM [the Pastoral Service Bureau for the Provence-Alpes-Côte d'Azur Region] to be provided with adequate support and guidance to ensure that the situation acquires official recognition. My impression is that it's not going anywhere at the present time, maybe because there aren't enough of us demanding action.

What Kind of Educational Approach Is Required to Gain Understanding and Respect for Us?

Hervé: In those specialized publications for mountain hikers that offer suggestions about the best trails to take, sometimes going into considerable detail, I have frequently come across references to our high mountain pasture, it's fairly well known. But never once have I noticed a reference to the fact that every summer, there is a herder up there with his or her flock, and that hikers should be on the lookout.

Roger: On the other hand, just this year I have read two tourist guides that tell you in idyllic tones, "You'll meet a friendly herder up there," or some such. We're becoming tourist attractions, just like a lake or a waterfall or the final pebble at the very summit that is a must-see. But we're nothing more than that.

Jean-Lou: I'd like to strike a slightly different note on what we've been saying about the way we're perceived by people who weren't born into farming or stock-raising families. In the department of Drôme, every spring we have a sort of "operation farm open house" that goes on for an entire weekend; it's called From Farm to Farm®. It's organized by the CIVAMs [Agriculture and Rural Environment Promotion Initiative Centers], and we've been participating in it for several years now. People hear about it on the radio or by reading the newspapers, especially city-dwellers or rurbanites. Farmers who wish to do so can stay at their farms to receive visitors during those two days. And all kinds of visitors turn up. There are superficial ones who just come to see a few sheep, as though they were something exotic, but there are also some who want to meet farmers to acquire a better understanding of what stock-raising involves. It's the same idea as going to buy your food directly from a farmer who belongs to an AMAP [Family Farm Support Association]. It's a form of consumption, but there's a direct link with the producer, and it's in the interests of both sides to get to know each other better. At our place, visitors see a few sheep outside, but they also go into the sheep barn to see the lambs. This gives them an entirely different image of our work. All that people see in the summer is the herding of the flock, pretty much. But our profession involves more than that. Lambing, for example, in my opinion, you can't omit lambing if you're talking about our profession.

Olivier: In the department of Hautes-Alpes, and I think in the department of Alpes de Haute-Provence as well, the Chamber of Agriculture and its partners organize what they call "high mountain pasture discovery days." It's somewhat the same idea as that farm open house initiative. It's an opportunity to explain to people how they should behave while hiking up there so as not to interfere with the work of the herders. But I'm not sure how many of them actually follow the good advice they've received once they're actually out on the trail.

Jean-Lou: Maybe the ones who attend your "discovery days" aren't the same as the ones who go out on the trail without a thought.

Roger: I'm sure they're not!

Olivier: Yes, but there are lots of people who attend those days. They're very popular, and yet they're very tightly structured and in many cases fairly technical in terms of the information that's provided.

Émilien: It's certainly important for people to be better informed about what we do, there's no doubt about that. All the same, let's stop and think. It takes time for a herder to receive a group of visitors in the middle of his or her flock, doesn't it? You're up there on that high mountain pasture to look after your sheep, you've got a job to do. It's the job I've chosen, and I haven't chosen it with the idea of finding myself doing the work of a teacher or a guide! No, I've chosen it in order to practice a technically demanding profession and deliver a flock of sheep in good condition at the end of the season, having regard to the world we live in, obviously. So, how are we supposed to participate in these "discovery days"? How are they organized? Because if it's going to rain the next day, you're going to have some reorganizing to do with your flock, and you won't be able to turn up on schedule for the guided tour.

Pascaline: Back where I come from, there was a tour leader who would come to see me on the high mountain pasture with his group. The best thing about his approach was that he did most of the talking, so that I had nothing to do until the chôme [the flock's midday rest period], when I was relaxed and had a little more time to answer questions. The rest of the time, he followed me around, and if the group had had enough of moving at the pace of the flock, he would stay with his tour and catch up with me later. So I didn't have to change my usual working procedure in any way. I thought it was an interesting initiative, because after all, it's desirable to be able to provide information. What I've noticed about tourists is that they don't mean any harm, but they have no idea how to behave with the flock and the dogs. So I think it's a really good idea to find ways of providing them with information. It's something that requires patience and determination.

Émilien: But it also has to be well organized, the way you've been describing it, because that's not what we're up there for, after all.

Collective Organizations?

Jean-Lou: We often hear it said that we don't have the time to organize collectively. But we have to make time! And what about union solidarity?

Olivier: With the Hautes-Alpes Shepherds and Cowherders Association [see chapter 12], it seemed for a time that it was going to be feasible for herders to organize. In fact, the original idea was to include the entire Alpine arc, but nothing ever came of it. But in the livestock sector, the farming sector, it's true that there is already a measure of organization.

Roger: There are some initiatives that could be expanded in the case of farmers who do their own herding, but as far as hired herders are concerned, I don't think the outlook is very hopeful [Roger has been the elected vice president of the association since 2004]. They don't have enough investment capacity to undertake the necessary effort. That's my opinion. But why not start with an informal group, like this group right here this evening, consisting of herders who are interested in the subject? We might just talk about it to people we know, and see who's interested.

Émilien: I don't have time, I can tell you that right away! I haven't been herding for very long, I'm just getting started, and I'm having to work really hard. Sometimes I have to find someone to replace me for a couple of days, because I have to cut firewood to heat my cabin. So we need people to help us organize in the way we've been talking about, people who are more established. In this profession, there should be exchanges, among ourselves to begin with, but also between hired herders and farmers, and between young farmers and more experienced ones who can manage to find the necessary time. At present there is nothing like that, or at any rate I've never come across it.

Jean-Do: Individualism is a factor at that level. And another serious problem, one that we've encountered with our meeting this evening, is the fact that we're so widely separated. It takes a good deal of time, because over and above the time we spend actually talking to each other, you have to allow for the time it takes to get here. So organizing any kind of event that involves a number of people is bound to be difficult. Herders are never going to have an easy time getting together.

Olivier: I think that there have to be people who are more dedicated than others if a collective initiative of that kind is going to get anywhere. It seems to me that some hired herders might be useful in that connection, ones who have acquired a bit of experience, to put forward our demands in terms of our work, our job descriptions.

Roger: There are plenty of hired herders who don't look any further than wage demands. For anything more, a comprehensive look at our profession, our practices, I suspect there's not much that we can expect from hired herders. I don't mean that none of them are interested in that aspect at all, but I may as well say at once that I have more faith in our younger colleagues than in herders of my own generation!

Olivier: Yes, but a good many of those younger herders have turned to this profession because they reject the consumer and leisure society that we were talking about just now. That rejection tends to make an individual closed in on himself or herself, in a sense. You often find that with the trainees. As soon as you start talking to them about more general issues, problems having to do with the clash of cultures between pastoral practices and modern society, they more or less stop listening. And in my opinion, that's precisely the aspect that needs to be emphasized. That's why more experienced herders could play a key role.

Roger: There are a lot of experienced herders who have become disillusioned with their careers, because they have never really got ahead, they haven't got ahead as they would have liked to do. Working conditions, housing, all that, those are the aspects that have been really significant for them, and consequently they're not very interested in throwing themselves into more comprehensive collective issues. They're still fighting for better wages, trying to get a cabin renovated, that sort of thing, but they aren't very receptive to other matters, whereas younger herders are still open-minded and comparatively flexible. So they're more interested, even though at the same time, during their initial years, they're primarily interested in devoting their efforts to concrete issues, learning how to do the job, before moving on to the next stage and turning to less immediate problems.

Pascaline: Say what you like, there are some who have had plenty of experience and are still fighting for more adequate recognition and professional status!

Roger: The whole issue of the agri-environmental measures that have been implemented, for example, not to mention the problem of wolves, there aren't many herders who have become really involved, and I suspect that that may have something to do with the high turnover rates among herders who work on high mountain pastures.

Hervé: You mean that in two successive years, on the same pasture, the herder is frequently a different person?

Roger: Yes, and that's something that has implications for an individual's motivation when it comes to becoming involved in issues beyond the actual work of herding. We have to face facts.

Learning to Become a Herder: Acquiring a Variety of Experience

Jean-Do: My own approach, when I started out as a herder nearly thirty years ago, I had a permanent job in the Crau steppe, working for the same employer. I spent six successive winters at the same farm. On the other hand, I spent every summer herding on a different high mountain pasture, for a change of scene. That's what I did before signing on for a course at Le Merle. Frequent changes, for me, were a learning experience, and in the end I herded practically everywhere in the Alps. When you're just beginning your career, herding on a different high mountain pasture every summer brings you into contact with a number of different herding styles, different sheep farmers, and different regions. You'll learn lots of different things, but at the same time, you'll learn some general principles that you'll be able to apply later in other contexts. There are some things that are pretty much the same on any high mountain pasture: you'll find your sheep much the same wherever you are. One situation may not be exactly the same as another, but you'll find yourself thinking, "I remember this, this happened to me once before at wherever it was." And as you grow older and wiser, when you arrive at a new pasture, you'll try to put your accumulated knowledge into practice by optimizing your flock's impact. You'll think, "Now I don't want these ridges to become overgrazed," or, conversely, "I'll have to make sure that they graze that stand of larches properly." On the other hand, if you spend your entire career herding for the same employer, on the same locations, from the year you start to the year you retire, you won't have that open-mindedness. As far as herding in meadows was concerned, when I took that course at Le Merle after six years of practical experience I was pretty good, perhaps better than just good, in fact. But when I went to work for other employers, well, I realized that I still had a good many things to learn. It's important to keep an open mind. If you don't take the trouble to do that early on, once you're settled in a sort of comfortable routine, always in the same place, "your own place," so to speak, which you know by heart, you'll be taking things for granted: "I know exactly where the sheep are going to go, they'll go where they always go, they don't change their ways!" But it's just possible that by changing the way you start them off ever so slightly, or holding them back just a bit, well, you may end up by making them graze one area a little more satisfactorily, or avoid causing some erosion somewhere else.

Roger: But by herding on a different mountain every year, you don't see the impact that your herding approach has had on the environment, you don't observe the condition of the pasture the following year.

Jean-Do: True enough, a year isn't long enough to enable you to see the effect you have had. I myself have been herding on two high mountain pastures for six years now, and I'm barely beginning to see what we have accomplished, the impact of our brush control activities and how the grazing has maintained the pastures. But the essential thing is that even after twenty years of experience, you're still going to have to make an effort to find some way of improving the grazing environment even more. It may be that not everyone is going to be willing to make that effort. It's easier to settle into a comfortable routine.

Émilien: I'm having the same experience myself, herding at a number of different locations. Or let's say I'm being subjected to it, because what I found in that first year wasn't really all that great. So you find you *have* to change, you have to evolve in the direction of something that you hope will be better. That's one positive aspect of this profession, in fact one reason why I adopted it. You can have your own flock, while still having the pleasure of leading a nomadic life, moving on to new horizons. It's a pleasure to spend one summer herding in the department of Savoie and then move on somewhere else the next summer, perhaps to the department of Alpes de Haute-Provence.

Jean-Do: But it's more difficult to do it with your flock than if you only have to take a backpack, like me! And your approach to herding is going to be affected too, because your sheep get accustomed to one particular mountain pasture. You can always adapt, but your sheep may find it more difficult, don't you think? A stint in Savoie, a stint in Alpes de Haute-Provence. . .

Émilien: My long-term goal is a stable situation on one mountain pasture, but. . .

Hervé: In the 1970s and 1980s, we had trouble finding a mountain pasture that we could obtain under a long-term contract, because that was a period when those pastures were under heavy pressure. No sooner had you found one than it would be snatched out from under you by another sheep farmer. The grazing rights went to the highest bidder. No solidarity.

Jean-Do: Matters went further than that on occasion.

Hervé: At that time, a good many municipalities didn't award contracts for more than one year. Every year, their high mountain pastures were put up for auction. As long as the other guy knew how much you had paid the previous year, all he had to do was put in a slightly higher bid. And then he'd overstock; he would put more sheep on the pasture, to recoup the difference in the price he had paid. It was escalation, in a sense. And that's where it all started to turn sour, because you can afford to pay a good price for the grazing rights to a high mountain pasture if you put one hundred or two hundred additional sheep on it. The only trouble is that when you do that, you overgraze the pasture and ruin it. So it took us some time to find a good one. Relations with the municipality were another aspect, a matter of establishing mutual confidence. Now, we've been herding on the same mountain pasture for seventeen years, and we were able to rehabilitate the cabin after fifteen years. It was a slow business, but the fact remains that if you herd in a different place every year, nothing is going to get done. On the other hand, I admit willingly that at that time, when I was a good deal younger too, I relished the prospect of setting off to discover a new high mountain pasture. At the same time, it was costly on occasion, because accidents would happen, flock management accidents, sometimes really bad ones that cost us a good many sheep. So I'm not sorry that stage is behind me.

Herders Replaced by a Few Strands of Wire

Jean-Do: At the time when the grazing rights, not only to high mountain pastures but also to lowland pastures, were being awarded to the highest bidder in many municipalities, the herders were being "awarded to the highest bidder" as well, you might say. Some sheep farmers would pay a herder an extra $25 a month, and it was worth it to them. There again, there was very little solidarity within the pastoral community!

Olivier: Another factor that is very important in determining whether a herder works on the same high mountain pasture for a number of years is his or her relationship with the farmers. Most herders, even the ones who are working for wages, feel that "it's your flock," in spite of the fact that a herder doesn't have as much to think about as a farmer. The farmers we work for often have difficulty seeing that, especially farmers of the younger generation, who have lost the herding skills of their predecessors. Fifteen or twenty years ago, those farmers' parents were herding their own flocks and knew every inch of their mountain pastures. But young farmers nowadays don't herd any more. They put their flocks into fenced areas, even up on a mountain. The result is that they can't tell you what you're going to find up there, and that complicates relations with the herder.

Hervé: My impression is that the image of a herder tending his or her flock has been seriously downgraded. I don't mean that we have reverted to the 1950s and 1960s, when people said things like, "Look, the herder. He's got to be at the bottom of the heap, he's the village idiot." I think we've moved beyond that sort of thing. But now it's how well we measure up in terms of what's regarded as modern. We ourselves have been in this region for the past thirty-five years, and for the whole of that time, livestock sector development bodies have been advocating something new to replace herders, to replace this profession, this cost, this constraint. It has consistently been presented as a constraint and an activity that has outlived its usefulness. Thirty years ago, you would see elderly people, both men and women, herding small flocks of sheep everywhere you looked, flocks of fifty to one hundred sheep. But now sheep production has become a specialized branch of agriculture, and a flock has to comprise five hundred to six hundred animals at a minimum. I remember very clearly when CERPAM organized any number of training sessions for sheep farmers, all devoted to four-wire fencing. The reasoning was simple: in this day and age, it doesn't make economic sense to pay a herder! Better to use agricultural machinery. In actual fact, if anyone had thought to conduct an ecological assessment of the situation, they would have found that wire consumption had increased, industrial activity was up, but the rangelands in our regions were not necessarily being optimally grazed. Working people are removed from rural areas, and then you find land becoming overgrown with brush, and you get fires. With fences, the human presence is removed, because one function that herders serve is simply to be there. Many a herder has noticed a fire at an early stage and has identified people who may be at risk. Herders are present for a certain length of time in a particular area, and they'll be able to tell you what's going on there. This is a useful function, after all, but it's not one that is highly regarded at the present time. Another thing is that herding provides the herder with a perfect opportunity for keeping the flock under observation, developing an intense relationship with his animals, thinking about their welfare: in a word, everything that we don't get with fencing systems.

Émilien: Herding is a useful practice when it comes to dealing with climate change too! I thought I might be able to gain some time for myself on the way down from the high mountain pasture this fall by using electric netting to keep my sheep in meadows. Well, I had to herd them after all, because there hadn't been a single drop of rain and there hadn't been any regrowth, even for my 350 sheep. So in view of the changes in climatic conditions that we're going to be encountering more and more frequently, might not herding be a viable solution, not to say one that will inevitably have to be adopted, because we won't be able to do otherwise? After all, you can't very well fence an area of 2,500 acres just to enable 350 sheep to find something to eat.

Jean-Do: Well, say what you like, when you've got your unbred ewes on one side and your ewes with lambs on the other, a fenced area is one solution, because with only 350 sheep, you can't very well afford to pay a second herder. So you have to consider both the positive and the negative aspects. It's not a good thing to rely on fenced areas entirely, with electric fencing or other kinds of fencing, but it's a practice that's not all bad.

Émilien: I would have used electric netting to keep mine in, if I had been able to!

Hervé: I wasn't talking about stringing a few electric nets, I was talking about enclosing dozens or hundreds of acres!

Roger: In my opinion, there has been something of a reaction against the exclusive use of fencing, now that we have acquired some experience, and also because of several years of drought. But electric fencing can be used judiciously as a supplementary practice, along with herding.

Training Provided by Herding Schools

Émilien: I recently saw an interesting newspaper article titled "Competition for Herders Organized by the Region's Agricultural Training Schools." It was a competition to choose the best young herder enrolled in a training course. What do you think was involved? Handling ewes: you had to catch one, sit her down, turn her over and do her feet [trim the hooves]. There was also a maneuver with a quad, and stringing electric nets. But there was nothing about herding, not so much as getting your sheep out of a field of alfalfa, or giving them a *soupade* [the final phase of a meal] in a small area of a meadow. Herding wasn't part of the competition. I had to laugh. Even though it was a competition for herders, with the winner going on to the national finals in Paris, at the Agricultural Show!

Jean-Do: Not really what you could call typical of a herder's life and learning experience.

Émilien: Agricultural training programs, and herder training programs in particular, don't even discuss herding techniques. And if you raise the issue with the instructors, if you say to them, "I'd like to learn how to herd a flock of sheep," they tell you, "You'll get your practical training on pasture during the summer." I've taken courses at Le Merle Herders School and an agricultural vocational school in the Auvergne region, and I have a BTS ["Brevet Technicien Supérieur," i.e., higher technician's license] in agriculture.

Hervé: I took courses at the Rambouillet Herders School, back in 1972. Even then, herding wasn't on the radar. All they talked about was forage quality and feed rations. Not only that, but they had just stopped producing Beaucerons [a renowned breed of sheep dogs originally from the Beauce region, a large plain south of Paris]. How can you learn herding in a herders school if they don't even tell you what a sheep dog is? The relationship between the herder and his dog is half the job, maybe more.

Jean-Do: As far as herding goes, I'm sure there are some skills that can be taught, but it's primarily an individual adventure, a voyage of discovery. You develop your own approach to herding yourself. With a bit of experience, you can go into a sheep barn and tell immediately, from the way the sheep behave, what kind of person is usually in charge of them. If they start jumping up against the walls, you'll say to yourself, "The herder's dogs must be a little bit hyper," or else "The herder himself must be somewhat overanxious." The way you handle your sheep, that too is part of your own personal development and the accumulated experience that will enable you, by degrees, to take all sorts of factors into account. And that's something that can't very easily be taught to young trainees, true enough.

Roger: It also depends whether they've had some previous hands-on experience or whether they're coming into the training course cold, so to speak.

Jean-Do: In my day, before you were admitted to a training program, you were required to have had at least six months' personal experience. Now, the admissions board accepts you on the strength of a letter of interest and an interview lasting half an hour; those are the only selection criteria. That seems pretty rough-and-ready to me.

Olivier: I'd like to respond to that because training programs have never claimed to define and teach herding as such! Theory of Herding 101, eh? Now that would be something! I have often thought about this very matter when helping trainees prepare for their practical training on summer pasture. These days, the schools try to give them some indications of the kind of thing they're going to have to think about, some hints from experienced herders, but even that's not easy. One thing I can tell you is that there was an entire generation of herders who started from scratch to learn on the job, and during the first few years there was a pretty high dropout rate: some didn't last the summer, others found themselves confronted with impossible situations. Whereas nowadays, well, it's true that there are still trainees who drop out before completing their programs, but there are a good many who do make it through their first summer range season. And it's noticeable that many of those who do make it have succeeded in making a connection between the subjects they were taught about in their courses and the real-life situations they encountered out there with their sheep. So they hadn't been under the impression that they had to fend for themselves as best they could, not in all cases. That's why I think that training programs are useful, they save time. I myself started out herding with no previous training at all. My first season with a flock on summer range, well, I got through it, but just barely. I had no dog, I just had to do the best I could, and sometimes it was pretty makeshift. I had been through an agricultural vocational school, so I had a certain amount of theoretical knowledge, and as far as the health of the flock was concerned, I managed more or less all right. But when it came to herding, I had absolutely nothing to go on, I had to learn by doing; I just floundered ahead. It seems to me that with today's training programs, at least you get an approach, you're in touch with farmers, you meet experienced herders and various other people.

Pascaline: And during your first season on summer range, you do get some support and guidance. Because it's your first season, you're inevitably going to have a rough time of it. During that first season, if you even have a farmer who comes to see you sometimes, even such a little thing as that means a great deal.

Jean-Do: I say nothing against training programs; they give you an excellent grounding, but it's important to be aware that there's more to the job than that, your training is only the first stage in your professional career.

Olivier: That's putting it a bit strongly, wouldn't you say?

Jean-Do: Yes, but I work in a school, and I can see what kind of results we get. I know that trainees have expectations. But it is true that it's not easy to teach a person how to herd, or to express it in words.

Émilien: That may be why some people try to write books about it [a sly allusion to the present work, which was in the preparatory stage at that time].

A Profession in Which You Can't Fool Yourself

Hervé: As a matter of fact, herding is the time when a herder is on his own.

Jean-Do: And when he can't fool himself!

Hervé: And he doesn't need a school for that. In the last analysis, everything he has learned at school, even if he's a very competent technician, even if he has been a very good student, well, there will be times when he will be unable to bear the loneliness, up on a mountain. I had a very good friend, who had been through a herder training program, and during his first practical session with a flock on a summer range, he cracked, he couldn't take it. He couldn't stand the solitude. He brought in friends nonstop, but even so, he didn't complete the season. Just this summer I met another trainee who was much the same. So herding is unique to this type of livestock production. You have to enjoy a nomadic lifestyle, you have to have a taste for moving around, being alone, dealing with unforeseen situations.

Émilien: You have to be there every day!

Hervé: You have to enjoy a regular routine too, in some ways.

Jean-Lou: I'd like to say something about solitude. In actual fact, you're never alone while herding, you're with your sheep. The unique aspect for a herder is his rapport with his animals, with his sheep. What has actually gone wrong, for people who can't stand being alone, is that they haven't managed to establish that rapport with the sheep, which is a very close one. You can tell, herders and farmers who do their own herding have a distinctive look about them. A herder who has that rapport with his sheep may suffer from fatigue occasionally, but his rapport with his sheep cheers him up when he is feeling down and helps him get through moments of discouragement.

Pascaline: I knew a chap who had been a herder for twenty years and gave it up because he couldn't stand going back to an empty cabin every evening. He took on a pointless job down in the plains, but he didn't care, at least he knew he'd see his friends after work. Even after twenty years, he couldn't take it.

Jean-Do: Did he get the passion for the work itself?

Pascaline: I think so. You could tell that he loved the sheep, it's just that he couldn't stand being alone any longer. During the day it was all right, I think, but in the evenings, or during the *chôme* [the flock's midday rest period], being entirely alone, not having anyone to talk to, that got him down. Perhaps he didn't have the passion to the point of being able to put up with that.

Roger: Did he work as a herder all year round?

Pascaline: No.

Émilien: It's simple enough for a person to call himself a herder! He says proudly, "I'm going to be spending this summer on a high mountain pasture, working as a herder!" It's an image that he's trying to project. I'm talking about young novice herders here. But to my mind, a person isn't a herder just because he has spent one or two seasons with a flock on summer range and herded for a couple of winters down in the plains. You become a herder gradually. Is there one specific point in time when you can say, "Now, *he's* a herder"? As a matter of fact, I once met a former herder who saw me taking my flock out for the first time, and he said to me, "So, young man, you're off to be a herder, are you?" And it's true that when you're just starting out, you "set off to be a herder" before you've actually become a real one.

Jean-Do: But if you're just in it for the image, you're not going to last. Up on a high mountain pasture, maybe you'll be able to fool yourself for a couple of weeks, but no longer. After that, you're going to have to face reality! You're on your own, you have to do your own cooking, herd the sheep, fetch water, do the shopping, do your own laundry. . . . At the first thunderstorm, there you are in the rain, and if you don't have that rapport with the sheep, that feeling of sharing with them . . . it's all part of the experience. It's like being in a boat out at sea. Or you may decide to give it up, and in that case, you still have to be able to look yourself in the eye in a mirror. You have a passionate side, somewhere in there! You have to go on to the end. This is not a profession that allows you to be dishonest with yourself. You can be dishonest with other people, verbally, but you can't be dishonest with yourself. You can't do it, there's no way! With words, you can make a person believe anything. But in these situations, you can't lie to yourself. It can't be done! You may say, "I'm out in a thunderstorm," but if some of your sheep are struck by lightning while you were snug in your cabin, you may say that, but deep down you'll know that in reality, you were safe indoors.

Resistance in Response to a Takeover Threat?

Olivier: Those herders who were invited to participate in cabin up-grading projects, some of them were involved in the efforts of municipalities or national parks to determine things like cabin floor space, facilities, and so on. And I remember that some of them said, "We don't want any of this, we don't need solar panels!" I understand why some herders took that attitude, because there's such a disparity between a herder's lifestyle and the modern way of life and all the accompanying structures, trying to standardize the profession. . .

Roger: They had the impression that they were in danger of being taken over.

Hervé: It's a form of resistance.

Émilien: I must admit that we herders have sometimes been known to take a sort of pride in being able to live under rotten conditions.

Pascaline: *I* certainly don't!

Émilien: Neither do I, but the phenomenon does exist.

Hervé: Besides, that gives aid and comfort to farmers who try to justify poor cabins by saying, "In the old days, herders slept under sheets of corrugated iron!"

Pascaline: Yes, well, that's precisely what has to be stopped!

Jean-Do: Twenty years ago, I shared that impulse to resist myself. But now I'm forty years old, and I'm beginning to pay the price in the form of arthritis, bad knees, and so forth. I have metal plates and screws in various places, and I say to myself, "If that cabin had been better insulated, if I hadn't had to shift from place to place to avoid the leaks in the roof, or worse, perhaps I would have signed my hiring contract [as seasonal herder] sooner." Now I appreciate having a toilet, a shower, and electricity in a cabin. I'm prepared to accept all that. This year is my twenty-seventh season on a high mountain pasture, and I'm glad of a few creature comforts.

Pascaline: In my opinion, it's a shame to have to wait for over twenty years to have electricity in a herder's cabin.

Jean-Do: It didn't take me twenty years to change my views! But when I did my practical training, I was shown the cabin where I was going to be living in August: two sheets of corrugated iron, a dry stone wall, clods of earth by way of a roof, two stone benches to sit on, the door that had to serve as a table, and the guy said to me, "This is the cabin where you'll be living in August!" I was twenty-three years old, and already I was beginning to realize what I had let myself in for. But in those days, it was, "March or die!"

Pascaline: I think we should stop submitting to exploitation. Where I come from, in 2007, they've finally provided me with a decent cabin. But when you hear the mayoress stating firmly, "The herder has no need of a toilet!" I absolutely see red! I dearly love my profession, but I also dearly love hot showers. We have to bring about change in those matters as well. Why should a herder have to live in . . . nothing? What is this image of the herder who doesn't need to wash? We live as a family. I have my two children with me. We aren't asking for a lot. We want two rooms: a bedroom area and a kitchen area, no more than the necessary minimum. We exist, and we need to be able to wash and have drinking water on tap, and that's all. We have to speak up, and above all, not be afraid of telling it the way it is.

Roger: Resistance in response to a takeover threat; that's a question I asked myself fifteen years or so ago when CERPAM turned up with a lot of "agri-environmental measures" for high mountain pastures. I had colleagues who told me, "Don't work with them, or they'll take us over!" or something to that effect. But today, I can see clearly that with pastoral husbandry in the state it's in, if we don't change our outlook, we probably won't exist fifteen years from now.

Olivier: This reminds me of the controversy over the establishment of the Shepherds Center in the department of Hautes-Alpes [inaugurated in October 2007]. Different hired herders are reacting in diametrically opposite ways. Some of them think it's going to be a museum, and as such will reinforce the image of the herder as a figure out of folklore. Others take the view that full-scale participation, working within the project, will be the key to sending a message, bringing about change. So it's controversial! And we're not talking about something that happened ten years ago, we're talking about something that's happening now.[*]

Roger: It's the same thing with sheep farmers.

Jean-Do: It's true that herders are in a small world, but even so, they often have difficulty communicating and reaching agreement. Everyone knows everyone else, more or less, by word of mouth, but at the same time there's not much that binds us together, partly because we don't have the time to concern ourselves with these things. Besides, it may be a small world, but it's a highly diverse one: there are year-round herders, seasonal herders, and farmers in high mountain regions, the Alps, the Pyrenees, Crau, or in other countries. You don't find quite the same working cycles or the same approaches everywhere.

Hervé: What frightens me is that right now I don't see any way of overhauling our profession in the context of a society that's going in the

---

* *Editors' update:* In 2011, the Shepherds Center at Champoléon, department of Hautes-Alpes, recruited new director Guillaume Lebaudy, an anthropologist. The center makes constant and valuable efforts to keep at a distance any forms of folklorization or "muséification" of herders' living and working conditions. To our knowledge, this has eased the controversy amongst herders.

exact opposite direction. I don't see how we can do that either through the profession itself or through its image as presented by the media. Our present society has an increasingly artificial relationship with animals and nature; why should it want to encourage young people to understand and appreciate shepherding, which means a commitment to individual animals, to an environment, to a type of social relationships, a type of commitment that is relatively comprehensive and complex. The areas where we pasture our flocks are being progressively closed off, sanitary standards are becoming more important than what a herder thinks about livestock breeding, and we are increasingly dependent on the AEMs [European Agri-Environmental Measures], which we use as crutches to support ourselves financially.

Jean-Do: And have been for some time now, in fact.

Hervé: That's our situation!

Jean-Do: The positive aspect is that in every herding school, every year there are three or four young trainees who stand out, who have that interest and drive, regardless of whether they are interested in becoming sheep farmers or even, initially, in working as hired herders. In view of the conditions that they're offered when they finish their training, if they still want to do it, they must be strongly motivated. So perhaps there's some point in continuing along that road.

Jean-Lou: Yes, and when people see us, they may think we're relics from the past, but we may also be a source of solutions for the future. At least for those who are currently taking a hard look at their consumption habits and trying to find something better.

Bibliography

Adam, E., 1993. Editorial. *Terre Sauvage* Monthly Magazine, 73: 4.

AFMR Etcharry, LEPA Oloron Sainte-Marie, 1995. *Référentiel métier berger vacher pluriactif en montagne pyrénéenne 1993–1995*. AFMR & LEPA Self-published document: 22 pp.

Agreil, C., Meuret, M., 2004. "An improved method for quantifying intake rate and ingestive behaviour of ruminants in diverse and variable habitats using direct observation." *Small Ruminant Research,* 54/1-2: 99–113.

Agreil, C., Meuret, M., 2007. "Évaluer la valeur alimentaire d'une végétation: la méthode GRENOUILLE s'intéresse au point de vue des troupeaux." *Espaces Naturels*, 19: 30–31.

Agreil, C., Meuret, M., Fritz, H., 2006. "Foraging on varied and variable environments: adjustment of feeding choices and intake in domestic sheep." *In:* Bels, V., (ed.), *Food and Feeding: From structure to behaviour.* CABI Pub., Wallingford, UK, New York, USA: 302–25.

Agreil, C., Greff, N., Polis, P., Magda, D., Meuret, M., Mestelan, P., 2008. *Des troupeaux et des hommes en espaces naturels: une approche dynamique de la gestion pastorale.* Guide technique du Conservatoire Rhône-Alpes des Espaces Naturels, Self-published document, Vourles, France: 87 p + annexes.

Albaladejo, C., Hubert, B., Roche, B., 2009. "Chercheurs en situation de partenariat: prescrire la subjectivité. Réflexions à partir du programme de pérennisation de l'agropastoralisme au Pays Basque." *In:* Béguin, P., Cerf, M., (coords.), *Dynamique des savoirs, dynamiques des changements,* Octarès Eds., Toulouse, France: 131–54.

Alphandéry, P., Billaud, J-P., (eds.), 1996a. "Cultiver la nature." Études Rurales, 141–142: 233 pp.

Alphandéry, P., Billaud, J-P., 1996b. "Introduction." *In:* Alphandéry, P., Billaud, J-P., (eds.), *Cultiver la nature.* Études Rurales. 141–142: 9–19.

Arnold, G.W., 1977. "An analysis of spatial leadership in a small field in a small flock of sheep." *Appl. Anim. Ethology,* 3: 263–70.

Arnold, G.W., 1981a. "Associations between individuals and home range behaviour in natural flocks of three breeds of domestic sheep." *Appl. Anim. Ethology,* 7: 239–57.

Arnold, G.W., 1981b. "Grazing behaviour." *In:* Morley, F.H.W., (ed). *World Animal Science,* B1: Grazing animals. Elsevier, Amsterdam, the Netherlands: 79–104.

Assemblée Pyrénéenne d'Economie Montagnarde (APEM), 2007. "SIG Pyrénées: couche unités pastorales." http://www.sig-pyrenees.net/map/composer/ (*consulted on:* August 25, 2013).

Association des Anciens Élèves de la Bergerie Nationale de Rambouillet, 1986. *La Bergerie Nationale de Rambouillet: Histoire du mérinos et d'une école.* Self-published document: 150 pp.
Bachelart, D., 2002. *Berger Transhumant en formation: pour une tradition d'avenir.* L'Harmattan Eds., Paris, France: 273 pp.

Balent, G., 1987. *Structure, fonctionnement et évolution d'un système pastoral. Le pâturage vu comme un facteur écologique piloté dans les Pyrénées Centrales.* Thèse Doctorat d'État, Université Rennes I, France: 146 p + biblio. et annexes.

Balent, G., Barrué-Pastor, M., 1986. "Pratiques pastorales et stratégies foncières dans le processus de déprise de l'élevage montagnard en vallée d'Oô (Pyrénées Centrales)." *Revue Géographique des Pyrénées et du Sud-Ouest,* 57: 403–47.

Baumont, I., 2005. *Berger, un authentique métier moderne.* Master 2 de recherche en sociologie, Département des Sciences Sociales, Faculté des Sciences Humaines et Sociales, Université René Descartes-Paris V-Sorbonne, Paris, France: 150 p + annexes.

Baumont, R., 1989. "État de réplétion du réticulo-rumen et ingestion des fourrages: incidence sur le contrôle de la quantité de foin ingérée par le mouton." Thèse de Doctorat, Institut National Agronomique Paris-Grignon, France: 159 pp.

Baumont, R., Champciaux, P., Agabriel, J., Andrieu, J., Aufrère, J., Michalet-Doreau, B., Demarquilly, C., 1999. Une démarche intégrée pour prévoir la valeur alimentaire des fourrages pour les ruminants: PrévAlim pour INRAtion." *Inra Productions animales,* 12: 183–94.

Becker, H-S., 1963. *Outsiders: Studies in the Sociology of Deviance,* Free Press of Glencoe, Collier-Macmillan, New York, USA, London, UK: 179 p + index.

Benarous, A., Sourd, L-J., 2002. *Les bergers sans terre dans les Pyrénées Atlantiques.* Rapport au Comité permanent de coordination des inspections, Ministère de l'agriculture, de l'alimentation, de la pêche et des affaires rurales (MAAPAR), Paris, France: 21 p + annexes.

Blanchard, R., 1945. *Les Alpes Occidentales. Tome IV Grenoble,* Arthaud Ed., Paris, France: 561 pp.

Blanchemain, A., 1979. "Parcours méditerranéens: quelques aspects historiques." *In:* Molénat, G., Jarrige, R. (coord). *Utilisation par les ruminants des pâturages d'altitude et parcours méditerranéens.* Éd. INRA, Paris, France: 343–60.

Blond, H., 2012. *Parcours poétique du Berger Albert.* Ed. L'Édition à façon, Forcalquier, France: 180 pp.

Bobbé, S., 2000. "Un mode de garde écologiquement correct: le chien de protection." *Ethnologie française,* XXX (3): 459–72.

Bodin, B., Bardiau, P., 1997. *Bergers: gardiens de l'Alpe.* Ed. Didier Richard, Claix, France: 128 pp.

Boltanski, L., Thévenot, L., 1991. *De la justification. Les économies de la grandeur.* Gallimard Ed., Paris, France. (English translation published as *On Justification: Economies of Worth,* Princeton University Press, Princeton, NJ, 2006, 400 pp.).

Bourdieu, P., 1980. *Le sens pratique.* Les Éditions de Minuit, Paris, France. (English translation published as *The Logic of Practice,* Stanford University Press, Palo Alto, CA, USA, 1992, 333 pp.).

Bourdieu, P., 2002. *Le bal des célibataires: crise de la société paysanne en Béarn.* Eds. Le Seuil, Paris, France: 266 pp.

Bourrelly, M., Borel, L., Devaux, J.P., Louis-Palluel, J., Archiloque, A., 1983. "Dynamique annuelle et production primaire nette de l'écosystème steppique de Crau." *Biologie-Écologie méditerranéenne,* 10: 55–82.

Boutin, J., 2002. "Plaine de la Crau: la réserve Naturelle des Coussouls de Crau." *Garrigues,* 30: 4–5.

Bouy, M., 1988. *Le comportement d'un troupeau d'ovins en montagne.* Étude de la dispersion spatiale au cours d'une séquence de pâturage. D.E.A. d'Écologie expérimentale, Université de Pau et des Pays de l'Adour, Pau, France: 44 pp.

Brard, L., 1996a. "Joyeux Noël au loup des Alpes." *Sciences et Nature* Monthly Magazine, 71: 83.

Brard, L., 1996b. "Manifeste pour un loup libre, vivant, sauvage, hors de toute idée de zonage barbelé." *La Lettre du Hérisson, Revue de France Nature Environnement*, 177: 9–2.

Brisebarre, A-M., 1978. *Bergers des Cévennes: histoire et ethnographie du monde pastoral et de la transhumance en Cévennes.* Eds. Berger-Levrault, Coll. Espace des Hommes, Paris, France: 192 pp.

Brossier, J., Brun, A., Deffontaines, J-P., Fiorelli, J-L., Osty, P-L., Petit, M., Roux, M., Leclerc, V., 2008. "Quels paysages avec quels paysans? Les Vosges du Sud à 30 ans d'intervalle." Eds. Quæ, Versailles, France: 152 pp.

Buisson, E., Dutoit, T., 2006. "Creation of the natural reserve of La Crau: Implications for the creation and management of protected areas." *Journal of Environmental Management*, 80: 318–26.

Buller, H., 1995. "Regards croisés: Angleterre, Irlande," France. *In:* Alphandéry, P., Billaud, J-P. (eds.), *Cultiver la Nature.* Études Rurales, 141–42: 171–74.

Calendre, I., 2007. "Tribunal de police: l'éleveur, le loup et le patou." *Le Dauphiné Libéré* Daily newspaper, edition du 7 septembre 2007.

Caraguel, B., Castanieris, J., Chenal, A., Four, L., Lebaudy, G., Breteau, E., 2011. *Un berger, des bergères: nouveaux enjeux d'un métier en mutation.* Maison du Berger de Champoléon, Fédération des Alpages de l'Isère, Cardère Ed., Lirac, France: 46 pp.

Cavaillès, H., 1931. *La vie pastorale et agricole dans les Pyrénées des Gaves, de l'Adour et des Nestes.* Librairie Armand Colin Ed., Paris, France: 413 pp.

Cazaurang, J-J., 1968. *Pasteurs et Paysans béarnais: naissance, mariage, décès.* Eds. Marrinpouey, Pau, France: 359 pp.

Chabert, J-P., Lécrivain, E., Meuret, M., 2002. Livestock farmers, researchers and scrub. *In: INRA Faced with Sustainable Development: Landmarks for the Johannesburg Conference. Dossiers Environnement INRA*, 22: 135–41. http://www7.inra.fr/dpenv/chabed22e.htm (*consulted on:* August 26, 2013).

Chabert, J-P., de Sainte Marie, C., Vincent, M., 2004. "La régularisation du loup, 1990–2004." *Forêt Méditerranéenne*, XXV-2: 131–42.

Charbonnier, Q., 2012. *1972 - la loi pastorale française.* Association Française de Pastoralisme & Cardère Eds., Lirac, France: 144 pp.

Cheylan, G., Bence, P., Boutin, J., Dhermain, F., Olisio, G., Vidal, P., 1983. "L'utilisation du milieu par les oiseaux de la Crau." *Biologie-Écologie méditerranéenne*, 10: 83–106.

Chiche, J., Bertrand, J.P., Ramdane, A., 1991. *L'appréciation des ressources par les pasteurs marocains. In:* Association française de pastoralisme, Gaston, A., Kernick, M., Le Houerou, H-N., (eds). *Proc. IVth International Rangeland Congress,* Montpellier, France. 22-26/05-2: 912-613.

Citoyen Daubenton, 1794. Extrait de l'instruction pour les bergers et propriétaires de troupeaux. Paris, Imprimerie de Didot Jeune, 216 p., An 2e de la République (1794). http://gallica.bnf.fr/ark:/12148/bpt6k436810 (*consulted on:* August 26, 2013).

Claude, J., Grouzis, M., Milleville, P., 1991. *Un espace sahélien: la Mare d'Oursi (Burkina Faso).* Eds. ORSTOM, Paris, 241 p + cartes et planches couleurs.

Colas, S., Muller, F., Meuret, M., Agreil, C., (coord.) 2002. *Pâturage sur pelouses sèches: un guide d'aide à la mise en oeuvre.* Fédération des Conservatoires d'espaces naturels, Programme LIFE-Nature Protection des pelouses relictuelles de France. Eds. Espaces Naturels de France, Orléans, France: 152 pp.

Cote, S., 2004. *Stockmanship: A powerful tool for grazing lands management.* Eds. USDA Natural Resources Conservation Service & Butte Soil and Water Conservation District, Boise, Arco, Idaho, USA: 150 pp.

Dagget, D., 2005. *The Gardeners of Eden: Rediscovering Our Importance to Nature.* University of Nevada Press, Reno, Nevada, USA: 180 p.

Darré, J-P., 2006. *La recherche coactive de solutions entre agents de développement et agriculteurs.* GRET Ed., Paris: 112 p.

Décret, J.O. 198, 1990. Executive order No. 90-756 of August 22, 1990, containing the text of the Convention on the Conservation of European Wildlife and Natural Habitats, opened for signature at Bern on September 19, 1979. *Journal Officiel*, France. http://www.legifrance.gouv.fr/affichTexte.do?cidTexte=JORFTEXT000000343578 (*consulted on:* September 2, 2013).

Deffontaines, J.P., Landais, E., Savini, I., 1989. *L'espace d'un berger*. Pratiques pastorales dans les Ecrins. Garabédian, D., (réal.), INRA-SAD/ENS St-Cloud, producteurs associés, France: 60 min Video documentary.

Deffontaines, J.P., Lardon, S., 1989. "Surfaces en herbe et système agraire. Réflexions méthodologiques sur l'espace pour la gestion des surfaces en herbe." *Études et Recherches sur les Systèmes Agraires et le Développement*, 16: 209–18.

Degioanni, B., 2003. "Des stages en montagne pour réconcilier les 'pro' et 'anti' loups." http://www.hurlements.info (*consulted on:* November 7, 2007; article no longer available).

Deverre, C., 1994. "Rare birds and flocks: agriculture and social legitimization of environmental protection." *In:* Symes, D., Jansen, A.J., (eds.), *Agricultural restructuring and rural changes in Europe*, Wageningen Agricultural University Press, The Netherlands: 220–34.

Deverre, C., 2005. "Les dispositifs réglementaires et institutionnels pour la gestion des usages agricoles du territoire. De l'aménagement au ménagement." *In:* Laurent, C., Thinon, P. (dir), *Agricultures et Territoires*, Eds. Hermès-Science, Paris, France: 269–81

Deverre, C., de Sainte Marie, C., 2008. "L'écologisation de la politique agricole européenne. Verdissement ou refondation des systèmes agro-alimentaires." *Review of Agricultural and Environemental Studies*, 89: 83–104

Deverre, C., Hubert, H., 1994. "Agriculture et Environnement: Derrière un nouveau slogan, de nécessaires reformulations pour la recherche." *In:* Sebillotte, M. (dir.) *Systems-Oriented Research in Agriculture and Rural Development*. Proc. Int. Symp., Montpellier, France: 483–88.

Dion, R, 1991 (first edition 1934). *Essai sur la formation du paysage rural français*, Eds. Flammarion, Paris, France: 173 pp.

Dodier, H., 2005. "Le pastoralisme collectif français: une dynamique nationale." *Revue des Chambres d'Agriculture*, Supplément au n° 940: 4–7.

Doisneau, R., 1999. *La transhumance de Robert Doisneau*. Eds. Actes Sud, Arles, France: 106 pp.

Dubar, C., 1991. *La socialisation. Construction des identités sociales et professionnelles*. Armand Colin Éd., Paris, France: 280 pp.

Dubost, M., 2000. "Corse: une montagne authentique et vivante: Le recensement 1999 des unités pastorales en Corse." *In:* Bornard, A., Bruan-Nogué, C. (coord.), *Le pastoralisme en France à l'aube des années 2000. Pastum,* Bulletin de l'Association Française de Pastoralisme, Numéro hors-série: 147–50.

Duclos, J-C., 1994. "La transhumance, la fête et le paysage." *In:* Duclos, J-C., Pitte, A. (coord.), *L'homme et le mouton dans l'espace de la transhumance*. Eds. Glénat, Grenoble, France: 301–8.

Dudzinski, M.L., Schuh, H.J., 1978. "Statistical and probabilistic estimators of forage conditions from grazing behaviour of merino sheep in a semi-arid environment." *Appl. Anim. Ethology,* 4: 357–68.

Dumont, R., 1956. *Voyage en France d'un agronome* (2e édition), Eds. M-Th. Genin: Librairie de Médicis, Paris, France: 485 pp.

Dupieux, N., 1998. *La gestion conservatoire des tourbières de France: premiers éléments scientifiques et techniques*. Fédération des Conservatoires d'espaces naturels, Programme LIFE-

Nature Tourbières de France, FCEN et Office National des Forêts. Eds. Espaces Naturels de France, Orléans, France: 244 pp.

Dureau, R., Fabre, P., 1999. "Analyse des pratiques pastorales sur les parcours steppiques de Crau." *Rencontres Recherches Ruminants*, 6: 131–34.

EC Habitats Directive, 1992. Council Directive 92/43/EEC of May 21, 1992 on the Conservation of natural habitats and of wild fauna and flora ("EC Habitats Directive"), *Official Journal of the European Communities*, No. L 206, July 22 1992: 7–50. http://eur-lex.europa.eu/LexUriServ/LexUriServ.do?uri=OJ:L:1992:206:0007:0050:EN:PDF (*consulted on:* September 2, 2013).

El Aïch, A., Bourbouze, A., 1999. *Parole d'éleveurs en montagne*. Arragon, P., (prod.), Eds. CIHEAM-IAMM, Montpellier, France: 60 min Video documentary.

Ernoult, C., Favier, G., (dir.), 1997. *Atlas pastoral Provence-Alpes-Côte d'Azur*. Self-published document, Agreste, Maison Régionale de l'Élevage, Cemagref & DRAF PACA: 64 pp.

Ernoult, C., Favier, G., Dobremez, L., (dir.), 1999. *Atlas pastoral Rhône-Alpes*. Self-published document, Cemagref Grenoble, DRAF Rhône-Alpes, GIE Alpages et Forêts: 96 pp.

Estrosi, C., Spagnou, D., 2003. "Prédateurs et pastoralisme de montagne: priorité à l'homme. Rapport fait au nom de la commission d'enquête sur les conditions de la présence du loup en France et l'exercice du pastoralisme dans les zones de montagne." *Assemblée Nationale*, n° 825, 2 mai 2003. http://www.assemblee-nationale.fr/12/rap-enq/r0825-t1.asp (*consulted on:* September 2, 2013).

Etienne, M., Hubert, B., Jullian, P., Lécrivain, E., Legrand, C., Meuret, M., Napoléone, M., Arnaud, M-T., Garde, L., Mathey, F., Prévost, F., Thavaud, P., 1990. Espaces forestiers, élevage et incendies. *Revue Forestière Française, n° spécial Espaces forestiers et incendies*, 42: 156–72.

Etienne, M., Armand, D., Grudé, A., Girard, N., Napoléone, M., 2002. "Des moutons en forêt littorale varoise." *Réseau Coupures de combustible*, Cardère Ed., Lirac, France: 73 pp.

Eychenne, C., 2006. *Hommes et troupeaux en montagne: la question pastorale en Ariège*. L'Harmattan Ed., Paris, France: 314 pp.

Fabre, P., 1997. "La Crau: depuis toujours terre d'élevage." *In:* CEEP & Chambre d'Agriculture des Bouches-du-Rhône (coord.), *Patrimoine naturel et pratiques pastorales en Crau*. Rapport LIFE-ACE Crau sèche, Self-published document: 34–44.

Fabre, P., 2002. "Bergers aujourd'hui en Haute-Tinée." *In:* Fabre, P., Lebaudy, G., (dir.), *1951: Transhumance sur la route des alpages*. Eds. Image en manœuvre, Maison de la Transhumance Eds., Marseille, France: 130–33.

Fabre, P., 2004. "Un réseau des Maisons du Pastoralisme." *Pastum*, Bulletin de l'Association Française de Pastoralisme, 71: 4–7.

Fabre, P., Duclos, J-C., Molénat, G., (dir.), 2002. *Transhumance: relique du passé ou pratique d'avenir?* Actes des journées euro-méditerranéennes de la transhumance. Eds. Cheminements, Le Coudray-Macouard, France: 339 pp.

Fabre, P., Lebaudy, G., 2004. "La mémoire longue d'un métissage: la 'métisse' ou la race ovine mérinos d'Arles." *Anthropozoologica*, 39: 107–22.

Faure, S., 1990. *Du pâturage en forêt au sylvopastoralisme*. Eds. INRA-MAF/DERF, Paris, France: 45 min Video documentary.

Favre, Y., 1979. Étude de l'*organisation sociale et de l'utilisation de l'espace par des ovins (Ovis aries L.) en liberté*. Thèse de Docteur Ingénieur, Université Aix-Marseille II, 211 pp.

Favre, Y., 1976. "Aménagement et utilisation du domaine pastoral." *B.T.I.* 314–15: 66I–70.

Fayn, M., 1973. "La formation professionnelle au Domaine du Merle." *Pâtre*, 205: 11–21.

FERUS, 2004. *Témoignages 2004.* http://ours-loup-lynx.info/spip.php?article263 *(consulted on:* November 7, 2007; article no longer available).

FERUS, 2007. *Le loup en France.* Plaquette 16 p. http://www.ferus.fr/wp-content/uploads/2007/11/PLAQUETTE_LOUP_.pdf *(consulted on:* August 26, 2013).

Formation des Pâtres de Haute Montagne, 2005. http://www.pamiers.educagri.fr/cfppa/formations/detailpatre.cfm *(consulted on:* August 26, 2013).

Foucault, M., 1975. *Surveiller et punir. Naissance de la prison.* Éds. Gallimard, Paris, France: 318 pp.

Foucault, M., 2001. *Dits et Ecrits II (1976–1988).* Coll. Quarto, Éd. Gallimard, Paris: 1736 pp.

France Nature Environnement, 2005. Le loup à la loupe. *La voie du Loup,* 20: 4 p.

Garde, L. (coord.), 2007. *Loup & Élevage: s'ouvrir à la complexité.* Actes du séminaire technique des 15 et 16 Juin 2006, Aix-en-Provence. Self-published document from UCP "Pastoralisme Méditerranéen" & CERPAM, Manosque, France: 248 pp.

Giono, J., 1953. *L'Homme qui plantait des arbres.* Published in the USA as: Giono, J., McCurdy, M., Lipkis, A., 2005. *The Man Who Planted Trees,* Chelsea Green Publ., White River Jct., Vermont, USA: 72 pp.

Goïc, A.M., I977. "Comportement de troupeaux ovins libres ou gardés en alpage. Cohésion du groupe et utilisation du terrain." Mémoire de fin d'étude, ENSA-Montpellier & INERM, France: 124 pp.

Golé, S., 2002. *Un Puy de savoirs: concilier production en élevage et préservation des milieux naturels au tire de Natura 2000.* Mémoire de fin d'études, ENITA Clermont-Ferrand, France: 66 pp.

Grosclaude, M. *(translation, notes and commentary by),* 1993. *La Coutume de la Soule.* Izpegi Eds., Pau, France: 164 p.

Guérin, S., Bellon, S., 1990. "Analyse des fonctions des surfaces pastorales dans les systèmes fourragers en zone méditerranéenne." *In:* Capillon, A. (ed.), *Recherches sur les systèmes herbagers: quelques propositions françaises. Études et Recherches sur les Systèmes Agraires et le Développement,* 17: 147–57.

Guérin, G., Bellon, S., Gautier, D., 2001. "Valorisation et maîtrise des surfaces pastorales par le pâturage." *Fourrages,* 166: 239–56.

Gerrish, J., 2004. *Management-Intensive Grazing: The Grassroots of Grass Farming.* Green Park Press, Ridgeland, MS, USA: 314 pp.

Guet, J., 1991. "André fait-il bien?" *In:* Landais, E. (éd.), *André L. Contrepoint,* Self-published document, INRA-SAD Versailles-Dijon-Mirecourt, Versailles, France: 75–77.

Hénault, M., Jolicœur, H., 2003. *Les loups au Québec: meutes et mystères.* Société de la faune et des parcs du Québec, Direction de l'aménagement de la faune des Laurentides & Direction du développement de la faune, Québec, Canada: 129 pp. http://parcsaintecroix.com/wp-content/uploads/2013/06/loupsQuebec-MichelHenault-HeleneJolicoeur.pdf *(consulted on:* September 2, 2013).

Hubert, B., 1991a. "Changing Land Uses in Provence: Multiple Use as a Management Tool." *In:* "Land Abandonment and its Role in Conservation," *Options Méditerranéennes,* Série Séminaires, 15: 31–52.

Hubert, B., 1991b. "Comment raisonner de manière systémique l'utilisation du territoire pastoral?" *In:* Gaston A., Kernick M., Le Houéou H-N. (eds), *Proc. IVth Intern. Rangeland Congress,* Montpellier, France, 3: 1026–1043.

Hubert, B., Rigolot, E., Turlan, E., Couix, N. 1993. "Forest Fire Prevention in the Mediterranean Region: New Approaches to Agriculture-Environment Relations." *In:* Brossier, J., de Bonneval, L. (eds.) *Systems Studies in Agriculture and Rural Development,* Eds. INRA, Paris, France: 63–86.

Hubert, B., Coudel, E., Coomes, O., Soulard, C., Faure, G., Devautour, H., 2012. "Conclusion: En route . . . but which way?" *In:* Coudel, E., Soulard, C., Devautour, H., Faure, G., Hubert, B. (eds.). *Renewing innovation systems in agriculture and food: how to go towards more sustainability?* Wageningen Academic Publishers, Wageningen, The Netherlands: 221–30.

Institut de l'Elevage, 1999. *Référentiel pastoral parcellaire.* Eds. Institut de l'Elevage, Paris: 30 pp + 412 technical data sheets.

Jallet, M., Fabre, P., 2007. "Organisation du travail face à la prédation: redéfinition des métiers d'alpage." *In:* Garde, L. (coord.), *Loup & Élevage: s'ouvrir à la complexité.* Actes du séminaire technique des 15 et 16 Juin 2006, Aix-en-Provence. Self-published document, UCP "Pastoralisme Méditerranéen" & CERPAM, Manosque, France: 108–16.

Jarrige, R. (coord.), 1978. *Alimentation des ruminants.* Eds. INRA, Paris, France: 621 pp.

Jarrige, R. (coord.), 1988. *Alimentation des Bovins, ovins et caprins.* Eds. INRA, Paris, France: 471 pp.

Jehan de Brie, 1541. *Le bon berger ou le vrai régime et gouvernement des bergers et bergères.* Paris, Isidore Liseux, 1879, Reprinted from the original edition in Paris, 1541. http://gallica.bnf. fr/ark:/12148/bpt6k54694869 (*consulted on:* August 18, 2013).

Joffre, R., Hubert, B., Meuret, M., 1991. "Les systèmes agrosylvopastoraux méditerranéens: réflexions à propos de la gestion des espaces fragiles." *MAB Digest,* 10. UNESCO, Paris, France: 96 pp.

Juillard, E., (dir.), 1976. *Histoire de la France rurale,* Vol. III: 1789–1914, Ed. Seuil, Paris, France: 568 pp.

Julien, M-P., Rosselin, C., 2005. *La culture matérielle.* Éds. La Découverte, Coll. "Repères," Paris, France: 121 pp.

Kaczensky, P., Chapron, G., Arx (von), M., Huber, D., Andrén, H., Linnell, J., (eds), 2013. *Status, management and distribution of large carnivores –bear, lynx, wolf & wolverine–in Europe: Wolf, France.* Self-published document, Boitani, L., (chair.) IUCN/SSC Large Carnivore Initiative for Europe, European Commission: 144–45. http://www.carnivorescience. org/files/2013_EUCommission_carnivore-status-2.pdf (*consulted on:* September 9, 2013).

Kauffman, J-C., 1996. *L'entretien compréhensif.* Ed. Nathan Université, Coll. Sociologie 128, Paris, France: 126 p.

Kilgour, R., Pearson, A.J., De Langen, H., 1975. "Sheep dispersal patterns on hill country: techniques for study and analysis." *Proceedings of the New Zealand Society of Animal Production,* 35: 191–97.

Kuhnholtz-Lordat, G., 1944. "La Silva, le Saltus et l'Ager de garrigue." *Annales ENSA Montpellier,* Montpellier, France, XXVI, IV: 1–84.

Lamour, P., 1980. *Le cadran solaire,* Eds. Robert Laffont, Paris, France: 464 pp.

Landais, E., (ed.), 1991. *André L. Contrepoint.* Self-published document, INRA-SAD Versailles-Dijon-Mirecourt, Versailles, France: 139 pp.

Landais, E., (ed.), 1993. "Pratiques d'élevage extensif: identifier, modéliser, évaluer." *Études et Recherches sur les Systèmes Agraires et le Développement,* 27, 389 p.

Landais, E., Deffontaines, J-P., 1988. *André L.: un berger parle de ses pratiques.* Self-published document, INRA-SAD Versailles-Dijon-Mirecourt, Versailles, France: 111 p.

Landais, E., Deffontaines, J.P., 1989. "Analysing the management of a pastoral territory. The study of the practices of a shepherd in the Southern French Alps." *Études et Recherches sur les Systèmes Agraires et le Développement,* 16: 199–207.

Landais, E., Deffontaines, J.P., 1991. D'abord comprendre. *In:* Landais, E., (ed.), *André L. Contrepoint.* Self-published document, INRA-SAD Versailles-Dijon-Mirecourt, Versailles, France: 117–21.

Landais, E., Deffontaines, J.P., Benoît, M, 1989. "Les pratiques des agriculteurs. Points de vue sur un courant nouveau de la recherche agronomique." Études Rurales, 109: 125–58.

Landrot, P., 1999. "L'alpage, une tradition vivante et modernisée." *Agreste – Les cahiers*, 41: 25–33.

Lapeyronie, P., 2000–2003. *Parcs à troupeaux et parcs de protection nocturne dans le Parc National du Mercantour et les Alpes du Sud: incidences paysagères, impact sur les pelouses des estives.* Self-published document, SupAgro Montpellier, ONCFS, Parc National du Mercantour (Eds.). Programme LIFE99 NAT/F/006299 "Le retour du loup dans les Alpes françaises": 39 pp.

Lassalle, D., (coord.), 1998. *Transmettre le métier de berger: une formation développement. Présentation du processus pédagogique et de la didactique par alternance.* Self-published document, AMFR Etcharry, France: 89 pp.

Lassalle, D., 2007. *Berger pyrénéen: une identité professionnelle, culture et sociale, en question (Pyrénées Occidentales et Centrales).* Thèse de Doctorat, Université Toulouse Le Mirail, France: 396 pp.

Launchbaugh, K., (ed.), 2006. *Targeted grazing: a natural approach to vegetation management and landscape enhancement.* Handbook copyrighted by: Peischel, A., Henry, Jr., D.D., for the American Sheep Industry Association, University of Idaho, Moscow, Idaho, USA: 208 pp. http://www.webpages.uidaho.edu/rx-grazing/handbook.htm (*consulted on:* September 2, 2013).

Lavoux, T., Tuddenham, M., Racape, J., 1999. "Premier bilan des mesures agri-environnementales européennes (1993–1998)." *Les données de l'Environnement*, 50: 1–4.

LCI/TF1, 2004. *Entre brebis et loups. Chaque été, des bénévoles aident les bergers à surveiller leurs troupeaux . . .* Témoignage. http://tf1.lci.fr/infos/ (consulted on: July 8, 2004; article no longer available).

Le Pape, G., Blanchet, M., Durand, C., 2001. *Interactions entre les promeneurs et les chiens de protection de troupeaux ovins dans le massif du Queyras.* Self-published document, Université de Tours, PNR du Queyras, Programme LIFE-Loup, ONCFS, 47 pp.

Le Roy Ladurie, E., 1975. *Montaillou, village occitan de 1294 à 1324.* Eds. Gallimard, Paris, France: 642 pp.

Leclerc, B., Lécrivain, E., 1979. Étude du comportement d'*ovins domestiques en élevage extensif sur le Causse du Larzac.* Thèse de Doctorat, Université de Rennes, 165 p.

Leclerc, B., Lécrivain, E., 1994. Incidence du retour quotidien en chèvrerie sur le comportement alimentaire et spatiale de caprins dans un taillis. *Annales de Zootechnie*, 43: 295.

Leclerc, B., Lécrivain, B., Hauwuy, A., 1989. Consommation des ressources ligneuses dans un taillis de chênes par des brebis en estive. *Reproduction, Nutrition, Développement,* suppl. 2: 207–8.

Lecomte, T., Le Neveu, C., Nicaise, L., Valot, E., 1995. *Gestion écologique par le pâturage: l'expérience des réserves naturelles.* Eds. Atelier Technique des Espaces Naturels, Coll. Outils de gestion, Montpellier, France: 76 pp.

Lefebvre, H., 1963. *La vallée de Campan: étude de sociologie rurale.* Eds. PUF, Paris, France: 224 p.

Legay, J.M., 1986. Quelques réflexions à propos d'écologie: défense de l'indisciplinarité. *Acta Œcologica, Œcol. Generalis,* 7: 391–98.

Legeard, J-P., 1996. *Les bergers d'alpage en chiffres:* résultat des enquêtes auprès des responsables d'*alpages et de leurs bergers en fin d'estive 1995.* Self-published document, CERPAM, Manosque, France: 51 p. + annexes.

Legeard, J-P., 1999. *Territoires pastoraux et gardiennage des troupeaux en Provence-Alpes-Côte d'Azur: valorisation de l'enquête pastorale 1997.* Self-published document, CERPAM, Manosque, France: 29 p. + annexes.

Legeard, J-P., 2002. "Les transhumances ovins provençales dans le massif des Alpes du Sud." *In:* Fabre, P., Duclos, J-C., Molénat, G., (dir.), *Transhumance: relique du passé ou pratique d'avenir?* Eds. Cheminements, Le Coudray-Macouard, France: 153–63.

Legeard, J-P., 2003. *La transhumance ovine provençale dans les Alpes du Nord: gestionnaires d'alpages et gardiennage des troupeaux.* Self-published document, CERPAM, Manosque, France: 6 p. + annexes.

Legeard, J-P., 2006. "Le pastoralisme en France au carrefour des questions agricoles et environnementales." *In:* Bonnemaire, J., (coord.), *Actualités et modernité du pastoralisme, C. R. Acad. Agric. Fr,* 92, n° 4, Session of May 31, 2006. Complete text published in *Pastum,* Bulletin de l'Association Française de Pastoralisme, 84: 20–34.

Léger, F., Bellon, S., Meuret, M., Chabert, J-P., Guerin, G., 1999. "Technical approach to local agro-environmental operations: results and means." *In:* Rubino, R., Morand-Fehr, P., (eds.), *Options Mediterranéennes,* Serie A, 38: 163–67.

Leopold, A., 1949. *A Sand County Almanac.* Oxford University Press: 240 pp.

Leroy, A., 1943. Élevage rationnel des animaux domestiques: *zootechnie générale.* Encyclopédie des Connaissances Agricoles, Eds. Hachette, Paris, France: 364 pp.

Leroy, M., Gaubert, C., 2000. "Témoignage: accepter la précarité territoriale." *Campagnes solidaires,* n° Spécial Moutons: 10.

Life-Coex, 2006. Les éco-volontaires, bilan 2005: "Des moments inoubliables, mais pas un voyage d'agrément précisait le dossier d'inscription" *Coexistence Infos,* 2: 3.

Ligue de Protection des Oiseaux (LPO), 2007. *Agir ensemble pour les oiseaux et l'homme.* http://www.lpo.fr/ (*consulted on:* November 29, 2007; article no longer available).

Lynch, J.J., Alexander, G., 1973. "Animal behaviour and the pastoral industries." *In:* Alexander, G., Williams, O.B., (eds.), *The pastoral industries of Australia: practices and technology of sheep and cattle production.* Sydney University Press, Sydney, Australia: 371–400.

Maître, P., 1991. *Chevrier en forêt.* "Mémoire de fin d'études, BTS-Productions animales," LEGTA Besançon, France: 109 pp.

Mallen, M., 1995. *Paroles de bergers: analyse de l'évolution d'un métier entre passion et désilusion.* Self-published document, CERPAM, Manosque, France: 58 p. + annexes.

Mallen, M., 2001. "En quête d'identité, les bergers salariés dans les Alpes du Sud." http://adam.mmsh.univ-aix.fr/activites/rencontres/pastoralisme/Pages/bergers-salaries.aspx (*consulted on:* August 26, 2013).

MAP (Ministry of Agriculture and Fisheries), 2006. "Les Unités capitalisables d'adaptation régionale et à l'emploi." http://www.chlorofil.fr/certifications/textes-officiels/referentiels-fiches-rncp-et-grilles-horaires/ucare.html (*consulted on:* December 23, 2007; article no longer available).

MAPAR (Ministry of Agriculture, Fisheries and Rural Affairs), 2002. *Rapport du Groupe interministériel sur le pastoralisme au ministre de l'agriculture, de l'alimentation, de la pêche et des affaires rurales.* http://www.ladocumentationfrancaise.fr/rapports-publics/024000454/index.shtml (*consulted on:* August 26, 2013).

Martinand, P., 1991. "Rapport introductif aux témoignages d'actions de développement pastoral." *In:* Association française de pastoralisme, Gaston, A., Kernick, M., Le Houerou, H-N., (eds). *Proc. IVth International Rangeland Congress,* Montpellier, France. 22-26/05-3: 1227–1229.

Mauss, M., 1950. *Les techniques du corps. In:* Mauss, M., Sociologie et anthropologie, Eds. PUF, Paris, France: 363–86. (Originally published in 1934: *Journal de Psychologie,* XXXII, 3–4).

Mech, D. L., 1995. "The Challenge and Opportunity of Recovering Wolf Populations." *Conservation biology,* 9: 270–78.

MEDD (Ministry of Ecology and Sustainable Development) and MAAPAR (Ministry of Agriculture, Food, Fisheries and Rural Affairs), 2004. *Wolf Action Plan, 2004–2008*. November 8, 2004. http://www.ecologie.gouv.fr/IMG/pdf/Planactionloup.pdf (*consulted on:* November 15, 2007; site no longer available). Updated Wolf Action Plan, 2013–2017, May 2013. http://www.developpement-durable.gouv.fr/IMG/pdf/Planloup2013-2.pdf (*consulted on:* August 26, 2013).

Mendras, H., 1967. *La fin des paysans*, Eds. SEDEIS, Paris, France. Republished 1992, Eds. Actes Sud, Coll. Babel, Arles, France: 440 pp.

Mestelan, P., Agreil, C., de Sainte Marie, C., Meuret, M., Mailland-Rosset, S. 2007. "Mise en place d'une contractualisation agri-environnementale basée sur le respect de résultats écologiques mesurables: le cas des surfaces herbagères du Parc Naturel Régional du Massif des Bauges." *Rencontres Recherches Ruminants*, 14: 173–76.

Meuret, M., 1988. "Feasibility of *in vivo* digestibility trials with lactating goats browsing fresh leafy branches." *Small Ruminant Research*, 1: 273–90.

Meuret, M., 1989. *Fromages, feuillages et flux ingéré*. Thèse de Doctorat, Faculté Sciences Agronomiques de Gembloux, Belgique: 249 pp.

Meuret, M., 1993. Piloter l'ingestion au pâturage. *In:* Landais, E. (coord.) Pratiques d'Élevage Extensif: identifier, modéliser, évaluer. Études *et Recherches sur les Systèmes Agraires et le Développement*, 27: 161–98.

Meuret, M., 1997. How do I cope with that bush? Optimizing on less palatable feeds at pasture using the MENU model. *In:* Lindberg, J.E., Gonda, H.L., Ledin, I. (eds.), *Recent advances in small ruminant nutrition. Options Méditerranéennes*, A-34, 53–57.

Meuret, M., 2006. *Pages de garde: les raisons de garder les chèvres*. Documentary film, Eds. INRA, Paris, France: 30 min. http://mediatheque.inra.fr/media/detail/187798/private.

Meuret, M., Giger-Reverdin, S., 1990. "A comparison of two ways of expressing the voluntary intake of oak foliage-based diets in goats raised on rangelands." *Reproduction, Nutrition, Développement*, Suppl. 2: 205.

Meuret, M., Landais, E., 1997. Quoi de neuf sur les systèmes d'élevage? *In:* Blanc-Pamard, C., Boutrais, J. (coord.), *Thème et variations: nouvelles recherches rurales au sud*. Eds. ORSTOM, Paris, France: 323–55.

Meuret, M., Chabert, J-P., 1998. "Retour du loup: ses protecteurs sont des éleveurs." *Terroir Magazine*, 49: 7.

Meuret, M., Chabert, J-P., 1999. "Le pastoralisme à fins environnementales en question dans le *Saltus* rhône-alpin." *In:* Sebillotte, M. (coord.), *Proc. Recherche, Agriculture et Développement Régional en Rhône-Alpes*. INRA, ENS-Lyon, France: 109–11.

Meuret, M., Dumont, B., 2000. "Advances in modelling animal-vegetation interactions and their use in guiding grazing management." *In:* Gagnaux, D. *et al.* (eds.), *Livestock Farming Systems: Integrating animal science advances into the search for sustainability*. EAAP Pub., Wageningen Pers., 97: 57–72.

Meuret, M., Léger, F., 2001. *Conservation des milieux: les références pastorales face aux attentes environnementales*. Rapport final d'activité Aip INRA 'Pâturage'. Self-published document, INRA, Avignon, France: 85 p. + annexes.

Meuret, M., Agreil, C., 2006. *Des broussailles au Menu*. Mimeographed document: 4 pp. http://www.chevredespyrenees.org/wordpress/wp-content/uploads/2012/07/Plaquette_Broussaille_Inra.pdf (*consulted on:* August 26, 2013).

Meuret, M., Bellon, S., Guérin, G., Hanus, G., 1995. Faire pâturer sur parcours. *Rencontres Recherches Ruminants*, 2: 27–36.

Meuret, M., Bartiaux-Thill, N., Bourbouze, A., 1985. "Évaluation de la consommation d'un troupeau de chèvres laitières sur parcours forestier: méthode d'observation directe des coups de dents; méthode du marqueur oxyde de chrome." *Annales de Zootechnie*, 34: 159–80.

Meuret, M., Viaux, C., Chadoeuf, J., 1994. "Land heterogeneity stimulates intake during grazing trips." *Annales de Zootechnie*, 43: 296.

Meuret, M., Gonzalez-Pech, P., Agreil, C., Wolff, A., Minard, R., 2013. "L'intelligence alimentaire des brebis conduits au printemps par des bergers en steppe de Crau." *In:* Tatin, L., Wolff, A., Dutoit, T., Colliot, E., Boutin, J., (coord.), *La Crau, écologie et conservation d'une steppe méditerranéenne*. Eds. Quae, Versailles, France (in press).

Meyer, D., 1983. "Vers une sauvegarde et une gestion du milieu naturel de la Crau." *Biologie-Écologie méditerranéenne*, X: 155–72.

Micoud, A., 2003. "Ces bonnes vaches aux yeux si doux." *Communications*, 74: 217–37.

Miellet, P., Meuret, M., 1993. "Savoir faire pâturer en S.I.G.," *Mappemonde*, 2/93: 12–17.

Moneyron, A. et al., 1995. *Formation berger vacher pluriactif en montagne pyrénéenne: Référentiel Métier*. Self-published document, AFMR Etcharry & LEPA Oloron, 22 pp.

Moneyron, A., 2003. *Transhumance et Éco-Savoir: reconnaissance des alternances écoformatives*. Eds. L'Harmattan, Paris, France: 236 pp.

Morand-Fehr, P., Sauvant, D., 1988. "Alimentation des caprins." *In:* Jarrige, R. (coord.), *Alimentation des bovins, ovins et caprins*. Eds. INRA, Paris, France: 282–304.

Moret, A., 2007. "L'utilisation du chien de protection dans les Alpes françaises." *In:* Garde, L. (coord.), *Loup & Élevage: s'ouvrir à la complexité*. Actes du séminaire technique des 15 et 16 Juin 2006, Aix-en-Provence. Self-published document, UCP "Pastoralisme Méditerranéen" & CERPAM, Manosque, France: 118–29.

Morley, F.H.W., 1981. "Grazing animals." *In:* Neimann-Sorensen, A., Tribe, D.E., (eds.), *World animal science B1*, Elsevier Ed., the Netherlands: 411 p.

Noschis, K., 1984. *La signification affective du quartier*. Éds. Librairie des Meridiens Klincksieck, Paris, France: 170 pp.

Osty, P.L., 1993. "The Farm Enterprise and its Environment: Proposals for Structuring an Appraisal of Strategy." *In*: Brossier, J., de Bonneval, L. (eds.) *Systems Studies in Agriculture and Rural Development*, Eds. INRA, Paris, France: 360–72.

Ott, S., 1993. *Le cercle des montagnes: une communauté pastorale basque*. Eds. CTHS, Paris, France: 267 pp. Translated from: *The Circle of mountains: a Basque shepherding community*. 1993, University of Nevada Press, Reno, Nevada, USA: 242 pp. (1st ed. 1981, Oxford University Press).

Ouedraogo, C., 1991. *Cinétique d'ingestion par des chèvres laitières au pâturage: étude dans deux exploitations en région méditerranéenne*. Mémoire de DAA Productions animales et fourragères, ENSA Rennes, France: 72 pp.

Peillon, A., Carbonne, G., 1993. "Bienvenue aux loups." *Terre Sauvage*, Monthly Magazine, 73: 23–42.

Pinton, F., Alphandéry, P, Billaud, J.P, Deverre, C., Fortier, A., Geniaux, G., 2006. *La construction du réseau Natura 2000 en France*. Eds. La Documentation Française, Paris, France: 249 pp.

Plana, C., 1989. *Utilisation d'un maquis à chêne liège par des ovins: étude de l'influence de la structure de l'enclos*. Rapport de stage DESU, Université Toulouse-III, France: 46 pp.

Planhol (de), X., 1969. "Le chien de berger: développement et signification géographique d'une technique pastorale." *Bulletin de l'Association des Géographes français*, 370: 355–68.

Polanyi, K., 1944. "The great transformation: the political and economic origins of our time." Eds. Beacon Press, Boston, MA, USA: 317 pp.

Provenza, F.D., 2003. *Foraging behavior: managing to survive in a world of change. Behavioral principles for human, animal, vegetation, and ecosystem management.* Self-published document, Utah State University, Dept. Wildland Resources, Logan, UT, USA: 63 pp.

Provenza, F.D., Villalba, J.J., 2006. "Foraging in domestic vertebrates: linking the internal and external milieu." *In:* Bels, V. (ed.), *Food and Feeding: From structure to behaviour.* CABI Pub., Wallingford, UK, New York, USA: 210–40.

Provenza, F.D., Villalba, J.J., Dziba, L.E., Atwood, S.B., Banner, R.E., 2003. "Linking Herbivore Experience, Varied Diets, and Plant Biochemical Diversity." *Small Ruminant Research,* 49: 257–74.

Provenza, F., H. Pringle, D. Revell, N. Bray, C. Hines, R. Teague, T. Steffens and M. Barnes. 2013. "Complex Creative Systems: Principles, Processes, and Practices of Transformation." *Rangelands* 35: 6–13.

Ravis-Giordani, G., 1983. *Bergers corses: les communautés villageoises du Niolu.* Eds. Edisud, Aix-en-Provence, France: 512 pp.

Répertoire National des Certifications Professionnelles (RNCP), 2007. "Berger vacher transhumant." http://www.rncp.cncp.gouv.fr/grand-public/visualisationFiche?format=fr&fiche=12962 (*consulted on*: August 26, 2013).

Robin, G., 1988. *Guide en reconnaissance des acquis: plus qu'un CV, un « portfolio » de ses apprentissages.* Eds G. Vermette, Bourcheville, Québec, Canada: 125 pp.

Robinson, J., 2008. "Being undisciplined: Transgressions and intersections in academia and beyond." *Futures,* 40: 70–86.

Rosoux, R., 2013. "Le pastoralisme ligérien: une pratique agricole au service de la Loire." Self-published document, Pasto'Loire project, Conservatoire des espaces naturels de la region Centre, Chambre d'agriculture du Loiret: 12 pp. http://www.cen-centre.org/du-local-au-regional/projetstransversaux/35-projets-coordonnes/72-pastoralisme-en-bords-de-loire (*consulted on:* September 6, 2013).

Roucolle, M., Plainecassagne, L., 2003. "Une cartographie interactive du domaine pastoral Pyrénéen: le volet pastoral du SIG Pyrénées." *Pastum,* Bulletin de l'Association Française de Pastoralisme, 70: 19–22.

Roux, L., Duclos, J-C., Fabre P., 2011. *Pastreja: Paysages et pastoralisme du Pays d'Arles.* Co-Eds. Images en Manœuvres & Maison de la Transhumance, Marseille & Saint-Martin-de-Crau, France: 128 pp.

Russel, A.J.F., Doney, J.M., Gunn, R.G., 1969. "Subjective assessment of body fat in live sheep." *Journal of agricultural science,* 72: 451–54.

Salmona, M., 1994. *Les paysans français, le travail, les métiers, la transmission des savoirs.* Eds. L'Harmattan, Paris, France: 371 pp.

Savini, I., Landais, E., 1991. "Comment gardent les autres bergers?" *In:* Landais, E. (éd.), *André L. Contrepoint.* Self-published document, INRA-SAD Versailles-Dijon-Mirecourt, Versailles, France: 57–62.

Savory, A., 1998. *Holistic Management: A New Framework for Decision Making.* Island Press, Washington D.C., USA: 664 pp.

Schilder, P., 1950. *L'image du corps* (réédition 1968). Eds. Gallimard, Paris, France: 350 pp.

Schwartz, B., 1994. *Moderniser sans exclure.* Eds. La Découverte, Paris, France: 244 p.

Senft, R.L., Coughenour, M.B., Bailey, D.W., Rittenhouse, L.R., Sala, O.E., Swift, D.M., 1987. "Large herbivore foraging and ecological hierarchies. Landscape ecology can enhance traditional foraging theory." *BioScience,* 37: 789–99.

Smith, B.M., 1998. *Move 'em: a guide to low stress animal handling.* The Graziers Hui: 352 pp.

Smith, Moroni A., 1918. *Herding and Handling Sheep: On the Open Range in U.S.A.* Self-published document, Salt Lake City, Utah, USA: 69 pp.

Sociétés d'Économie Alpestre de Haute-Savoie (SEA-74) (coord.), 2007. *Un berger dans mon école.* http://www.echoalp.com/un-berger-dans-mon-ecole.html (*consulted on:* August 26, 2013).

Sociétés d'Économie Alpestre de Savoie et Haute-Savoie (SEA-73 et 74), 2001. *Profession berger: synthèse.* "Opération "revalorisation du métier de berger." Self-published document, Deuxième rencontre internationale des bergers, May 14–15, 2001, La Motte-Servolex, France: 27 pp.

Soulet, J.F., 1974. *La vie quotidienne dans les Pyrénées sous l'ancien régime du XVIᵉ siècle au XVIIIᵉ siècle.* Eds. Hachette littérature, Paris, France: 319 pp.

Squires, V.R., 1975a. "Environmental heterogeneity as a factor in group size determination among grazing sheep." *Appl. Anim. Ethology,* 35: 184–90.

Squires, V.R., 1975b. "Leadership and dominance relationships in Merino and Border Leicester sheep." *Appl. Anim. Ethology,* 1: 263–74

Squires, V.R., 1978a. "Effects of management and the environment on animal dispersion under free ranging conditions." *In:* Proc. 1st World Congress Ethology Applied to Zootechny, Madrid, Spain: 323–34.

Squires, V.R., 1978b. *Flock configurations and orientations of individuals among grazing sheep. In:* Proc. 1st World Congress Ethology Applied to Zootechny, Madrid, Spain: 335–43.

Suaci Alpes du Nord (coord.), 2007. *Bergers-vaches: des métiers d'interfaces.* Fiche de Synthèse Alpes, Emploi. Self-published document, Suaci Alpes du Nord: 4 pp.

Taillefer, F., (dir), 1974. *Les Pyrénées de la montagne à l'homme.* Eds. Privat, Toulouse: 520 pp.

Thepot, N., I977. "Influence des processus socio-démographiques sur le système agraire dans la région des Préalpes: 1. Essai d'analyse historique; 2. Compte rendu d'enquête dans six communes." Self-published document, Fédération départementale ovine (FDO) des Alpes de Haute-Provence & CTGREF Antenne Élevage Ovin, Montpellier, France: 152 pp.

Thiault, M., 1979. "Parcours méditerranéens: réflexions à partir de quelques aspects bioclimatiques." *In:* Molénat, G., Jarrige, R. (coord.) *Utilisation par les ruminants des pâturages d'altitude et parcours méditerranéens.* Éds. INRA, Paris, France: 361–73.

Thompson, P.B., 1995. *The Spirit of the Soil: Agriculture and Environmental Ethics,* Eds. Routledge, London, UK: 196 pp.

Tolley, C., 2004. "Formation scolaire ou formation sur le tas chez les bergers de Provence: différenciation des pratiques et conflit de légitimité?" *Sociétés Contemporaines,* 55: 115–38.

UNESCO, 2005. *Ecosystems and Human Well-Being: Synthesis (Millennium Ecosystem Assessment Series).* Island Press, Washington, D.C., USA: 160 pp.

Van Soest, P.J., 1994. *Nutritional ecology of the ruminant,* 2nd ed., Eds. Cornell University Press, New York, USA: 476 pp.

Viaux, C., 1992. *Par ici la relance!* Mémoire DESS Informatique, Université d'Avignon: 58 pp.

Vincent, M., 2005. "Loup: un éleveur devant la justice pour son patou." *La lettre du Mérinos,* 149: 4.

Vincent, M., 2011. *Les alpages à l'épreuve des loups.* Eds. Quae & Maison des Sciences de l'Homme (MSH), Coll. Nature Sociales, Versailles, Paris: 352 pp.

Vissac, B., 2002. *Les vaches de la République: saisons et raisons d'un chercheur citoyen.* Eds. INRA, Coll. Espaces ruraux, Paris, France: 505 pp.

Warnier, J-P., 1999. *Construire la culture matérielle. L'Homme qui pensait avec ses doigts.* Eds. PUF, Paris, France: 190 pp.

Weber, E., 1976. *Peasants into Frenchmen. The Modernization of Rural France, 1870–1914.* Eds. Stanford University Press, Stanford, California, USA: 615 pp., (French edition 1983: *La fin des terroirs. La modernisation de la France rurale. 1870–1914.* Eds. Librairie Arthème Fayard/ Éditions Recherches, Paris, France: 844 pp.

White, C., 2008. *Revolution on the Range: The Rise of a New Ranch in the American West.* Island Press, Washington D.C., USA: 248 pp.

Wolff, A., 1997. "Impact de la conduite pastorale sur la répartition de trois espèces d'oiseaux nichant dans les coussouls." *In:* CEEP & Chambre d'Agriculture des Bouches-du-Rhône (coord.), *Patrimoine naturel et pratiques pastorales en Crau.* Self-published document, Rapport LIFE-ACE Crau sèche, Saint-Martin-de-Crau, France: 94–97.

Wolff, A., Fabre, P., Vincent-Martin, N., Paulus, G., Becker, E., 2008. *La Réserve naturelle des Coussouls de Crau: Plan de gestion 2009-2013, section A, diagnostic et enjeux,* Self-published document, CEEP & Chambre d'Agriculture des Bouches-du-Rhône, Saint-Martin-de-Crau, France: 183 p + annexes.

Yin, R.K., 2003. *Case study research: design and methods*, 3rd edition, Eds. Sage Publications, Thousand Oaks, California, USA: 181 pp.

Young, A., 1909. *Arthur Young's Travels in France during the Years 1787, 1788, 1789.* Eds. Miss Betham-Edwards, London, George Bell & Sons, UK. http://oll.libertyfund.org/simple. php?id=292 (*consulted on:* September 6, 2013) (first edition: 1792; French edition 1976: *Voyages en France.* Eds. Armand Colin, Paris, France: 490 pp.).

Index

The Editors

Michel Meuret

Michel Meuret obtained degrees in agronomy and ecology from Brussels University in 1983. The French National Institute for Agricultural Research, INRA, was interested in his innovative scientific approach and methodological developments for measuring food intake on forested rangeland and proposed that he join a research staff in southern France

 that was studying the use of livestock grazing to prevent wildfires in Mediterranean forests and scrublands.

Michel got his PhD in animal ecology sciences in 1989 and was immediately recruited by INRA as permanent researcher to study grazing practices and animal nutrition on rangelands. He has since led several interdisciplinary research projects on the implementation of European policies, in particular the value of livestock grazing for improving wildlife habitat and biodiversity conservation. In 2012 he joined SupAgro agronomy school at Montpellier as consultant professor.

From the beginning, Michel's research has been conducted in communities with family farmers and herders. Working also with social scientists, he focused on the experiential know-how and practices that positively impact feeding motivation in domestic herbivores on rangeland. Michel is regularly asked by farmers, herders, and nature conservationists to teach and promote debates on herding techniques. On several occasions, Michel has been invited to present his experience in the United States and other countries that are intrigued by the unique French experiences of nature-friendly shepherding. Michel now serves as a director of research at INRA.

Fred Provenza

Fred Provenza is from Colorado, where he worked on a ranch near Salida while earning a bachelor of science in wildlife biology from Colorado State University. Upon receiving his degree in 1973, he became ranch manager. He and his wife Sue left the ranch in 1975 so he could work as a research

assistant and technician at Utah State University, where he earned MS and PhD degrees. He was a professor in the Department of Wildland Resources at Utah State University from 1982 to 2009. He is now professor emeritus, and he and his wife are living once again in the mountains of Colorado.

For the past forty years, his group's work has inspired researchers and managers in disciplines including nutrition and foraging behavior of wild and domestic animals and humans, phytochemical ecology, pasture and rangeland science and management, and restoration ecology and targeted grazing, among others. Along with colleagues and students, he has authored or coauthored over 250 publications in scientific journals and books. He has been an invited speaker at over 350 conferences.

Fred's efforts led to the formation in 2001 of an international network of scientists and land managers from five continents. That consortium, known as BEHAVE (www.behave.net), integrates behavioral principles and processes with local knowledge to foster healthy relationships among soil, plants, herbivores, and people as social, economic, and ecological environments ever transform. We no longer view organisms, including ourselves, as machines and genes as destiny but learn to work with behavioral relationships to create opportunities as environments ever transform.

Fred has received numerous awards for research, teaching, and mentoring. These awards represent the productivity that flowed from warm personal and professional relationships with over seventy-five graduate students, post-doctoral students, visiting scientists, and colleagues he worked with during the past thirty-five years.